Sheep
Production

Sheep
Production

JOHN B. OWEN *BSc, PhD, MA, FI Biol*

Professor of Animal Production and Health,
University of Aberdeen

BAILLIÈRE   TINDALL
LONDON

A BAILLIÈRE TINDALL book published by
Cassell & Collier Macmillan Publishers Ltd
35 Red Lion Square, London WC1R 4SG
and at Sydney, Auckland, Toronto, Johannesburg
an affiliate of
Macmillan Publishing Co. Inc.
New York

First published 1976
ISBN 0 7020 0577 0

Printed by Page Bros (Norwich) Ltd, Norwich, England.

Contents

Preface

The aim of this book is to collect under one cover a wide spectrum of knowledge about sheep production and the factors that influence efficiency in sheep systems, and to consider how recently acquired knowledge might be profitably used to improve traditional methods and to create new systems. It is a difficult task to achieve comprehensive coverage of such a varied activity as sheep keeping and although an attempt has been made to keep a world perspective, the author's own experience and interest have inevitably influenced the emphasis achieved. Most previous sheep books have concentrated on wool because of its former pre-eminence but the emphasis in the present book is more in tune with the trend of the increasing importance of meat from sheep.

The book is intended to fill a gap in the literature for students of agriculture at degree and higher diploma level. Whilst the book is aimed at satisfying the requirements of such students in any part of the world, it remains essential that lectures and class work are soundly complemented with practical classes implementing the principles in the context of the local breeds and practices of the area. It is hoped that the book should also meet the need of the great number of those with agricultural degrees and diplomas in every walk of the agricultural life—farmers, advisers, feed formulators—all those who are concerned with the efficiency of sheep production. It is also hoped that it will be of value to research workers, veterinary practitioners and those concerned with planning the future of our rural environment.

Sheep keeping is a crucial sector of human activity and if the industry declined rapidly large tracts of the earth's surface would be laid bare, which would lead to the loss of a people and a culture that have survived with less change than in almost any other section of human activity.

I am deeply indebted to many colleagues who have made the writing of this book possible; in particular to the many research students and staff colleagues who have contributed the enthusiasm and shared the burden of some of the development work reported. Mr D. A. R. Davies of Liverpool University has made a major contribution on the artificial rearing of lambs and the development of the Cambridge sheep breed. Many farmers have also contributed as cooperators in the sheep breeding scheme.

At the School of Agriculture, Aberdeen, I am much indebted to Miss L. E. Brook for assistance in much of the final research for the book and to Mr J. Stauvers and Mr J. F. Reaper for assistance with the visual material. I am most indebted to Mrs I. M. Watt for master-minding the typing and undertaking much of the work herself.

Parts of the draft at various stages were read by kind colleagues— Dr R. C. Roberts, Dr M. L. Ryder and Dr A. W. Speedy of Edin-burgh; Dr J. J. Robinson, Dr E. R. Ørskov, Mr D. C. Macdonald and Mr D. J. Pearson of Aberdeen, and Dr D. W. Walker of Sydney, Australia.

Finally, but not least, my wife Margaret and my children provided assistance in all sorts of ways.

Aberdeen   J. B. Owen
October 1975

Systems of *Sheep Production*   1

The Development of World Sheep Systems

Sheep give rise to three major products—meat, wool and milk. In many parts of the world, particularly the temperate regions, meat is the major product and the importance of meat in sheep production is increasing. Australia is still the world's major sheep keeping country and fine wool production is the basis of its economy, although meat production is gradually increasing in importance. In many areas of the world, particularly the Mediterranean countries, the Middle East and Eastern Europe, ewes are still kept for dairying so that their sheep production is based on the three major products although meat production is gaining in relative importance.

Table 1.1. *Efficiency of Meat Production**

	Poultry	Pigs	Cattle	Sheep
DM eaten per kg carcase	3.1	4.7	30	36
DM eaten per kg usable meat	4.5	6.2	35	44

* Based on feed input to the whole system.

Table 1.1 shows the efficiency of sheep as converters of their feed to meat relative to other farm animals at current average rates of production. It is evident that the ruminants are much inferior to pigs and poultry on this basis, largely because of the overhead of breeding stock that has to be carried by every slaughter animal. Because the lamb is sold at a relatively low body weight as compared to the beef animal, sheep production is less efficient than beef production. Sheep, however, consume a lower proportion of expensive concentrate feed than any other farm stock.

Sheep production is concentrated, throughout the world, around the poorer mountainous regions and is largely associated with less developed peasant farming systems. Table 1.2 shows the sheep population and main products of several countries together with the trend of changes in a recent period of years. It was an exception to this trend that arable areas in Western Europe, particularly in the Britain of the nineteenth and early twentieth century, supported an intensive agriculture, based on a large number of sheep. However, it was on the lighter soils of the dry Eastern arable areas that the main concentrations of sheep were to be found. It is the sheep's ability to live and produce on land unfavourable for other forms of agriculture, that has made it so important in world agriculture.

In better areas the sheep system has existed as a complement to other enterprises, often utilizing by-products that would otherwise be wasted. As farming becomes more 'developed' and labour use has to become more intensive, there is a trend towards simplification and specialization in farming systems and a trend away from the traditional farm with its whole variety of complex interacting enterprises.

Transhumance and Nomadic Systems

One of the most interesting systems of farming that has ever evolved, is still widely practised in some sheep keeping areas and goes back in history right to the threshold of domestication. This is the system, found in mountain areas, where farming people and their flocks and herds migrate annually in the spring, from their wintering grounds in the valleys to the high moun-

Table 1.2. *Features of the sheep industry in several important sheep countries*

Continent/Country*	No. of sheep (thousands)		Sheep per hectare of land surface	Ewe's milk as % of all milk produced	Washed wool /1000 sheep (metric tons)	Mutton + goat produce/1000 population (metric tons)
	1967	1972	1972	1972	1972	1972
Europe						
Albania	1 670	1 590	0.55	25.38	1.13	12.88
Bulgaria	9 998	10 127	0.91	18.82	1.52	9.31
France	9 816	10 115	0.18	2.90	0.84	2.41
German DR	–	1 607	0.15	–	2.10	0.63
Greece	7 829	7 620	0.58	33.40	0.58	10.30
Hungary	3 274	2 271	0.24	2.94	1.89	0.48
Eire	4 239	4 277	0.61	–	2.33	16.38
Italy	8 212	7 846	0.26	4.42	0.68	1.00
Poland	3 321	3 200	0.10	0.003	1.69	0.75
Portugal	5 760	5 700	0.64	12.54	0.60	1.84
Romania	14 109	14 071	0.59	9.54	1.28	4.00
Spain	18 716	17 863	0.35	3.93	0.72	3.97
UK	28 885	26 877	1.10	–	1.19	3.90
Yugoslavia	10 329	8 326	0.33	5.15	0.82	2.41
USSR	135 483	139 916	0.06	0.12	1.80	3.95
North & Central America						
Mexico	6 695	5 480	0.03	–	0.56	0.63
USA	23 898	18 710	0.02	–	1.99	1.15

Contd,

Table 1.2. (*Contd*)

Continent/Country*	No. of sheep (thousands)		Sheep per hectare of land surface	Ewe's milk as % of all milk produced	Washed wool /1000 sheep (metric tons)	Mutton+goat produce/1000 population (metric tons)
	1967	1972	1972	1972	1972	1972
South America						
Argentina	48 700	42 000	0.15	—	2.00	7.60
Bolivia	6 170	7 000	0.63	38.10	0.53	3.88
Brazil	22 102	24 400	0.29	—	0.82	0.59
Chile	7 600	6 900	0.09	—	1.67	2.15
Peru	15 500	16 918	0.13	—	0.41	2.42
Uruguay	21 900	15 614	0.88	—	2.25	11.84
Asia						
Afghanistan	48 700	23 000	0.36	41.49	0.75	5.93
China	69 700	71 300	0.07	—	0.50	0.73
India	42 100	43 000	0.13	—	0.52	0.67
Iran	28 000	36 000	0.22	30.18	0.36	7.49
Iraq	11 040	16 000	0.37	45.50	0.48	8.85
Mongolia	13 065	13 420	0.09	19.92	0.94	65.84
Nepal	2 000	2 220	0.16	—	0.99	1.44
Pakistan	11 000	16 720	0.21	—	0.71	1.18
Syrian Arab Republic	5 569	6 500	0.35	41.94	1.15	6.96
Turkey	34 379	36 760	0.47	21 45	0.71	5.11
Yemen Arab Republic	11 800	3 751	0.19	20.23	—	8.89

Africa					
Algeria	7 000	8 420	0.04	21.71	0.75	2.86
Ethiopia	121 000	12 950	0.11	0.79	0.0154	3.67
Lesotho	1 500	1 720	0.57	—	0.67	3.69
Mali	4 900	5 500	0.04	16.26	0.0364	6.18
Morocco	10 600	17 500	0.39	29.17	0.41	5.14
Nigeria	5 095	8 000	0.09	—	—	1.84
South Africa	35 570	30 700	0.25	—	1.89	8.05
Sudan	8 670	14 800	0.06	7.04	0.22	6.24
Tunisia	4 205	3 100	0.19	22.16	0.71	2.96
Oceania						
Australia	164 237	162 939	0.21	—	2.79	58.86
New Zealand	60 030	59 900	2.23	—	3.81	190.44
Continent Totals						
Europe excluding USSR	133 718	127 533	0.26	1.90	1.10	2.22
N. America	24 643	19 430	0.01	—	1.46	1.09
S. America	135 091	118 000	0.07	0.14	1.39	1.91
Far East	71 195	66 551	0.08	0.75	0.52	0.55
Near East	129 043	146 344	0.12	13.16	0.62	5.43
Africa	115 385	143 301	0.05	5.76	0.15	2.20
Oceania	224 281	222 853	0.26	—	3.06	65.41

* Includes countries that have 5 million sheep or more or have 1 million or more sheep at more than 0·1 sheep per hectare.

tain pastures, returning in the autumn to the valleys for their shelter and the winter food.

The system survives in several modified forms. In parts of Europe, Asia, and North Africa, the system remains almost unchanged as it must have done for thousands of years and involves whole groups of people, existing as isolated tribes of several families, sharing a distinct culture and participating in the communal migration involving many flocks.

The relics of the system can still be seen in more developed countries and persisted in many parts of Britain until the beginning of the nineteenth century, e.g., the Welsh '*hafod a hendre*' system (Jones, 1967). It has left its mark not only in the names of farms in the valleys of Western Britain but also in the present hill sheep farming system in those areas, which is based on a close 'symbiosis' of mountain summer pasture with lowland wintering resources. Thus, elements of this method of farming, developed over centuries as a balanced ecological system, still make sound sense in terms of using land resources.

Whilst transhumant systems usually involve two main territories, usually differing in altitude, nomadic systems in their extreme may involve much more movement and the tribal groups involved may live in tents all the year. These systems are associated with the semi-arid areas of the world where the movement is dictated by the rainfall pattern rather than by altitude. The Bedouin nomads of the Middle East and North Africa are well known but only a few detailed studies of their sheep management are available. Bhattacharya and Harb (1973) have studied the Bedouins of the Lebanon and show that they follow broadly traditional routes in a seasonally cyclic fashion searching for pastures and water for their stock. Often the standard of living of the nomad is higher than that of the farmer of the settled village that he passes on his route. The nomadic flocks lamb in January before the pastures are green and the fat tail provides a reserve to bridge the gap before pasture growth while the lambs are suckled. They then enjoy good pasture from April to July coinciding with the period of milking which commences after the lamb reaches 2–3 months of age, although the lambs are not necessarily completely weaned at this stage. Pasture gradually deteriorates from July to September when the ewes are dried off. The Bedouin then move over the border into Syria for the winter, in some cases paying rent for privately owned land. Some of the land is seeded with barley and vetch before the nomads move on.

Settled Villages.

In the nomadic and transhumant areas there are also a proportion of tribes which have settled into villages near sources of water or oases. These people cultivate land but still usually own livestock, particularly sheep (Faulkner, 1973). Often the sheep are tended by hired shepherds in communal flocks and may still take a limited part in movements to other grazings.

A whole history and culture is bound up with the traditional practices of the nomadic and transhumant people and the expertise and cultural sense embodied in these systems and their practitioners have been too little valued in the modern world. They still utilize in the only possible way important resources of a vast but poor terrain, which would otherwise be barren. The system is but a memory in Britain but great areas of the Near East, Asia and North Africa are entering on a period of traumatic change. Over-grazing and deterioration of ranges has been continuing for centuries in some parts, but present day livestock transport and the demands of developed society are putting intolerable strains on the lives of the nomadic and transhumant populations. Unless serious attention is given to the merits of these practices and some attempt made to reconcile their essentials with modern society then a large proportion of the earth's surface may become barren.

Fencing and Sheep Systems

Of all human innovations, the fence has had as much impact as any on the sheep. Systems used in the long enclosed lowland areas of some developed countries are often quite different from those found in large areas of the world which have not been enclosed. In enclosed areas, sheep management on arable land involves the closely herded flock, tended closely by a man and his dog. Subdivision of grazing into small fenced fields is still comparatively less important on a world basis, and even in developed countries like Britain many mountain areas have no fenced boundary between separately owned sheep flocks.

The Territorial Instinct

In many mountain and range areas sheep adopt distinct territories whereby, without any fences, a flock or 'heft' of sheep sticks to one area of grazing (see Chapter 7). This tendency in the sheep has been developed over several generations and reinforced by shepherding and the culling of strays. It is developed to such an extent that an open hill farm cannot operate without its 'hefted' flock and the flock is sold with a farm at a premium for 'acclimatization value'.

Sheep Herding

Sheep, under most systems of husbandry, are kept in large numbers and scattered over a large area of land. Since the days of early man a third animal has formed one of a triangle of relationship with man and his sheep. Without the sheep dog, sheep management would demand too much labour to be viable and it is only because of the dog that one man systems, involving many hundred or even thousands of sheep, can be contemplated. Essentially, in the sheep dog, man has capitalized on the primitive stalking instinct of the predator dog and sublimated it into a disciplined array of conditioned and learned reflexes. This strange partnership of dog and man has turned out to be one of the most useful examples of man-trained animals.

Labour use in Sheep Systems

Because the sheep is the farm animal most strictly influenced by the season, the sheep enterprise has special problems with regard to labour use. A successful lambing is often claimed to be the one that is concentrated into one intense period in the year of little more than two weeks duration. Many of the subsequent operations are related to lambing, or the age of the lamb, and are therefore synchronized. Added to this are other intensely seasonal operations like shearing which result in the characteristic uneven demand for labour in the sheep industry.

Traditionally, such peaks were overcome by the planned staggering of some of the operations like shearing, from farm to farm, so that the co-operation of several neighbours could easily provide a gang of operators to deal with the need. These activities also strengthened the strong co-operative social bond in otherwise largely isolated and independent farms.

The breakdown of traditional co-operation, associated with the increased industrialization of agriculture, has resulted in a grave labour problem for sheep farming. The increasing specialization of farm workers and of farming systems has reduced the role of sheep, as subsidiary enterprises on large farms, and the consequent benefit derived in such systems from the pooling of all hands on any farm to cope with any peak sheep job required. In the USA, New Zealand and Australia, the formation of contract gangs has been one means of meeting the need for labour and, to some extent, sheep farmers in Europe and other developed areas have adopted a similar policy.

Another possible means of combating the problem, is to break up the peaks of demand and plan a system where the labour load is better spread. So far, only little progress has been made along this line but it seems to be a logical trend to follow and examples of how this can operate in a breeding flock are given in the description of detailed systems in Chapter 10.

In some of the American West and Midwest states such as Colorado, lamb feed lots have been in operation for many years, which operate on a year round large scale operation. Such units may have a capacity for several tens of thousands of lambs at any time with store lambs purchased every week of the year from a large catchment area south and north of the Rocky Mountain ranges. The spread of throughput is achieved because Texan lambs come early in March/April to be followed from late summer until the spring by the Northern lambs from the ranges north of Texas right up to the Canadian border. Such units are extremely efficient in labour use and often operate to a high standard of management and animal welfare.

Sheep Predators

Another factor in the development of present day systems has been the number of natural enemies that plague the sheep. Important among these are the predators of the dog family, and the close herding and night confinement of sheep found in some parts of the world is to ward off predators like wolves, coyotes, dingo dogs, hyenas and foxes. In the modern world the domestic stray dog has become a menace to the sheep keeper within reasonable proximity to cities and towns, and there is a heavy annual toll from this source.

In the USA sheep predators, chiefly the coyote, are being increasingly protected because of the concern for the maintenance of wild life, and legislation is such that sheep keepers feel they have no effective means to protect their flocks. Many forecast the demise of the Western range sheep industry in the States, if the present trend continues. Although adult sheep are sometimes attacked and killed by the larger predators, the young lamb is often the main target of predator attacks.

World Systems of Sheep Production

It is not easy in a short space to paint a coherent picture of such a vast and varied industry. There are countless breeds and varieties of sheep, let alone all the facets of management and husbandary that change from one district to another, and from one farm to the next. The following major types of sheep production are distinctly different and clearly regionalized:

1. *Finewool production.* The production of finewool is found in the semi-arid plains of Australia, South Africa, South America and Asia—based on large scale herding of Merino sheep or their

close derivatives. Although called finewool production the wool varies in fineness and meat is a by-product.

2. *Dairy production.* Dairy production is widespread on mountainous land in Southern and Eastern Europe, Northern Africa and Asia—based on small scale peasant farming or communal tribal ownership of a wide variety of native sheep types. Meat, wool and pelt production are other important products.

3. *Mountain or range sheep production.* In addition to the subsistence farming associated with transhumance there is specialized range farming of the type found in Northern Europe and North America. These flocks vary considerably in size, and are generally complementary to lowland systems, supplying lambs to be finished in feed lots as in central North America or on grass and arable crops as in Britain and Northern Europe. The mountain farms are also an important source of breeding ewes for lowland lamb producing flocks. Wool is usually an important product on such farms.

4. *Lowland lamb production.* This system is found in good temperate or coastal areas suitable for the growth of grass as in New Zealand, Northern Europe and North America. Generally the small scale breeding flocks involved are either self contained or based on cross bred hill sheep. The main product is young lamb slaughtered towards the end of the growing season.

To put sheep production in its context, an attempt is made in the following section to give a brief review of sheep production on a world basis. To reduce the size of the task, it is mainly countries that have a sheep industry with more than five million ewes or with a million sheep at a density of 0·1 per ha of land surface are included. There is a wide disparity in the amount and type of information available in English on sheep and sheep production systems in the world and there has been much more emphasis on wool production than on any other aspects. The following account is based on a variety of sources in addition to the author's own limited acquaintance with some of the countries involved. These include Ryder and

Stephenson (1968), Onions (1962), Mason and Maule (1960), Mason (1969), Faulkner (1974) and Draz (1974). Other specific sources are referenced in the text.

In order to make some intelligible order out of the myriad of sheep breeds and types that occur throughout the world, Table 1.3 attempts to group the main sheep breeds in some kind of logical order. Fig. 9.9, (Chapter 9; kindly supplied by Dr M. L. Ryder of the Animal Breeding Research Organisation, Edinburgh.) is an attempt to group breeds by function and development. Most, but not all, of the breeds mentioned in various countries fit into the broad pattern given.

Table 1.3. *List of main world sheep groups.*

1. *Groups of world-wide distribution and influence*	*Examples of constituent breeds*
Merino	Australian merino, Caucasian merino, German Mutton merino, Précoce, Rambouillet, Russian merino, Sopravissana.
Longwool	Blue-faced Leicester, Border Leicester, Devon Longwool, English Leicester, Galway, Île de France (Corriedale) [Merino cross], Lincoln, Roscommon, Teeswater, Wensleydale.
Down	Dorset down, Hampshire, Oxford down, Southdown, Suffolk.
Romney	Lowicz, New Zealand Romney, Romney (Kent).
2. *Regional groups of historical and widespread importance*	
Northern Short-tailed (N. Europe)	Finnsheep, North Ronaldsay, Romanov, Shetland (includes primitive multihorned e.g., Soay, Jacob).
Marsh (N. W. Europe)	East Friesian, Oldenburg, Texel.
Heath (N. W. Europe)	Danish Landrace, Dutch Heath, German Heath, Polish Heath.
Zackel (S. E. Europe)	Albanian Zackel, Bulgarian Zackel, Greek Zackel, Racka, Sumava, Țurcana, Valachian, Voloshian.

Table 1.3. *contd*

2. *Regional groups of historical and widespread importance—cont.*	*Examples of constituent breeds*
Tsigai (S. E. Europe) (Merino derivative)	Azou Tsigai, Romanian Tsigai, Ruda, Russian Tsigai.
Karakul (USSR)	Arabi, German Karakul, Malich.
Fat-rumped (USSR)	Chuntuk, Kalmyk, Karanogai, Kazakh.
Fat-tailed (Asia, Europe, Africa)	African long fat-tail, Barbary fat-tail, Caucasian fat-tailed, Han-yang, Hu-yang, Mongolian, Tan-yang, Tung-yang.
Indian (India and Pakistan)	Bikaneri, Chanothar, Gujarati, Hassan, South India Hairy, Thal, Waziri.

3. *Local groups of varying importance*	
Scottish Blackfaced hill (UK)	Lonk, Scottish Blackface, Swaledale.
British Whitefaced hill (UK)	Cheviot, Herdwick, Llŷn, Radnor, Welsh Mountain.
Awassi (Middle East)	Awassi, Israeli Improved, N'emi, Shafali.
Somali (Africa)	Adali, Blackhead Persian, Toposa.
Churro (Spain & Portugal)	Bragança, Castilian, Galician, Mancha, Segura.
Sardinian (Italy)	Large Lowland Sardinian, Medium Hill Sardinian, Small Mountain Sardinian.
Irish (Eire)	Galway, Roscommon.
French (France)	Berrichon, Bluefaced Maine, Causses, Contentin, Lacaune, Préalpes du Sud.
Tibetan (Asia)	Northern Tibetan, Southern Tibetan, Steppe Tibetan.
Lop-eared Alpine (Alps)	Bergamo, Biella, French Alpine, Swiss White Alpine, Tyrol Mountain.
Chios (Greece & Turkey)	Greek Chios, Turkish Chios.
Dahman (South Central Morocco)	Dahman.
British Whitefaced Shortwools (S. W. Britain)	Devon Closewool, Dorset Horn, Exmoor Horn, Kerry Hill, Ryeland, Wiltshire Horn.

The continents and countries within continents are dealt with broadly in the order of the numerical importance of their sheep industry, although this order is not adhered to when there is an obviously coherent geographical or other order that is preferable.

AUSTRALIA

Australia is well established as the main sheep producing country of the world. This vast continent, first settled by Europeans as late as the end of the eighteenth century, has since developed an agriculture dominated by wool producing sheep. The suitability of extensive sheep systems for the exploitation of the dry environment and of finewool as an export product, have resulted in the rapid development and continuing importance of the sheep industry (Fig. 1.3) Australia's sheep industry depends largely on wool production from Merino sheep, run at very low rates of stocking. Three main areas can, however, be distinguished, which are distinct climatic zones and which also broadly distinguish between sheep systems in Australia.

The High Rainfall Area

This relatively high rainfall area extends in a narrow band along the southern coast of the country from the south west of Western Australia, includes the south eastern tip of South Australia, southern Victoria and the eastern coast of New South Wales, reaching up to the south eastern border of Queensland. It also includes much of Tasmania. The most southerly part of this narrow belt, virtually from Perth to Canberra, has winter rainfall which is reliable, by the uncertain standards of the remainder of the continent. The area contains a number of coastal hill and mountain ranges where productivity is limited by soil poverty but it also includes the best farm land in Australia. On the better land there is a high proportion of fat lamb producing flocks, based on Merino ewes crossed with Down breed rams or crossbred Merino or non-Merino ewes crossed with rams such as the Dorset Horn. As might be expected, farm sizes

Fig. 1.1 *An Australian Kelpie sheepdog takes a short cut. (by courtesy of the Australian News & Information Bureau)*

Fig. 1.2. *Merinos being gathered for shearing—southern Tablelands New South Wales, Australia. (by courtesy of the Australian News & Information Bureau).*

are lower than in other areas of Australia, although the number of sheep per flock may still be large by world standards. Lambing in these flocks takes place in the autumn and winter usually before the main grass growth, except in areas like the higher and more northerly tablelands where the severity of the winter makes spring lambing more common.

Even these areas are not immune from drought, particularly summer drought, and supplementary feeding may be provided during the drought period.

The Medium Rainfall Area

In between the high rainfall area and the dry interior of the continent lies an extensive area of the country with a medium but unreliable rainfall which has long been utilized for wheat and sheep farming. These areas extend west from the slopes and plains inland from the main eastern dividing mountain range, to the vast plateau of Western Australia and northwards into the predominantly summer rainfall areas of northern New South Wales and Queensland. Farms in these areas are run on a mixed sheep and wheat system with wheat alternating with pasture for grazing, although there is no rigid standard rotation characteristic of the whole area. The improvement of pasture by the use of fertilizer, particularly by the introduction of subterranean clover leys, has been a marked feature in recent years.

As in the high rainfall areas, sheep are kept for fat lamb production as well as wool production and several flocks in the area are based on crossbred Merino ewes for this purpose. In the winter rainfall areas of the South, with their relatively mild winters, lambing takes place in the autumn, so that lambs can be slaughtered before the food supplies dry up in the spring. In the summer rainfall areas of eastern Australia lambing is in the spring so that the lambs have their main growth period on the summer pasture.

The Low Rainfall Area

Next to the barren deserts of the centre of Australia is the arid zone, which has long been associated with large scale sheep farming. In some parts, particularly in the north of the continent, large scale ranching is practised. The size of enterprise is large, with some sheep stations covering several hundred thousand hectares and the average size of the sheep flock is larger than those of the higher rainfall areas. The basis of the system is the Merino breed, kept for wool production in flocks with a high proportion of wether sheep. A high proportion of wether sheep has been a feature of most sheep systems, throughout the world where conditions are poor and wool is an important product. Lambing in these flocks may take place at any time from the autumn to the spring according to area; moving northwards into Queensland, there is a trend to spring lambing.

Table 1.4 gives a summary of the position in the Australian sheep industry according to the state and the rainfall area.

The future of much of the Australian sheep industry depends on the future for wool and although wool is likely to continue as an important product for many decades, it is probable that there will be increasing emphasis on fat lamb production in the higher rainfall areas. It is difficult to see a suitable alternative for wool production in the low rainfall pastoral areas of Australia. Another important factor for the future is the marked increase that has occurred since 1945 in the proportion of lamb meat consumed by the domestic consumer, as opposed to mutton (Tribe & Coles, 1966). The increase in the Australian population and the continuation of the long term trend towards shortage of meat supplies are likely to provide a strong future demand for high quality lamb. Other areas of the Far East, notably Japan, are also increasing their demand for sheep meat.

New Zealand

New Zealand is more heavily stocked with sheep than any other important sheep country (Table 1.2), and a significant part of its development and economy has been based on the

Table 1.4. *Average sheep property characteristics for Australia, 1970–71 to 1972–73. Source: Bureau of Agricultural Economics, Canberra.*

State	Zone	Property size Av. over 3 years 1972–73 (hectares)	Sheep shorn Av. over 3 years 1972–73 (number)	Lambs shorn Av. over 3 years 1972–73 (number)	Total sheep shorn Av. over 3 years 1972–73 (number)	Sheep carried 1972–73 (number)	Stocking rate 1972–73 (sheep/hectare)	Total sheep numbers 1971 (million)	Merino 1971 (%)
New South Wales	Pastoral	10 645	4 277	1 025	5 302	4 788	0.4	15.9	
	Wheat/sheep	999	1 515	429	1 944	1 692	1.5	37.5	75
	High rainfall	677	1 876	232	2 108	1 888	2.8	16.9	
Victoria	Wheat/sheep	789	984	281	1 265	1 073	1.1	11.0	50
	High rainfall	465	1 553	442	1 995	1 616	2.6	22.7	
Queensland	Pastoral	14 200	5 048	958	6 006	5 548	0.4	12.8	98
	Wheat/sheep	2 978	1 469	155	1 624	1 473	0.7	1.9	
South Australia	Pastoral	34 161	4 173	873	5 046	3 495	0.1	2.5	
	Wheat/sheep	946	858	259	1 117	984	1.1	9.0	85
	High rainfall	483	1 637	488	2 125	1 967	3.6	7.7	
West Australia	Pastoral	237 219	9 836	1 123	10 959	9 212	0.1	3.7	
	Wheat/sheep	1 412	2 189	617	2 806	2 629	1.7	22.9	93
	High rainfall	732	2 139	562	2 701	2 333	3.1	8.1	
Tasmania	High rainfall	652	1 586	438	2 024	1 664	2.6	4.5	9
Australia	Pastoral	23 177	4 852	957	5 809	4 948	0.2	34.9	
	Wheat/sheep	1 047	1 410	396	1 806	1 605	1.4	82.3	75
	High rainfall	563	1 715	406	2 121	1 818	2.9	59.9	
	*Outside of zone							0.7	
Australian Total								177.8	

* Refers to areas which do not come within the boundaries of the three zones.

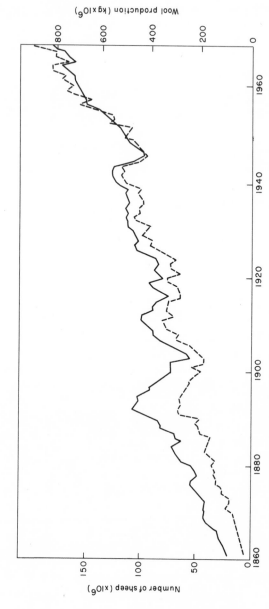

Fig. 1.3. *Wool production (greasy basis) and number of sheep in Australia, 1861–1970 showing effects of major droughts. (From Alexander & Williams, 1973; By courtesy of the Commonwealth Bureau of Census and Statistics, Australia).*

export of prime lamb carcasses to the UK. The sheep was introduced to New Zealand in the 1830s shortly after the country was colonized by European settlers and in the 1840s sheep were brought over in large numbers, so that by 1880 there were thirteen million sheep. The early sheep were largely based on the Spanish Merino, although a number of British breeds were also introduced. At first, wool was the main product, but the commencement of export to London of frozen carcasses in 1882 was the start of an enterprise that has since dominated the New Zealand sheep industry.

New Zealand sheep farming is more uniform than that of most countries but shows the common features of a simple stratification system where higher lands farms produce breeding stocks for the lowland farms. Merinos are now kept only on the most unfavourable native tussock pastures in the mountains of the South Island. In the better mountain areas of the South Island, Corriedales and Halfbreds (based on Longwool × Merino matings) are maintained to produce wool and breeding ewes. Some farms on the lowland plains of the South Island use draft ewes from the hill Corriedale and Halfbred flocks for producing lamb, sired by the Southdown breed. Alternatively, as is the general custom in the North Island, they use Romney ewes for lamb production.

The pattern of sheep production in the North Island of New Zealand developed rather differently, partly due to the delay in settlement because of the Maori wars and because the milder, moister, climate favoured a dense rain forest vegetation which was not so easy to clear. After reclamation and the establishment of sown pastures, the Merinos, which were the first sheep introduced, were quickly replaced by the larger Lincoln Longwools which in turn have been almost entirely replaced by the New Zealand Romney. Large self-contained flocks of Romneys are kept on the higher hill country of the North Island and provide a reservoir of breeding ewes for the lamb producing flocks where the Romney ewe is crossed with the Southdown ram. Some of the larger lamb producers both in the North and South

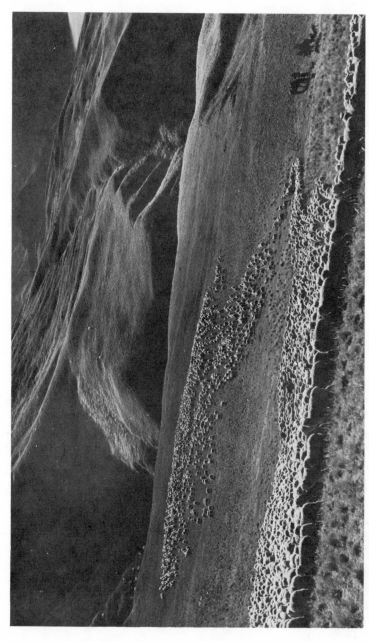

Fig. 1.4. *Sheep return to their hill grazings—West Wanaka, New Zealand. (by courtesy of the High Commissioner for New Zealand).*

Islands keep virtually two flocks on the same property—one self-contained to supply replacements for both flocks and the other crossed with the Southdown for lamb production.

Some other breeds have recently made progress in the North Island, notably the Cheviot in crosses with the Romney on the worst of the hill country. As a result of continued breeding a breed called the Perendale has been developed for use on the harder hill areas.

The flocks in New Zealand, as in Australia, are mostly in excess of one thousand ewes and the industry is noted for its use of dogs and its labour efficiency. Apart from the poorest hill and mountain areas where there may be less than one sheep kept per hectare, New Zealand sheep are heavily stocked with all year stocking rates of more than ten ewes per hectare on the best farms.

The future of New Zealand sheep farming may change with the entry of Britain into the European Common Market. Although this may mean a diversification of exports to the USA and Japan, the efficiency of lamb production and the fact that the NZ supply complements that of the Northern Hemisphere will ensure that New Zealand lamb is a continuing formidable competitor for the north-west Europe winter lamb market.

Asia—the Near East

FAO statistics (FAO, 1972) suggest that more than 90 per cent of the land area of the Near East has no other use than grazing. Over most of the area 50 per cent or more of the population is engaged in agriculture and sheep are the most important livestock in their agriculture; Turkey and Iran each have more than 35 million sheep. Sheep meat is most important in countries with a high population of Muslims and Jews where little pigmeat is consumed. Sheep also provide a high proportion of the milk consumed in the area. Because of the arid conditions, fat-tailed sheep, adapted to such conditions are dominant—a good example of a natural buffering system against seasonal variation in food supply.

TURKEY

The land of Turkey is dominated by a large central plateau over 800 m above sea level with spring and autumn rainfall and dry summers. The sheep in the area are run during the summer in large flocks, looked after communally for the whole village. During the winter the flocks are often brought indoors because of the intense cold.

The majority of Turkish sheep are fat-tailed and sheep produce about 20 per cent of the milk produced in the country. As in most sheep countries of the world there has been some Merino influence—the Turkish Merino being the result of crossing native sheep with German and Hungarian Merinos.

IRAN

Iran is a mountainous country and the sheep is the most important livestock kept; it has also a high population of goats. Most of the sheep are fat-tailed sheep belonging to various breed types, e.g., the Baluchi, with coarse, partly black, wool; the sheep are used to produce meat, milk and wool. Iran is well known for its carpets and the coarse carpet wool of their sheep is suited to this outlet. Almost 30 per cent of the milk produced in Iran is sheep's milk.

Transhumance and nomadic systems are an important feature of Iranian sheep farming with groups of several families banding together with their sheep in seasonal movements between winter and summer pastures. It is estimated that 70 per cent of the total sheep and goat population of Iran belong to the nomad and transhumant people (Sharafeldin, 1974). As in other countries in the area, attempts have been made to settle the nomads but only a small proportion of people live in settled villages. Nomadic and transhumant activity is concentrated largely around the central Zagros Mountain where the tribal system is strongly developed.

In these settled villages small family flocks are grazed on nearby grazing during the day and the sheep brought back in the evening for milking, kept confined overnight, and milked in the morning before pasturing for the day.

IRAQ

Iraq has the third highest sheep population of the area. The sheep are mainly fat tailed and belong to three main groups.

The Awassi breed is widespread throughout the Near East area and the greatest number of Awassi are found in Iraq. This breed has been subjected to selection to form the 'improved Awassi' in Israel. In Iraq, it is numerically the most important sheep and is concentrated in the middle of the country. In the south east, Arabi sheep are important, whilst the Kurdi sheep are most important in the Kurdish mountain areas of northern Iraq.

In Iraq, the sheep are owned either by nomadic graziers or by richer settled cultivators. The nomads move with their flocks into the desert each autumn and winter as the grass becomes available. When pasture and water in the wells dry up the nomads bring their flocks back to the fringes of the irrigated land and the waste land along canal and river banks. In the northern mountains, movement is between the plains and the mountains with the season.

The cultivators use the sheep as scavengers on stubbles and weeds and for grazing winter wheat. They usually pay hired shepherds to take their sheep to the desert grazings for the spring and early summer.

SYRIA

Syria has over 6 million sheep, mainly of the fat tailed Awassi type, which utilize the extensive range and waste land. A high proportion of the sheep are owned by rich merchants and town dwellers, and are shepherded by the bedouins with their own flocks. The nomads move east to west or north to south in annual migrations according to the dry and wet seasons. With a very variable rainfall, losses in droughts are common. Recently, changes in legislation governing the protection of ancient tribal grazing rights, has resulted in overgrazing and much range deterioration.

Other near east countries including Jordan, Cyprus and Lebanon have sheep populations which figure prominently in their agriculture. Although the sheep is not so important in relation to other activities in Israeli agriculture, a number of well developed Awassi flocks are kept.

The Far East including USSR

USSR

Symons (1971) has described some of the salient features of the Soviet sheep industry. It is not easy to make a sensible survey of such a big country, including as it does one-sixth of the world's land surface and about one-seventh of the agricultural land. It spans two continents and conditions vary from some of the northernmost inhabited latitudes to a Mediterranean type climate. It also demonstrates the first and most ambitious design for state organization of agriculture. The short history of the modern Soviet Union is very much affected by this large scale experiment in State run agriculture and the future of a large part of the world depends on the outcome of the experiment not only in Soviet Russia but in the other countries that have followed suit.

Livestock are relatively less important than crops in the USSR as compared with many other countries and sheep are less important than cattle. In spite of this, the recent sheep population of more than 130 million is second only to that of Australia. Sheep numbers have fluctuated widely in Soviet history during the civil war and collectivization and later during the Second World War and the recent steady increase in sheep has been achieved mainly in the state and collective farms. Of the total number of sheep only about 20 per cent were recently estimated to be privately owned.

There is much variation in the density of sheep through the various Soviet Republics, the most important being the RSFSR with more than 40 per cent of the total sheep population and Kazakhstan with more than 20 per cent. In the Central Asia and Caucasian regions where there are sharp seasonal differences in pasture production, seasonal transhumance is practised whereby the flocks move to the mountain pastures in the summer and winter on the drier, warmer lowlands nearby.

Wool is the chief product of Soviet sheep but meat and sheepskin are also important. Sheepskin includes the production of astrakhan from Karakul sheep and that of sheepskin from young sheep.

The organization of Soviet agriculture has provided an unparalleled opportunity for effecting genetic improvement in sheep since the majority of sheep are served by artificial insemination and performance recording is widespread. The Soviet Government has fostered the production of finewool by setting up large state farms for breeding Merino sheep in the North Caucasus, the Volga area, Siberia, Kazakhstan, Central Asia and the Ukraine. An all-Union Research Institute for sheep and goat breeding was set up at Stavropol and sheep breeding departments opened in a number of other institutes and research stations. State farms play a leading role in the genetic improvement of sheep and one of the finest Soviet breeds of fine fleece sheep, the Caucasian, was developed by crossing Novocaucasian finewooled ewes with American Rambouillet and Askanian rams. The new breed has been widely used in many sheep-raising districts. On the State Breeding Farm at Rubtsovsk, in Altai Territory, the Altai breed of sheep was formed by crossing Siberian Merino ewes with rams of the Caucasian breed, Australian Merinos and American Rambouillets. This breed is good for wool and meat production and adapted to the severe conditions of Siberia.

Several mountain breeds of sheep have been developed in the

Soviet Union for the millions of hectares of high mountain pasture. Karakul sheep are bred mainly in Uzbekistan, Turkmenistan, Tajikistan and Kazakhstan and some state and collective farms have flocks of up to 70 000 sheep producing the high quality Karakul skins. One of the largest sheep breeding farms in the Soviet Union is a collective farm in the Kalmyk Autonomous Republic which has 180 000 ha of pastures and about 150 000 fine fleece Stavropol sheep.

On collective and state farms a full time specialist is responsible for recording all the sheep flocks, and records of weight, fleece yields and milk production, are kept. The records provide data for management purposes as well as for testing young rams to be used in artificial insemination.

THE CHINESE PEOPLE'S REPUBLIC

Epstein (1969) has given a detailed description of sheep in China. Sheep are found in twenty out of the twenty-six provinces of the Chinese People's Republic, the six provinces without sheep being the rice growing provinces of the south and south-east. About 75 per cent of the sheep population of China is concentrated in the sparsely populated pastoral provinces of the north and south-west, particularly in the Sinkiang Uighur Autonomous Region. Wool is an important aim of Chinese sheep production and the government have fostered an expansion in the production of fine wool. Meat, milk, lamb skins and sheep skins, are also produced.

In spite of the importance of sheep in modern China there is no true native sheep evolved from indigenous stock in China proper. The earlier sheep were all derived from Mongolia or Tibet, and recently several breeds have been introduced e.g., the Merino, Karakul, Rambouillet and Corriedale.

The sheep of China can be roughly classified into four groups: fat-tailed; fat-rumped; Merino and Merino crossbreds; other thin tailed breeds. The fat tailed and fat rumped sheep produce carpet wool and some are used for milking. In parts of northern China the Mongolian fat tailed sheep is kept as a lowland ewe on the better areas whilst the thin tailed Tibetan sheep are used on higher land. The Tibetan sheep is noted for its hardiness and is often managed on a nomadic or transhumance basis with movements from the valleys to high mountain pastures for the summer. The Tibetan sheep produce a high quality carpet wool and in some areas they are trained to carry light loads because of their agility and ability to traverse difficult territory.

The Kazakh fat rumped sheep form the majority of sheep in the Sinkiang province and it is normal practice for them to be sheared twice a year; they are also used to produce lamb pelts.

Much emphasis is placed on developing fine wool production in China and the Merino breed has been widely used to this end. The Sinkiang fine wooled sheep were developed in China, with the assistance of Soviet specialists, from a basis of Kazakh fat rumped and Mongolian fat tailed sheep mated to Précoce Merino and Novocaucasian Merino rams imported from the USSR.

INDIA

India is another vast country and although it is usually associated with hot humid climates, it has areas of the North which are mountainous and cold in winter. The 42 million sheep in India are almost equally divided between the plains and semi-arid regions of the south and the colder hills and plains of the north. The sheep of southern India are hairy sheep, well adapted to hot conditions, and are kept mainly for milk and meat, whereas the sheep of northern India, particularly the north west, produce carpet wool, some of it of very high quality. The sheep on the southern plains are kept in small flocks by poor people and are grazed on waste land or on other people's stubble, where they contribute valuable manure for the coming crop. The sheep act largely as scavengers with little in the way of a fixed breeding policy. In the semi-arid areas wool is more important and a more consistent breeding policy is usually employed.

In the northern mountain regions many of the flocks are

migratory, grazing in summer on the higher mountain pastures. Some very large flocks are grazed to great heights in the Himalayan foot hills.

PAKISTAN

Most of the sheep of the former Pakistan were in fact in West Pakistan, which is now Pakistan. The sheep are similar to those of north West India and produce the better quality type of carpet wool. Wool is the main product of the Pakistan sheep and much of the finer wool is exported.

Transhumance is again an important feature of some areas in Pakistan. In Baluchistan, for example, the tribes have their home areas in the highland plateau and mountain areas, but they migrate to the lowlands of the Indus Valley and the Kachhi Plains for the winter. Here they spend the winter on irrigated areas of sorghum and other crops. Whilst they have vacated their highland grazings, Afghan nomads come down from the more severe mountains of Afghanistan to winter their flocks on the overgrazed summer pastures of the Baluchistan tribesmen.

AFGHANISTAN

Of the sheep population of over 20 million, approximately eight million are Karakul sheep concentrated in the Northern and Western Provinces and they contribute significantly to the country's important exports of sheep products. Sheep production is relatively unimproved and most are kept on a transhumance system by nomadic tribal people living in their goat-hair tents. In addition to the Karakul sheep and their specialized production, a variety of breeds are kept for coarse wool, meat and milk.

South America

The sheep population of South America is not much lower than that of the Near East and is concentrated in the southern part of the continent, particularly in the western half. The South American countries were settled from Europe by the Spanish and Portuguese and became colonies of those countries. The early colonists first brought their Churro sheep with them. Later, however, the Merino and the Lincoln longwool became the main contributors to the sheep of the area, including the more recently imported Corriedale sheep. Wool production is the main object of sheep production with some Merino fine-wools as well as some coarser wools being produced. Conditions in the continent vary markedly—Uruguay being temperate and wooded whereas Patagonia in southern Argentine is cold and dry with little shelter from the high winds.

ARGENTINA

Argentina has a population of more than 40 million sheep, a number that has been steadily reduced from much higher levels by encroachment of cattle and cultivation. The country can be divided into fairly distinct areas as far as sheep production goes. The southern area of Patagonia is a large exposed plateau, rising from the Atlantic to the Andes, where sheep are run on large ranches (*estancias*) with flocks up to 100 000 in size. The enormous plains are mainly unfenced and there is seasonal movement of flocks from winter to summer pastures. In the north, conditions are less severe with large plains of savannah and grass in the La Pampa and Buenos Aires area, with rolling pampas areas of cleared pasture with ample rainfall in the north east. In the north, there is more mixed farming with cropping and mixed grazing with cattle is common.

URUGUAY

Although a relatively small country compared with its neighbours, Uruguay has a population of nearly 20 million sheep. The conditions are somewhat similar to those of Northern Argentina—temperate with good rainfall—although it is drier in the central region.

There is less cropping in Uruguay than in Northern Argentina, but sheep are kept along with cattle in large, fenced *estancias*.

BRAZIL

Brazil has the second highest population of sheep of the South American countries, and these are concentrated towards the south of the country bordering on Uruguay. A type based on the Criollo is the most important sheep in Brazil with Merinos, Romneys and Corriedales making up most of the remainder.

CHILE

There are marked differences in the sheep systems in Chile. In the southern tip of the country in the area around Punta Arenas, most of the sheep flocks are the property of one commercial organization which produces much of the wool exported from Chile. The wool from Corriedale sheep is well known for its quality as 'Punta Arenas' wool. In the rest of the country sheep farming is less developed and based mainly on Hampshire Down, Criollo, Romney and Merino, for both meat and wool production.

PERU

The sheep of Peru are mainly kept in high plateau area of the Andes at a height of 3000–5000 m above sea level. The sheep, derived from Merino and Churro stock, are mainly kept by Indian peasants. The Government of Peru have imported Merino and Corriedale sheep with a view to improvement of Indian flocks, although production is often limited more by management practices than by sheep genotype.

Europe

Europe and the Near East contain the most densely stocked sheep areas in the world. Sheep are most important in the UK, Spain and the south east corner of Europe, but of little importance in some European countries such as Germany. Many of the sheep developed in Europe, notably the Merino from Spain and the various longwool and mutton breeds from Britain, have had a world wide influence as seen in Fig. 9.1 (*see* p. 324). Many of the countries colonized by Europeans in the last few centuries have adapted European sheep breeds to rather different conditions and spread their influence to neighbouring areas.

UNITED KINGDOM

The UK is a leading producer and consumer of lamb meat. The number of breeding ewes at 12 million in 1972 (MLC, 1972) is higher in relation to its human population than any of the highly industrialized nations. In spite of this, home production of lamb and mutton only accounted for 43 per cent of total consumption in 1973, the majority of the shortfall being imported from New Zealand; these imports from the Southern Hemisphere are complementary to British home production being concentrated on late winter, spring and early summer. The UK sheep industry has developed a complex structure which is distinctly stratified, broadly in relation to the range of land quality over which it is spread. A detailed description has been published (MLC, 1972) and only a summary of the salient points is included here.

The hub of the British sheep industry is the pool of pure-bred hill ewes, which in 1971 formed 4.6 million of the total of over 12 million breeding ewes. These ewes are mainly of the Scottish Blackface breed in Scotland and the Welsh Mountain in Wales with a smaller contribution from North Country Cheviot, Swaledale and several other localized breeds. These sheep graze the higher mountain land extending mainly from 300–1200 m above sea level, either on a year round basis at very low rates of stocking, as on the heather moorland of the Scottish Highlands, or mainly during the summer at much higher stocking rates, as in Wales and parts of Northern England. Under both management systems the chief products are the

Table 1.5

Environment	Ewe breed or cross	Number of ewes	Ram breed
Mountain and hill and mainly 300–1200 m	Blackface	1 669 ⎫	
	Welsh Mountain	1 331 ⎪	Bred pure or to rams of other hill breeds
	Swaledale	287 ⎬	
	North Country Cheviot	316 ⎪	
	Other hill breeds	1 000 ⎭	
	Total	4 603 (38% of all ewes)	
Lower hill land mainly 150–450 m	Blackface	563	Border Leicester (= Greyface)
	Welsh Mountain	140	Border Leicester (= Welsh Halfbred)
	Swaledale	185	⎰ Teeswater (= Masham) / Blue faced Leicester (= Mule)
	North Country Cheviot	128	Border Leicester (= Scottish Halfbred)
	Other hill breeds	135	Longwool
	Clun Forest / Kerry Hill / Other upland breeds ⎱	252	Pure bred or bred to other upland breed
	Hill breeds / Other crossbreds ⎱	142	Upland breeds
	Total	1 545 (13% of all ewes)	

Lowland mainly below 300 m

Welsh Mountain	413	
Other hill breeds	564	
Upland breeds	506	
Lowland breeds (including Romney, Devon and Longwools)	281	Down breeds (80% Suffolk)
Down breeds	232	
Longwool × hill crosses	1 808	
Upland × hill crosses	219	
Down × hill crosses	119	
Down × (Longwool × hill)	597	
Other crossbreds	396	
Total mated to Down rams	5 135	
Lowland ewes (excluding Down)	265	Bred pure
Ewes of all categories	527	Other lowland breeds
Total in lowland environment	5 927	(49% of all ewes)
Total ewes in Great Britain (excluding Shetland)	12 075	

store lambs in the autumn for sale to lowland feeders, the surplus cast or draft ewes, sold mainly for further breeding on farms of lower elevation, and wool, which forms a substantial proportion (25–40 per cent.) of the gross sales from these farms. The store lambs from these farms, fed on lowland pasture or arable crops, come to the market in autumn and winter. The ewes sold for breeding mainly go to farms of medium elevation; their progeny, from larger longwool breeds like the Border Leicester, are an important source of crossbred (called half-bred) ewes for lowland fat lamb production. On the lowland farms these halfbred ewes and a small proportion of the pure-bred hill ewes, are crossed with Down rams, primarily the Suffolk, to produce fat lamb.

A parallel, though more localized, stratification chain starts with the so-called semi-hill breeds, concentrated on the hills of lower elevation in the Welsh and Scottish Border country. These ewes include the Clun Forest and the Cheviots and again form a pool of breeding ewes, sold as 3–5 year old ewes to be crossed with Down rams on lowland pasture.

A simplified version of the system in 1971 is shown diagrammatically in Table 1.5 with approximate numbers in each category (MLC, 1972).

Sheep on lowland in the UK tend to be concentrated in the North and West, in areas near the source of breeding ewes although there is movement of breeding ewes to the large strip of mixed lowland farming that extends from Wiltshire up the Western side of the Midlands up to the Scottish borders.

These ewes form part of 'flying' flocks (not breeding their own replacements) used in a mixed system with cattle and arable crops. The main output is the fat lamb mainly from the Down (largely Suffolk) sire, sold during the summer and early autumn. Wool forms a much smaller proportion (about 10 per cent) of gross output on these farms.

A formerly widespread but progressively diminishing category of sheep keeping was associated with the lighter arable lands of the South and East where the traditional Norfolk four-course rotation included roots, fed off with sheep in the winter before barley was sown, together with a clover seeds break, to provide hay and late season grazing. These areas have progressively moved towards arable rotations with high proportions of cereals, particularly since 1939. The agronomic difficulties experienced with such intensive cereal cropping has caused farmers to think again about the value of grass breaks in the rotation and there could be a greater adoption of sheep systems in these areas if simple, large scale, grazing systems for sheep became widely adopted (Owen, 1972).

THE IRISH REPUBLIC

Ireland, like New Zealand and Denmark, is a relatively small advanced country whose agriculture, particularly its agricultural exports, are an important part of the country's economy. Traditional historical links, combined with proximity, has meant that the UK has been the main recipient of Irish agricultural exports, particularly of store cattle. Irish agriculture is pastoral, based on animal rather than cash crop production, but the cattle sector is substantially more important than the sheep. In 1963, there were 2.25 million cows in Ireland (both dairy and beef) compared with 1.8 million ewes. In 1973, there were 2.8 million cows and 1.4 million ewes, an increase in cow numbers and a decrease in the ewe population.

In the past, a considerable proportion of Irish lamb was consumed at home, with a small proportion exported, mainly as lamb carcasses to Britain. More recently, exports to France have increased with the periodic opening of the French market to imported lamb. In 1973, of the total mutton and lamb production of about one half a million tons (560 million kg), most was consumed at home and the remainder exported—900 tons (108 000 kg) to the UK and 10 000 (11 million kg) to France and other EEC countries.

Irish sheep production is mainly concentrated on the poorer land of the West and South West where the Scottish Blackface (Kerry) ewe is kept on the poorer land but the Galway and the

Galway × Blackface ewe (Greyface) is used as a breeding ewe on the better land. These ewes are crossed with a Down ram—mainly Suffolk—to produce the lamb for slaughter and are widespread throughout the country as a subsidiary enterprise on small farms rasing store cattle.

Ireland has a well organized Government service for the development of new practices in agriculture, and some important work on the development of new genotypes and techniques has been carried out in Ireland. The Irish are also concentrating on the marketing and quality of their products and they are well placed to develop a strong meat export trade within the EEC.

SPAIN

During the sixteenth and seventeenth centuries Spain dominated world fine wool production and much of the wealth of the Spanish empire stemmed from this basis. Sheep breeding was for a long time highly organized and protected in Spain and resulted in the development of the Merino sheep. With the spread of the Merino to the Spanish colonies and its exportation to the other developing colonies (mainly those of Britain) the dominance in fine wool production was lost and, judged by former standards, the production of fine wool in Spain has declined. Of about 18 million sheep in present-day Spain only about one-quarter are pure Merino sheep. The Churro, Mancha, and Castilian breeds are coarse or medium wooled sheep kept chiefly for their milk with meat and wool as subsidiary products. There are also a number of Karakul flocks in Spain specializing in the production of high quality lamb pelts.

The suitability of the Merino for the drier areas of the world is a reflection of the semi-arid conditions over a large part of Southern and Central Spain, where the main density of sheep is found. The Churro is the exception, being found mainly in the north west of the country. A large proportion of Spanish sheep are kept on a transhumance system where sheep in their thousands are moved from the southern wintering areas to the central plateaux further north for summer pasturing. In this system, lambs are born in the autumn so that they are capable of withstanding the long trek north. Like most semi-arid climates, conditions are variable with occasional prolonged droughts.

Attempts are being made to improve Spanish sheep production by recording performance and by selection of superior breeding stock, and there is some development of progeny testing of rams and artificial insemination. Poor nutrition arising from overstocking often, however, sets the limit to improvement. Some of the interesting developments in Spain include an assessment of the use of artificial rearing of lambs to improve the output of dairy ewes.

PORTUGAL

Portugal has a higher population of sheep, according to its size, than Spain, and conditions are more temperate. Production is somewhat similar to that of Spain, largely dependent on the same breeds—the Merino and its derivatives, and the Churro. There is a high proportion of black wooled, mainly Merino, sheep in Portugal.

FRANCE

France supported a much higher population of sheep in the last century, many kept in the central and southern areas on a transhumance system. With the restructuring of french agriculture and the abandonment of some of the transhumance movements, the sheep population has declined to relatively low levels after the Second World War. Quittet (1965) has produced a valuable guide to French sheep breeds and the pattern of the French sheep industry. In 1963, eight pure breeds in France comprised 4–9 per cent each, and 55 per cent in total, of the sheep population. These were (in order of numerical importance) the Lacaune, Caussenard, Charmoise, Île-de-France, Southdown, Mérinos d'Arles, Prèalpes du Sud and

Berrichon breeds. Between 1948 and 1962, there was a recovery and a redistribution of sheep numbers in France, with a continuing decline in a narrow central portion of Northern France around Paris, and an increase in much of the rest of the country, particularly in the south. The French sheep industry is spread out over a large area of the country and there are distinct differences in aims and husbandry practices, to some extent associated with the type of sheep.

The Lacaune dairy sheep are found in the mountain and plateau areas of the south of France, stretching southwards and westward from Aveyron almost to the South coast and the Pyrenees. The breed is closely associated with the production of Roquefort cheese and has emerged as the dominant breed of the area from a number of minor breeds found there before 1939. The commercial success of the cheese produced has enabled much development work to be done on the breed, including a well organized recording scheme with an associated scheme for selection of young dairy sires and the use of A.I. The district is subject to the severe Mediterranean climate with its cold winters and summer drought. The sheep are closely shepherded, often amongst mixed arable stocking and they are usually brought home for the night and milked evening and morning. The ewes lamb early in the season and the lambs are weaned at one month of age so that milking can take place over the months of the main grazing season. Traditionally, the lambs were slaughtered at weaning to provide much prized small lamb carcasses but there is now an increasing tendency to feed these lambs to greater weights. The other breeds of the area, collectively known as the Caussenards, have declined rapidly with the increasing dominance of the Lacaune as the major dairy ewe.

The Charmoise sheep are mainly located in the Vienne district but have extended their numbers and territory markedly since 1948. The breed is based on French native sheep combined with some of the Romney Marsh breed from Britain and is mainly developed as a meat breed for both good and poor pastures.

The Île-de-France breed is concentrated mainly in the region North and East of Paris and declined from being the dominant breed in France in 1932 with more than 1 200 000 sheep to about half that number in 1963. It developed from the work of Yvart at the veterinary school in Alfort in the 1830s, who was impressed by the Dishley Leicester in England and wished to combine its qualities with those of the Merino. It has developed as a major meat breed with a useful wool yield and has figured prominently in the recent breeding programmes of many countries. In France it is bred pure in lowland flocks in arable areas and also used as a crossing sire for other breeds and crosses. Nearer the North Eastern frontiers of France, breeds like the Texel and the German Württemberg Merino, fill the role played further West by the Île-de-France as a meat producing sheep.

The Southdown is a major French sheep breed concentrated in two main areas on the Western coast and in one part of the Eastern Central area. The breed is bred pure for lowland lamb production, as well as to produce sires for crossing with other maturing breeds.

The Mérino d'Arles breed is the important hill breed of the Pyrenees and the French Alps. They are small hardy sheep noted for their resistance to the rigours of the transhumance systems on which they are kept and produce wool and meat of high quality. The breed is associated with the great traditional transhumant movements, from the winter pastures of the Rhône delta in Provençe, in late May and June to the mountain pastures, from which they return to their home in October with the first snows on the mountain. Nowadays much of the movement is by truck and train.

The Prèalpes du Sud are found in the South East—eastwards of the main concentration of the Mérino d'Arles and Lacaune. The breed is kept under somewhat similar conditions to the Lacaune, which it resembles, and it is well adapted to the Mediterranean climate of the low hill area it occupies.

The Berrichon is an ancient French breed found in the centre of France and to some extent in the south west and near the

Swiss border. One branch of the breed, the Berrichonne du Cher, has been developed as a meat producer and used as a crossing sire as well as bred pure on the better pasture and indoors.

The many other breeds and crosses mainly occupy localized areas of France and are not as important and as widespread as those discussed.

Because of the strong demand for lamb in France and the general shortage of meat, vigorous efforts are made to foster the French sheep industry through various agencies. Mention has been made of the developments in relation to the Lacaune dairy sheep; there is also Government support for improving meat production. These include the development, since 1958, of a recording scheme as well as a number of breeding and feeding developments. Some large scale, indoor lamb production units have been set up primarily to produce lamb meat for the Paris market. With the formation of the EEC and the entry of the UK and Ireland, an active trade in lamb is developing, although at present there is no agreed sheep policy in the market and the French market is very closely protected.

ITALY

Like many other countries where transhumance is an important feature, the difficulties of the system in an era of change, particularly the cultivation of former wintering land, has resulted in a decline both in the system and in sheep numbers in Italy. There are now less than eight million sheep in Italy, mainly concentrated in the northern mountainous parts. In most countries where transhumance is practised, the winter abode is regarded as the sheep owner's home, and the summer pasture the temporary one. Often, as in Wales, the winter home 'hendre' was a substantial building whereas the summer home 'hafod' was a rather rude affair. In the Apennines, in central and southern Italy, however the sheep owners resemble the Baluchistan tribesmen of Pakistan who live in the mountains and leave their homes to go to winter pastures, just as in Wales today the hill farmer pays for wintering land for his flock. In the central and southern areas, breeds such as the Apulian Merino and the Sopravissana have been developed with much Merino influence and produce fine wool. The sheep of the Apennies were also traditionally milked on the long routes between the mountain home and the winter pasture, so that cheese could be sold in the towns on the way. The most widely kept dairy sheep is the Sardinian ewe, which produces poor wool but is highly developed as a docile dairy animal. As in Southern France, the lambs are weaned early, often at two or three weeks of age, to be slaughtered as a delicacy. In Northern Italy, sheep are an important livestock on the small, mixed peasant farms, with meat breeds like the Bergamo and the Biella (lop eared Alpine type). These sheep are often housed in the winter and graze the foothills and lower slopes of the Alps in summer. It is customary to shear the sheep in the autumn and in the early summer.

NORWAY

Norway is the only Scandinavian country where the sheep numbers exceed one million but a brief description is considered useful. The sheep population in Norway has shown some decline since 1967 although there is spare mountain land above tree level that can be used for summering sheep. There is a concentration of sheep around the western coast near the mountains, where sheep belonging to small flocks of 10–100 ewes (average 20–30 in 1969) are sent up to communal grazings above the forests in the summer. The sheep are brought down from the mountain in mid-September, and because of the lack of wintering facilities, 80 per cent of the surplus lambs are weaned and slaughtered after the 1st October. The meat is frozen and home freezers have long been a feature of Norwegian households. The remaining breeding sheep are housed in the winter and are usually shorn on going into the house in early November and again before the ewes return to the mountain in June.

Norwegian sheep are based mainly on the Cheviot which has

gradually ousted the Old Norwegian breed, one of the northern short tail group. There has been much interest in sheep improvement in Norway associated with the traditional autumn sheep shows, and recently there has been active development of objective recording and progeny testing. The Norwegian Meat Board has co-operated in this work by carrying out detailed carcass assessment.

Other Scandinavian countries and Iceland have small but rather similar sheep systems, depending largely on winter housing with the consequent need for high lamb production to cover costs. Although the major emphasis is on meat and wool, in Sweden particularly there is also some emphasis on sheep skin production to provide material for winter clothing. Sweden, Finland and Iceland have retained, to a much greater extent than Norway, their native (landrace) sheep, belonging to the northern short tail group. These sheep, particularly the Finn-sheep, are well known for their high prolificacy and have recently been exported all over the world for inclusion in sheep breeding programmes.

ROMANIA

Outside the USSR, Romania, with almost fourteen million sheep, has the highest population of sheep in Eastern Europe. The sheep are based mainly on the Ţurcana breed, a Zackel type, found in most of the mountain areas of Romania. In the lower plain areas the Tsigai sheep are common, a breed that is widely distributed in South East Europe. A small proportion of Karakul sheep are kept for the production of lambskins and there are several other breeds of minor importance. After the establishment of the Communist Government, Romanian agriculture was rapidly collectivized in the 1950s, reverting to some extent to the larger sized farming units common in Romania before the land reform of the 1920s. With collectivization and the establishment of State farms to act as development centres, changes are taking place in Romanian sheep practices. Artificial insemination is now used extensively and much improved breeding stock has been imported from the USSR and other countries.

BULGARIA

The sheep industry of Bulgaria has been described by Minev (1972) and has similarities with that of Romania, although Bulgaria, with almost 10 million sheep, is more densely stocked with sheep than any of its neighbours. The sheep are found in the mountain regions and were kept in very small flocks until the collectivization that occurred after the Communist takeover in 1944. Until then, Bulgaria had long been a country of small farms–the vast majority under 10 ha of cropping land and in 1939 the average sheep flock per private holding was fifteen. The native Bulgarian sheep of the Zackel type, like the Țurcana of Romania, was the major basis of sheep farming in Bulgaria. A number of local and improved derivatives have sprung from it, especially in the last few years. The Karnobat breed of the South East of Bulgaria is derived from the Tsigai sheep.

In the '40s and '50s Bulgarian agriculture has become almost entirely collectivized with very large units, in complete contrast to the land tenure of the pre-Communist era. The production of milk, meat, wool and some sheep skins continue to be important objectives in almost all breeds and crosses of sheep, and great emphasis is being placed on the use of superior breeding stock through the medium of Artificial Insemination. There are artificial insemination centres in each district of the country supplying a free insemination service, and in 1969 98 per cent of all ewes were artificially inseminated. The important breeds imported into Bulgaria, to improve finewool production, have included the Caucasian, 3420 rams and 3764 gimmers having been imported from the USSR in the period 1952–1963. Breeding animals from the Askanian and Stavropol breeds have also been introduced on some scale. For lowland conditions substantial introductions of Mutton Merino sheep have been made. Work on the East Friesian sheep has shown that the breed is not well adapted to Bulgarian conditions, but use is made of its high milk production in new crosses of sheep derived especially for dairy production. Other breeds introduced in smaller numbers include British breeds such as the Suffolk, Romney Marsh, Clun Forest and Oxford Down.

In addition to experiment and organization in sheep breeding, several developments have taken place in the 'industrialization' of sheep husbandry by creating large units, mechanized feedings and cleaning, and mechanizing the milking process.

Yugoslavia

Yugoslavia, with almost 9 million sheep, is another East European country that depends largely on a sheep of the Zackel type. The Yugoslav Zackel or Pramenka type encompasses a number of clearly defined breeds developed in certain localities, e.g., the Bosnian Mountain and the Dalmation–Karst. All provide milk, meat and wool in varying degree. Other breeds of lesser importance in Bulgaria include the Tsigai and a lop eared Alpine sheep—the Solčava. Since the communist régime came to power in the 1940s agriculture has been progressively collectivized, although the transhumant migration of flocks into the Bosnian mountains still continues.

Greece

Greece is a mountainous country and sheep have traditionally been an important part of its agriculture. One-third of the milk produced in Greece is from sheep and they also contribute substantially to the meat consumption. Greece has a marked Mediterranean climate with high rainfall in the winter and drought in the summer. Most sheep and their owners on the mainland move from the lower land and cultivated areas, where they spend the winter, to the mountain pastures for the summer. Of the sheep population of 7.5 million, about 80 per cent are of the Greek Zackel type, of which there are several local varieties. Also, amongst the remaining 20 per cent several local breeds have been developed in the islands under more intensive conditions than on the mainland. One of these, the Chios sheep, a semi-fat tailed sheep is prolific as well as a good milk breed and it has some promise for sheep improvement programmes in semiarid regions. Most of the Greek sheep are milked as well as providing meat and wool, and since 1965 a Government recording service has been made available to producers.

ALBANIA

There are far fewer sheep in Albania than in the other Eastern European countries discussed and their numbers have remained fairly static around 1.6 million for many years. Albania, unlike many of her neighbours, has much less mountain land that can be profitably exploited with sheep. The sheep are again mainly of the Zackel group with a small number of other types.

Africa

For such a large continent sheep numbers are low and rather unevenly distributed. Sheep are mainly concentrated in the Republic of South Africa and in the North and North East. The countries of Algeria, Ethiopia, Morocco, Nigeria, South Africa and Sudan contained almost 75 per cent of all African sheep in 1972. There is a wide variety of native sheep in Africa which are not organized into 'breeds' in the common meaning of the word. They can be mainly grouped by the type of tail and rump into three categories—thin-tailed, fat-tailed and fat rumped. Within these groups there are wide differences in many important characteristics, the most obvious being the difference in fleece type. Most of the African native sheep have little or no true wool and are best described as hairy although there is varying development of a woolly undercoat. The hairy sheep are adapted to hot conditions and are also widely found in Southern India. Some dwarf sheep types are found in Africa, for example the Congo Dwarf which stands only 40—50 cm at the withers.

SOUTH AFRICA

South Africa's sheep population is largely based on the extensive production of wool from Merino sheep. The Merino was introduced to South Africa in 1785 and has been much influenced by importations of Australian Merinos in the early 1900s. It has developed into a type adapted to their conditions—smaller than the Australian Merino and with rather shorter and finer wool; in some cases shearing takes place at 8 or even 6 months intervals giving rise to an even shorter staple. The Merino sheep, which comprise about two-thirds of all South African sheep, are mainly concentrated on the high plateau area of the Karroo, extending from Cape Province to the Orange Free State and the veldt region to the north and east; the rainfall is low and vegetation scarce and largely of a shrub type. The flocks are large (1000–10 000 or more sheep) and stocked at a low rate of several ha per sheep. In these areas the jackal is a serious menace and high fences have to be erected around the properties to protect the sheep. Formerly, sheep were 'kraaled' overnight to protect them against jackals, and this resulted in serious erosion of the overgrazed areas around the kraals.

East and South of the Orange Free State there is a belt of land, lying mainly in Natal, which is similar to the wheat and sheep zone of Australia with a fairly predictable winter rainfall. Flocks are smaller in this region and although good wool is important there is some emphasis on the meat characteristics. In the past it was customary to move the sheep ('trekking') from the high veldt area in the North to the wintering pastures in Natal, but this practice has largely died out.

In addition to Merino sheep there are several other types in South Africa. These include some European breeds and their crosses in the higher rainfall, coastal areas, where meat production is a more important aim. There is also a variety of native sheep, some of which utilize the areas that are too arid even for the Merino. The Karakul sheep are kept for quality lambskin production and are found mainly in the northern part of Cape Province. The Afrikander sheep, a long fat-tailed type, are of

Fig. 1.5. *Merinos on the veldt near Cape Province, South Africa. (by courtesy of the Republic of South Africa Embassy, London).*

Hottentot origin and are found mainly in the arid western parts of Cape Province. They are coarse woolled or hairy sheep, well adapted to these arid conditions and are owned both by white South Africans and by the native black people of the area. Although the fleece is of little value this type of sheep can produce meat and useful leather in a most unfavourable climate.

The Blackhead Persian sheep and its derivatives also figure prominently among the minor breeds of South Africa; the Dorper, developed from a cross of Blackhead Persian with the Dorset Horn, has recently gained popularity at the expense of the mother breed. It is now thought that the breed originated from Persia and it bears some resemblance to the Somali sheep. The Blackhead Persian is a very hardy, fat-rumped breed, well suited to the dry areas, and the ewes are mainly crossed with mutton rams to produce crossbred lambs for slaughter. The Blackhead Persians are mainly concentrated in an area of Cape Province, eastwards of the main areas of Afrikander and Karakul, and extending into the Orange Free State.

Lesotho

Lesotho (formerly Basutoland) lies in the middle of South African territory. It is a mountainous country with just under a million inhabitants and a sheep population of 1.75 million. As in many sheep keeping areas of the world, the country suffers from difficulties relating to traditional practices leading to overstocking and consequent erosion. Many of the traditional fat-tailed sheep are being replaced by Merinos for wool production. The sheep are kept on a system of seasonal movement from the lower altitudes in winter to the high mountain pastures in the summer.

Morocco

Extending from Morocco eastwards along the North African coast to the United Arab Republic, is an important sheep producing area largely bordering on a vast inland desert area.

Morocco, on the northwest sea-board has shown a substantial increase in sheep population since 1967 to the 17.5 million of 1972. The country has much land at high elevation and sheep are the most important livestock. These are kept mainly by nomadic people who also keep goats. Several sheep breeds are found in Morocco and they produce milk, wool and meat. The Berber sheep of the Atlas mountains have a high proportion of black and partly black sheep, and it is the custom for them to move with their nomad owners to the high mountains for summer pasture. On the high plateaux of Eastern Morocco, a breed called the Beni Guil is found, and on the western plateaux a breed called Tadla. The three breeds have been crossed together and a Middle Atlas type formed. On the plains are found the Atlantic coast type sheep—the Beni Ahsen and the Zemmour of the northwest, the Doukkala of the south west. Some of these sheep have some good quality wool, traditionally made into fine Arab robes, and there has been some importations of Précoce Merino sheep from France in order to further improve fleece quality by crossing. It is customary in much of Morocco to pen the sheep at night.

One of the most interesting sheep of the area–the Dahman or Tuareg–is found in the North Central area of Morocco between the Atlas mountains and the Sahara. These sheep appear to have a high level of prolificacy although there has been no known attempt, until recently, to improve them for this trait. It is estimated that there are 30 000–40 000 of these sheep in Morocco, kept in flocks of 3–10 in their owner's houses. It is one of the long-legged desert types with a hairy coat (D. D. Fox, 1973 private communication); This sheep is another possible candidate to provide genetic material in sheep improvement programmes.

TUNISIA

Sheep are also important in Tunisia where sheep mainly of the Barbary fat-tailed type are kept largely by nomads.

LIBYA

Although large in area, much of Libya is taken up by the Sahara desert and in the bordering semi-arid areas the sheep is very important. The Barbary fat-tail type is the shief sheep kept in Libya, and it is kept mainly in the traditional nomad flocks for its milk and its meat. Because of the importance of numbers to the nomads, flocks are often large (several hundred) and there are rapid fluctuations in numbers according to conditions; in some drought years a flock owner may lose most of his sheep. Recently, the age-long nomadic patterns have been somewhat disrupted with the development of motorized transport, which enables nomad flocks to be transported to the green areas over much larger distances. The improvement of sheep production in such a context is a difficult task, although regulation of stock numbers could be an important factor. Nomadism, like trans-humance, in spite of its drawbacks in today's world, has strong merits in utilizing the unpredictable and localized rainfalls that occur in the area.

With the exploitation of its oil resources, some of the new wealth in Libya is being invested in agricultural development. A major project, developed in conjunction with FAO, is the Kufra project, where underground water is pumped for irrigating virgin desert, upon which fodder is grown for intensive sheep production. The capital costs are substantial and the economic outcome as yet uncertain, but it is a possible means of utilizing for food production the vast desert areas of the earth's surface.

EGYPT

The sheep in Egypt are similar to those of the Middle Eastern countries to the East, based on a fat-tailed type found in numerous local varieties. These include the Ausimi and Rahmani of lower Egypt, the Fellahi of the Nile delta, and the Barki of the North West. The sheep are kept mainly for meat production, the wool being of low quality, and recent efforts have been made to improve sheep in the irrigated areas by crossbreeding and selection.

THE SUDAN

The Sudan is another North African country where sheep numbers have rapidly increased recently to their present number of over 13 million. In the Northern Sudan the sheep are mainly those adapted to arid and semi-arid conditions. Like other desert sheep they tend to be long-legged and hairy, with only a small proportion of real wool. The tails are long and thin and do not form the large fat deposits as in the fat-tailed sheep. The sheep are kept in nomadic flocks for milk, meat and skins. The skin is thin and used for the manufacture of high quality gloves. Because of their adaptation to the arid conditions, the desert sheep are less suitable for the riverside and irrigated pastures, and other smaller sheep such as the Gezira, are found under those conditions. Only relatively few sheep, in the Dongola region of Northern Sudan, have what can be described as a proper wool fleece.

In Southern Sudan a small type of sheep is found, mainly associated with the mountains and hills. These are hairy and are kept mainly for meat production.

ETHIOPIA

Sudan's neighbour, Ethiopia, has almost 13 million sheep associated largely with the mountainous areas of the country. The main sheep is the Abyssinian, an East African hairy fat-tailed type which resembles the fat-tailed sheep of Northern Africa and the Near East. Although the sheep are used to a small extent for their milk, the chief products are their meat and skins. The fleece is of low value but may be used for coarse clothing and blankets; they are often sheared twice a year.

KENYA

The sheep population of Kenya declined from almost 7 million in 1967 to the 1972 level of 3.7 million. Of the native sheep in Kenya, the Masai sheep largely owned by the Masai tribe of South West Kenya are the most numerous. These are sheep of the fat-tailed type with a coarse, hairy coat kept mainly for meat and skins. Varieties of the Masai include the Kipsigis, Luo and Nandi of Western Kenya and the Samburu of Northern Kenya.

On the highland plateau areas of Kenya a number of exotic breeds have been tried and the Merino has been successfully established for fine wool production on a number of large properties. In addition, in the grassier areas in the mountains and near the coast, native ewes are crossed to a limited extent with British breeds such as the Hampshire and Dorset Horn.

NIGERIA

Nigeria had over 8 million sheep in 1972, an increase of more than a half since 1967. The sheep are entirely of the hairy thin-tailed West African long legged type, kept primarily for their meat and skins. These include the Uda or Bali-Bali sheep of Northern Nigeria and the Bornu in the North West, both varieties of the Fulani sheep which is widely distributed in West Africa. Sheep are relatively unimportant in West Africa as a whole, compared with the Arab countries to the North and East.

North America

Apart from the Bighorn of the Rockies, sheep in the United States date back to the importation of Churro type sheep by the Spaniards in the sixteenth century. These were adopted by the Indians and are the origin of the Navajo sheep breed of Arizona, New Mexico and Utah. In the seventeenth century the British settlers brought their sheep with them and sheep breeding developed rapidly in the East. With the importation of the Spanish Merino, the Merino sheep became popular in the Eastern States in the early nineteenth century. The Rambouillet, a French derivative from the Merino, was also imported and has remained as an important sheep in the United States. With the increasing population of the Eastern states and the development of the Western part of the United States, Merino sheep moved westward so that the main concentration of sheep became centred on the 'range states', down which the Rocky mountains extend from the North to the South of the country. In addition to the redistribution of the sheep industry in the country there has been a sharp decline since 1940 when there were more than 50 million sheep, to below 20 million in 1972.

The sheep ranges of the West are the most important sector of the present day US sheep industry. The Western ewe is based on breeds such as the Rambouillet, Targhee and Columbia, American derivatives of Merino and Longwool types, and crossed with various breeds such as the Suffolk, Hampshire and the Rambouillet to produce a large bodied lamb. These lambs come off the ranges at the end of summer at about 35 kg liveweight and many are fed intensively in large feed lots to weights of 45–70 kg. Although wool is an important product of the Western range sheep industry the relative importance of lamb production has increased. In the rest of the United States sheep are widely scattered in relatively small flocks with meat as the primary product.

Vigorous efforts have been made in recent years to improve the American sheep industry but the lower preference for the large, rather fat lambs marketed there has resulted in a very low and uneven pattern of lamb production. The home producers are also having to face competition in recent years from imported New Zealand lamb.

Growth and 2
Carcass Quality

An outline of the main aspects of growth and development are given in this chapter, as they relate to meat production; wool and milk production are dealt with in the succeeding chapters. Aspects that relate specifically to reproduction are considered in Chapter 5. The chapter concludes with a consideration of quality and marketing aspects in relation to lamb and mutton.

Body Growth and Development

Growth and development describes the phase of change between the conception of the animal and its ultimate maturity (or its premature slaughter for meat purposes) and the various factors that influence the rate and quality of this development.

Before examining the effects of the main factors involved, it is necessary to summarize the normal course of development in a sheep, given optimal conditions from conception to maturity. In doing this, some concise description of the course of events is necessary as shown in the curve of growth (Fig. 2.1). This represents the normal pattern of change of body weight and a similar curve could describe the growth of any constituent part of the body that can be defined and measured. For example, if the scales are adjusted, body weight could be replaced by components such as the weight of the heart, the weight of the ram's testicle, the weight of the skull bones or the

57

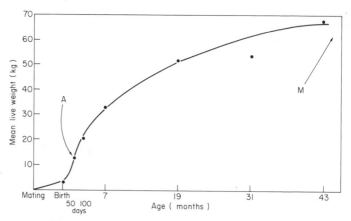

Fig. 2.1. *Growth curve in sheep (based on data for ewes).*

weight of magnesium in the body. The curve implies that the component in question commences its growth after conception and at first grows slowly in absolute terms because the initial mass is so small, then as the overall size increases the rate of growth reaches a maximum, shown by the steepest part of the curve A. The rate of growth then falls until body weight be-

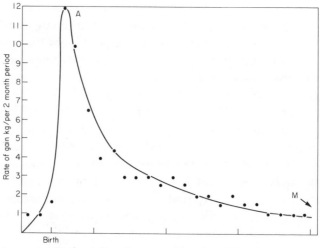

Fig. 2.2. *Growth rate curve (based on Fig. 2.1).*

comes relatively stable at maturity. Eventually, with old age some loss of weight may occur. In the lamb, the highest rate of growth in liveweight under optimal conditions, occurs between 1–5 months.

The data for the growth curve in Fig. 2.1 may also be expressed in a slightly different form as in Fig. 2.2, where rate of gain and not the absolute weight is plotted against age. The simplification of the growth process, implicit in its representation by Figs 2.1 and 2.2 although essential and helpful, should not obscure the fact that growth of body tissues is a much more dynamic process. There is a continuous turnover of all the components of the body readily apparent in the growth and replacement of wool fibres, but affecting all constituent cells of the body, particularly the protein component.

DIFFERENTIAL GROWTH OF BODY COMPONENTS

Development is an expression of the differential rate of growth of constituent parts of the body. It is obvious that the growth of a lamb, from conception to maturity, is no simple change from a small to a large scale but a progressive change in the proportion of the various tissues, which results from the fact that, although each component grows along the same basic pattern described in Figs 2.1 and 2.2, the time scales are different. Each component reaches the various stages in a different chronological order.

The present state of knowledge on the main principles governing the growth and development of the sheep's body can be summarized as follows:

1. The development period of body components (however defined) tends to be timed according to their function in the body (Hammond, 1960). In the development of various main tissues in the lamb, nervous tissue, for example, develops early, followed by essential organs, bone, muscle and lastly fat. In terms of the curves shown in Figs. 2.1 and 2.2 the significant points A and M tend to be concentrated at an earlier stage of the lamb's life in the case of the weight of the brain tissue,

for example, than for the weight of fat tissue in the body. The difference between these tissues is described as that between early (the brain) and late maturing (the fat). Similarly, a breed of sheep is considered early maturing if the curve for liveweight is displaced to the left on the age scale, as compared to another breed. The early maturing lamb tends to be a scale miniature, with the same body proportions as a late maturing lamb, at the appropriate heavier weight.

2. One convenient way to express the relative rates of growth of different body components (i.e., relative development), for the lamb under optimal condition, is the equation

$$Y = bX^{\alpha} \qquad \text{(Huxley, 1932)}$$

where Y is the weight of the component under study.

X is the weight of some suitable reference basis, e.g., body weight or carcass weight.

b and α are constants.

For most data the equation can be calculated as a linear regression equation of the form:

$$\log Y = \log b + \alpha \log X$$

The exponent α, sometimes called the growth coefficient, provides a concise measure of the rate of growth of the component, relative to the reference basis. For instance, if body weight is taken as X, any component Y, for which the value of α is greater than 1.0, will be late maturing in relation to body weight and vice versa.

As far as commercial lamb production is concerned the main body components of interest are bone, muscle and fat, although the killing out or dressing percentage, which estimates the yield of carcass from a given liveweight, is also important.

If the above equation held true, using carcass weight as a reference base, for example, then once the carcass composition at a series of carcass weights is determined from a sample of lambs within a defined group, the composition of any other lamb within the group could be estimated from its carcass weight.

An example of changes in the composition of lambs is shown in Table 2.1. These were ram lambs raised artificially on ad libitum feeding, slaughtered at different stages, with the carcasses subsequently ground up and analysed for the major chemical components (Morgan & Owen, 1973).

Table 2.1. *Carcass composition of lambs during growth*

No. of lambs	Body weight kg	Carcase weight kg	Dry matter per cent	Fat per cent	Dry matter basis		
					Ash per cent	Crude protein per cent	Gross energy kcal/g
6*	3.5	–	22.6	8.1	13.9	71.7	4.76
9	22.5	9.1	40.7	52.5	10.2	37.1	6.59
34	38.4	16.1	44.6	59.5	9.0	31.2	6.89

* Analyses carried out on the whole body and not on the dressed carcass.

Hammond and his colleagues at Cambridge (Hammond, 1932; Pálsson & Vergés, 1952) have described the growth and development of a number of body components including dissected components—bone, lean and fat—anatomical components—specific bones and muscles—and a variety of body measurements. Separation into lean, fat and bone is significant in the study of meat producing animals although these descriptions, particularly that of lean tissue, may obscure variation in chemical components such as water and protein. In a study of Suffolk cross Scottish Halfbred lambs, one side of each lamb's carcass was dissected from its various components and provided an opportunity to examine the chemical composition of these components. The results of the analysis of separated lean, bone and fat from the carcasses are shown in Table 2.2.

Important changes that occur in the main components of the lamb's body as it grows, as shown in these and other studies, are as follows:

Table 2.2. *Composition of dissected carcass components in lambs. (All values mean of 10 lambs)*

Component	Dry matter (per cent.)	Ether extracted fat (per cent.)	Crude protein (per cent.)	Ash (per cent.)
Bone	48.8	11.0	18.3	16.7
Lean	29.5	6.6	9.2	2.7
Fat				
subcutaneous	74.3	63.9	9.2	0.5
intermuscular	71.0	49.5	9.7	0.6

ANATOMICAL COMPONENTS

Brain and Nervous Tissue

The proportion of this component falls progressively as growth proceeds, e.g., in the high plane lambs studied by Pálsson and Vergés (1952) the brain as a proportion of live-weight fell from 1.6 per cent at birth to 0.1 per cent at 41 weeks of age.

Other Essential Organs

Other organs such as the heart and liver also form a lower proportion of the adult than of the lamb at birth. In the same study (Pálsson & Vergés, 1952) the heart and liver respectively fell from 0.7 and 2 per cent of liveweight at birth to 0.3 and 1.2 per cent at 41 weeks.

Bones

The skeleton as a whole is an early maturing component of the body; in the above study the proportion fell from 17.3 per cent at birth to 5.9 per cent of the liveweight at 41 weeks of age. Within the skeleton, individual bones vary in their rate of development. The skull bones, for example, are relatively earlier maturing than the whole skeleton, whereas the ribs are later maturing.

Muscle

The proportion of muscle as a whole, in the body, shows less change as the lamb grows. In the same data, the proportion fell from 27 per cent at birth to 24 per cent at 41 weeks. Within the total, however, individual muscles show large differences in earliness of maturity; the head and neck muscles, for example, are relatively early maturing compared with the total muscle mass, whereas the loin muscles are later maturing.

Fat

The adipose tissue depots of the lamb's body are later maturing than the body as a whole. At birth the lamb contains little fat and the high plane lambs referred to above showed only 3.7 per cent total fat (including kidney fat) at birth compared with fully 31 per cent of the live weight at 41 weeks. Much variation in rate of maturity exists between fat deposits, subcutaneous depots being later maturing than total fat, whereas intramuscular deposits and kidney fat develop earlier than the fat as a whole.

CHEMICAL COMPONENTS

Water

The water content of the body falls as the lamb matures (Table 2.1). This is a reflection of the increased proportion of fat to lean, fatty tissue being associated with little water, whereas lean muscle contains a high water content.

Ash Content

The ash content as a measure of the total mineral content of the body falls as the lamb grows; this is to be expected because the mineral content is largely associated with the skeleton.

Crude Protein

On a dry matter basis there is an appreciable fall in the crude protein of the lamb's body and carcass (Table 2.1) when comparing lambs at birth with older sheep. This reflects the substantial increase in fat—the other major component of the dry matter. It is the association of the crude protein with a relatively high proportion of water in muscle tissue that accounts for the much smaller decline of muscle proportion as carcass weight increases.

Fat Content

The fat content, as estimated from ether extracted samples of lamb carcasses (Table 2.1), is closely related to the dissected fat content, and shows a marked increase as the lamb grows. Expressed on a dry matter basis the increase in fat content is more marked and about 60 per cent of the dry carcass of the lamb is fat.

BODY CONFORMATION

Several studies, including those of Pálsson and Vergés, have assessed how the conformation of the body and carcass of the lamb develops with age. All the detailed measurements involved will not be commented on, but the main effects are that as the lamb grows its body trunk becomes a larger proportion of the whole, as compared to the head and legs. The body itself becomes thicker and deeper and the loin area becomes better developed, as compared with the neck and chest region. The roundness and smoothness of the body and joints that develop as the lamb grows, are largely a reflection of the laying down of fat, particularly subcutaneous fat, and not of muscular development.

FACTORS INFLUENCING THE PATTERN OF GROWTH AND DEVELOPMENT IN LAMBS

Body Weight

Due to the process of growth and development, substantial changes have been shown to occur in the body composition of the lamb as it grows and it is useful to consider to what extent these changes are accounted for by the increase in body weight. Reid et al., (1968), in an analysis of data from 221 wether lambs, slaughtered over a wide range of liveweight, showed that 63 per cent, 95 per cent and 88 per cent of the variation in ash, protein and fat content respectively, was accounted for by the variation in empty body weight. Over the more limited range of body weight, at which lambs are normally slaughtered, there is still appreciable variation in body composition, which is not accounted for by variation in body weight. For example, the data in Table 2.3 (Cuthbertson et al., 1973) shows the

Table 2.3. *Mean value of carcass and other traits for Suffolk × Scottish Halfbred lambs killed at the same target live weight (mean of 8 progeny per ram)*

Trait	Ram A	Ram B	Ram C	Standard deviation
Days of age	105.0	107.3	114.1	7.45
Fasted live weight (kg)	35.7	35.2	35.6	1.02
Cold carcass weight (kg)	16.6	16.4	16.5	0.76
Dissected fat (per cent)	20.2	20.1	21.3	3.12
Dissected lean (per cent)	58.9	58.6	57.6	2.33
Dissected bone (per cent)	18.8	19.0	19.0	1.40
Eye muscle area (cm^2)	14.1	12.4	11.2	2.42
Fasted body dry matter (per cent)	19.1	18.6	19.1	1.58
Carcass dry matter (per cent)	41.1	39.9	41.1	2.94
Carcass fat (ether extracted) (per cent)	18.7	17.6	19.0	3.11
Carcass crude protein (per cent)	16.6	16.4	16.4	0.53
Carcass ash (per cent)	4.7	4.5	5.2	0.82
Carcass energy (calories/g)	2.72	2.67	2.73	0.28

mean, range and standard deviation of various measures of carcass composition in the 24 Suffolk × Scottish halfbred lambs, killed as each reached 40 kg liveweight, which provided the data for Table 2.2. These lambs had been artificially reared from two days of age on a standard milk allowance and given a standard diet ad libitum during the growing period. These data indicate that variation still exists in the composition of carcasses from lambs killed at the same, or a very narrow range, of body weight.

Genotype

Under the same conditions of feeding, breeds of sheep can be broadly ranked according to rate of growth and according to earliness of maturity. For example, within the British Down breeds there is a gradation from Southdown to the Oxford Down where mature size and rate of growth tend to increase and earliness of maturity tends to decrease. Several studies have confirmed that rate of growth and earliness of maturity are closely associated with the mature size of the breed. However, there are exceptions to this generalization, as shown by Jackson (1974), and it is evident that there are some breed differences in the rate of growth and of development, that are associated with the mature size of the breed. Breed differences therefore exist in the shape of the growth curve for body weight and for the weight of some of the body components.

Sex

Sex differences in growth and development are a result of the operation of the sex hormones, steroids released from the gonads which influence a number of the animal's complex physiological systems. In addition to their direct effect on reproductive function the sex hormones are responsible for the so-called secondary sexual characteristics. The ewe differs from the ram in that it has a slower rate of growth, a more early maturing carcass and reaches a lower mature size, due to the effect of oestrogen in restricting the growth of the long bones of the body. Castration, or the removal of the testes of the ram, leads to a reduced growth rate, particularly to a restriction of muscle growth, giving an earlier maturing and fatter carcass with reduced food conversion efficiency (Table 2.4).

The appreciation of the central rôle of the sex hormones in growth and development, as manifested in the consequences of castration, have led to extensive study of the effects of the administration of natural or synthetic hormones to meat animals, in order to influence performance (Hafs et al., 1971). The results of these studies have shown that when administered in appropriate doses, some hormones can lead to substantial growth promotion, particularly in the castrate, associated with

Table 2.4. *Mean weight of body components, dry carcass composition and total weight of skinned empty-body components for lambs slaughtered at about 40 kg live weight*

	Sexes			
	Male		Female	SE
	entire	castrate		
Body components (kg)				
Head, liver, lungs and heart	3.7	3.4	3.3	0.05
Cleaned stomach	2.0	2.1	2.1	0.06
Cleaned intestines	1.8	1·6	1.8	0.05
Pelt	5.2	4.8	5.1	0.10
Carcass	18.6	19.1	19.2	0·27
Dry carcass composition (per cent)				
Dry matter	46.4	50.0	50.4	0.70
Ether extract	64.6	70.0	72.0	1.78
Crude protein	27.6	22.4	21.0	0.62
Ash	7.6	6.6	6.3	0.32
Gross energy (kcal/g)	7.1	7.2	7.4	0.06
Skinned empty-body components on dry-matter basis (kg)				
Dry matter	12.0	12.9	13.1	0.25
Ether extract	7.9	9.1	9.5	0.32
Crude protein	3.2	2.9	2.8	0.11
Ash	0.9	0.9	0.8	0.02
Gross energy (mcal)	84.9	94.6	94.8	2.42

increased muscle growth and the leaner carcass of a later maturing animal.

The male hormones, or androgens, have been shown to act as anabolic steroids, promoting muscle growth, in most species, but their use for ruminants have given disappointing results. Two synthetic compounds, diethyl stilboestrol and hexoestrol, have much the same action as natural oestrogens and have been shown to be effective in promoting growth in ruminants. The use of these synthetic hormones has been shown to have substantial effects on the growth and carcass quality, particularly of wether lambs but no consistent economic benefit has been widely established for their use, nor is their mode of action completely understood. Where feeding conditions are good ram lambs can often be slaughtered before there is any need for castration, thus avoiding any necessity for artificial hormones.

Another method of avoiding the penalties of castration is by using 'induced cryptorchidism'. This entails squeezing the testes into the abdominal cavity shortly after birth and sealing the neck of the scrotum with a rubber ring to prevent their descent. The scrotum and the ring eventually drop off and the intact testes are retained in the abdominal cavity. Normal sperm development is inhibited by the high temperature within the abdomen and the lamb, although similar in most respects to an entire ram, is sterile. Results with the use of this operation have shown that it is effective in its aims but that there seems only limited application for it in practice (Hudson et al., 1968).

The Effect of Nutrition on Body Composition

So far the pattern of growth and development under optimal conditions has been considered and it is important to see what modifications may occur when conditions are less than optimum, particularly when there is underfeeding. If the constants b and α in the equation on page 60 were unaffected by level of feeding, all components of the body or the carcass would be retarded to the same degree by underfeeding so that whatever the age of the lamb, a carcass of a given weight would always have the same composition. On the basis of numerous experiments at Cambridge, it was postulated that underfeeding during the rearing phase would retard body components differentially, according to their function, such that the earlier maturing components would be less retarded than the later maturing components (Hammond, 1960); the composition of the body would therefore be different for underfed animals as compared to well fed animals of the same body weight. Several studies on various species, including reassessments of the data used by the Hammond School (Elsley *et al.*, 1964), have subsequently shown that the carcass is far less affected by underfeeding than was once thought, particularly the fat free body components. The amount of fat, relative to the rest of the body, can be reduced by feed restriction during growth, and so can the distribution of the fat, but it is difficult to demonstrate any important effect on bone/muscle ratio, in carcasses compared at the same total fat-free weight. It can be concluded that differences in levels of feeding, and therefore of rates of growth, of the growing lamb, from birth to slaughter, will result in some differences of fat content in the carcass, but little effect on the fat free composition of carcasses compared at the same fat free weight.

Diet Quality

Although the animal body is relatively resistant to change in composition from the imposition of energy restriction, there is much evidence that changes in the composition of the diet can have marked effects. Diets deficient in protein, in particular, are known to lead to an increase in the fat to lean ratio in many species. Andrews and Ørskov (1970) have confirmed this effect for lambs when diets of varying protein content are compared as shown in Table 2.5. Jagusch et al. (1970) have also noted a similar effect for lambs on milk replacers, within the first month of life.

Table 2.5. *The effect of dietary protein concentration on the nitrogen and ether extract contents of the carcass dry matter of male lambs slaughtered at 27.5 and 40 kg liveweight*

Measurement	Live wt. at slaughter (kg)	Dietary protein concentration (per cent)					Residual SD
		10	12.5	15.0	17.5	20	
Nitrogen in	27.5	6.65	7.46	8.45	8.25	9.14	± 0.51
carcass	40.0	4.82	5.43	5.78	5.98	5.97	± 3.3
(per cent)							
Ether extract	27.5	49.9	45.7	39.0	38.9	32.6	± 3.3
in carcass	40.0	62.0	59.6	55.3	55.2	55.5	± 4.3
(per cent)							

PRENATAL INFLUENCES

Comparisons at Aberdeen (Owen, unpublished) made between lambs born in litters of various sizes and subsequently suckled as singles or twins or artificially reared, have shown that live weight at one hundred days of age is reduced for the lamb born in the larger litters. Having allowed for the season and the age of the ewe, there was a 2.5 kg reduction in the average one hundred day live weight of individual lambs for each extra lamb born to the ewe. This result was similar for twins raised as singles compared with single born lambs and for triplets reared as twins compared with twin born and twin reared lambs. It is not clear how much of this reduction is attributable to genotype, to effects of ewe lactation or to the prenatal restriction imposed.

Carcass Quality

Assessing the quality of lamb is a difficult task, particularly when such an assessment needs to be condensed into a single or very few measures. Quality is basically related to the preference of the eventual consumer but it also includes aspects of suitability for the processing, distributing and marketing industry at all stages from the producer to the consumer at the table.

CARCASS YIELD

Starting from the live lamb the first aspect of quality is related to the yield of carcass per unit liveweight, commonly called the 'killing out' or 'dressing' percentage. The specifications for dressing sheep carcasses vary in detail from country to country. British regulations (MAFF, 1973) stipulate the removal of the skin, head and tongue, rumen and digestive system, omental and depot fat, liver, spleen, heart, lungs, thoracic or heart fat, thymus and parathyroid glands, urinogenital organs excluding the kidneys, and the feet. A high proportion of young slaughter lambs yield 45–50 per cent carcass per unit liveweight.

The yield of dressed carcass for a given liveweight is markedly affected by many factors operating immediately before slaughter, particularly the level of feeding and type of diet and the degree of fasting. It is also affected by more permanent influences such as breed, age, level of nutrition and degree of body development. Because of the high level of uncontrollable variation in killing out percentage it is worthwhile to record carcass weight, if possible, in any assessment of meat output.

CARCASS QUALITY

The quality of the lamb carcass has long defied simple definition and no one has yet produced a completely satisfactory method. The attributes of the carcass that are known to comprise quality are as follows:

Yield of Lean Meat

Most consumers regard the lean as the desirable part of the meat and high lean content in a carcass is therefore important. This implies that the proportion of fat and bone in the carcass should be correspondingly low. It has already been shown that as carcass weight increases, the proportion of bone falls, that of fat increases, with relatively smaller changes in total lean content.

Fat Content

One of the most important criteria of consumer acceptability is the fat content of the carcass. Excess fat is unattractive to the housewife, particularly since sheep fat has a relatively high melting point and congeals easily when served. It therefore involves the retailer in wasteful trimming. On the other hand, a minimum amount of fat cover over the loin is considered desirable for carcass storage and for cooking the meat. It is not easy to assess fat cover satisfactorily in the lamb carcass because of the thinness of the fat cover and its variability.

Distribution of the Meat in the Carcass

In some countries the meat is boned before use (e.g., in the Far East); consequently, the distribution of the meat on the carcass is not so important. In many other countries, such as Britain, the traditional retail unit is the unboned joint and there are important price differentials between the various joints as shown in Table 2.6.

Table 2.6. *Average retail prices of various lamb joints (including bone) 1968–1973 (MLC Market survey) (£ per kg)*

	1968	1969	1970	1971	1972	1973
Home killed lamb						
loin	0.64	0.72	0.74	0.82	1.06	1.35
shoulder	0.46	0.51	0.50	0.56	0.72	0.93
leg	0.62	0.70	0.71	0.78	1.00	1.27
Imported lamb						
loin	0.51	0.56	0.58	0.60	0.86	1.20
shoulder	0.36	0.40	0.42	0.44	0.60	0.85
leg	0.55	0.61	0.62	0.68	0.89	1.22

Average retail prices expressed in relation to the price for leg (100)

	1968	1969	1970	1971	1972	1973	Average 1968–1973
Home killed							
loin	103	103	104	105	106	106	104
shoulder	74	73	70	72	72	73	72
leg	100	100	100	100	100	100	100
Imported							
loin	93	92	94	88	97	98	94
shoulder	65	66	68	65	67	70	67
leg	100	100	100	100	100	100	100

There is evidence that the distribution of lean in the carcass, at the same total weight of lean meat, does not vary markedly according to genetic and environmental factors. The ideal carcass in this respect is therefore a compromise between achieving the maturity required to give adequate development in the high price joints without leading to over-fatness.

The Composition of the Lean

Lean meat is a variable commodity and there are three important factors involved in its quality:

Tenderness. Although lamb, when properly processed and cooked, is usually good in this respect, tenderness and freedom from stringiness are of prime importance. This is partly a property of the lamb and partly a consequence of the treatment of the lamb before slaughter and of the carcass after slaughter. Stress at slaughter is known to lead to a watery lean with a consequent loss of moisture in the carcass when it is hung and it may affect other aspects of quality. Tenderness is particularly subject to various processes, that are not yet well understood, but which continue in the meat during a period of storage. The length of time the meat is left hanging and the method of freezing, through an effect called 'cold shortening', can affect the tenderness. There is some evidence that tenderness of meat is reasonably heritable as are fat content and lean content (Botkin et al., 1969).

Juiciness Lamb that is dry when cooked is not desirable. Maltreatment of the lamb before slaughter causing stress or exhaustion can lead to excessive moisture loss. This may be one factor causing variation in juiciness although the fat content of the lean is also an important factor.

The data on the composition of the various components of the lamb carcass (Table 2.2) shows that lean meat contains a significant proportion of fat when chemically analysed.

Flavour The housewife's attitude to flavour is often negative, being more concerned with the presence of obnoxious smells and flavours than with positive aspects. The fat content of the lean meat, as well as contributing to juiciness, may also influence flavour.

In some parts of the world there is some consumer resistance to the odour of lamb meat when cooking. This has been studied in the USA where such aversion is widespread (Hornstein & Crowe, 1963).

SLAUGHTER WEIGHT

Several attributes, important in the economy of lamb production, are affected by the weight chosen for lamb slaughter. These are:

Yield of Usable Meat

For any type of lamb the yield of usable meat shows a sharp increase as slaughter weight increases. This is partly a reflection of the increased killing-out percentage and partly a reflection of decreased bone content as shown in Table 2.7.

Table 2.7. *Yield of usable meat, i.e., weight of boneless carcass as percent of liveweight in well-fed lambs. (Based on Pálsson & Vergés, 1952)*

	Birth	9 weeks	41 weeks
Liveweight (kg)	3.5	27.8	81.7
Usable meat (per cent)	28	40	54

For many markets the larger the portion of meat that can be cut from a carcass, the better. Small carcasses, whatever else their merit, tend to give chops and other joints that do not compare favourably in size with meat from cattle and pigs.

Another aspect is that many of the costs of handling and processing lamb carcasses are related to the carcass as a unit, thus increasing the costs per unit of meat for small carcasses.

Fat Content

It has already been shown how sensitive the fat content of the carcass is to increases in carcass weight. Within the range of normal lamb slaughterings, carcass fat content is increasing exponentially. This factor limits the extent to which carcass weights can be increased in order to increase the yield of usable meat. In this respect the choice of genotype is crucial because of the effect on fatness at a given carcass weight. MLC (1973) have suggested the weight class of fat lambs some common British crosses would be expected to produce, assum-

Table 2.8. *Body weight of parent breeds and lamb carcass weight (K.O. 50 per cent). (Based on data given in "Planned crossbreeding and lamb carcass weights" (MLC, 1973))*

Carcass weight range	Breed		Mature adult body weight			Crossbred fat lamb	
	Ewe	Ram	Ewe breed	Ram breed	Crossbred fat lamb	Body weight at slaughter	Carcass weight
			kg	kg	kg	kg	kg
12–15 kg	Welsh Mountain	Southdown	45	61	53	26	13
	Cheviot	Southdown	63	61	62	31	15
16–19 kg	Scottish Blackface	Dorset Down	70	77	73	37	18
	Welsh Halfbred	Dorset Down	72	77	75	38	19
20–23 kg	Romney Halfbred	Suffolk	77	91	84	42	21
	Mule	Suffolk	84	91	87	44	22
24 kg plus	Scottish Halfbred	Oxford Down	88	106	97	49	24
	Suffolk × Scottish Halfbred	Oxford Down	88	106	97	49	24

ing that a lamb is slaughtered at around half the mature adult weight of the cross and killing-out at 50 per cent (Table 2.8). For heavier lambs, such as those common in the USA, Bradford (1974) has recommended much higher slaughter weights as shown in Table 2.9.

Table 2.9. *Recommended slaughter weight for lambs in the USA.*

Mature weight (kg) of ewes of		Recommended range of slaughter weights (kg) to avoid overfatness
Sire breed	Dam breed	
90	90	54–60
70	70	42–46
50	50	30–34
90	70	48–53
	50	42–46
70	50	36–40

Unit cost of production

The cost of producing lambs can be conveniently divided into two categories:

1. Those associated with the breeding ewes and rams. The total costs of the breeding flock are not much influenced by the numbers of lambs produced nor by how long the lambs are kept before slaughter.

2. The variable costs associated with the lambs themselves. The total for the flock depends on the number of lambs and the length of time they are kept.

For given values of overhead costs and of increases in variable cost with increased gain, the slaughter weight which minimizes total cost per kg of lamb carcass can be determined.

Fig. 2.3 illustrates this approach when the assumptions are based on data from a ram performance test.

The assumptions are:

Overhead cost per lamb including labour = £10
Variable costs per kg feed consumed   = £00.05
    live weight gain of lambs per day   = 0.38 kg

live weight of lambs at 50 days   = 20 kg
killing-out percentage at all weights   = 50 per cent
Feed requirement per kg live weight
   increases at the rate of 0.35 kg per 10 days
Food consumed to 50 days   = 1.0 kg

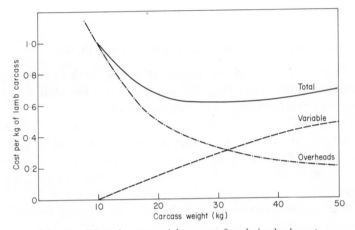

Fig. 2.3. *Effect of carcass weight on cost of producing lamb meat.*

The figure shows that, in the early stages of growth, the effect of spreading the breeding flock overheads leads to marked decreases in cost per kg carcass and, in spite of the rapid deterioration in feed conversion efficiency, costs per kg carcass only begin to rise when lamb carcass weight exceeds 30 kg.

The effect of delay in slaughtering on the variable costs can vary substantially according to the system of production. Where lambs are grazing outside in the peak of the grazing season delay in slaughtering may lead to little extra cost since the grass is already available and unlikely to be used for any other purpose if the lambs were slaughtered at low weights. On the other hand where lambs have been weaned and are consuming expensive feed, delay in slaughtering gives considerably increased variable costs.

An added complication is that price levels for lamb fluctuate and in most countries prices tend to fall as the lamb slaughtering season proceeds.

The choice of optimum slaughter weight for lamb is therefore a complex one, depending not only on the weight which minimizes total cost per kg carcass, but on the changes in the value per kg of carcass, which in turn depends on the effect on carcass quality and on the seasonal price trends.

The evaluation of carcass quality in the sheep

Having considered the attributes of the lamb carcass that are important in determining its quality, it is essential to consider the methods that can be used in practice to measure these attributes. Those used for the scientific investigation of the lamb carcass, which have contributed to our knowledge of the factors involved, are usually much more laborious and expensive than those that can be contemplated for commercial purposes.

The main methods used in scientific work can be briefly summarized:

Carcass Dissection

This method varies from the delicate surgical separation of individual muscles and other anatomical features to the rougher separation, using butchers' knives, into lean, fat and bone. The method is very expensive and even the simpler separation of one side may lead to the loss of about one-quarter to one-third of the value of the carcass as well as demanding about half a man-day in skilled labour (Cuthbertson, 1974).

The method has the merit of identifying either an anatomical entity or an entity meaningful to the meat trade. Because of cost its use can only be justified in rare studies to establish criteria for calibrating less expensive methods.

Chemical Analysis

This method involves the grinding of the carcass to produce a uniform sample for analysis into fat (ether extract), crude protein (Kjheldahl) and mineral matter (ash). The method is expensive because of the loss of carcass value and the labour involved, particularly in the grinding and mixing process (Morgan & Owen, 1973).

Specific Gravity

The specific gravity of a carcass is closely associated with its fat content and, conversely, with its lean meat content. The method based on estimating carcass composition from specific gravity has the advantage that little sacrifice in the value of the carcass is involved. However, accurate weighing of carcasses in air and in water has to be carried out under carefully standardized conditions, as well as adequate calibration with the first two methods in order to derive predictive equations (Timon, 1968).

Sample Joint Analysis

An analysis of sample joints using any of the above three methods is much cheaper to apply and can give useful estimations of the total carcass values. In a study of 435 lamb carcasses of different breeds and crosses Cuthbertson (1974) found that the 'best end of neck' (a joint cut from the dorsal part of the thorax immediately posterior to the shoulder) and the 'shoulder' joint were the most valuable predictors of the total lean content of a lamb carcass. Uniformity of cutting is essential for the accuracy of this method.

Carcass Measurements

A variety of length and area measures have been proposed and investigated in order to describe the lamb carcass. None of these have been shown to approach the predictive value of the best of the sample joint analyses.

The area of the longissimus (eye) muscle measured at the twelfth rib has not been shown to have much predictive value for assessing the lean or fat content of the lamb carcass. In the analysis of twenty-four lamb carcasses, described earlier (Table

2.3), the correlation between eye muscle area and lean content of the carcass was not significant ($r = +0.28$). Measurements of fat depth in the carcass either measured by calipers at the twelfth rib of a carcass cut transversely, or by subjective measures of fat cover, have been shown to be the most useful of the simple measurements in predicting carcass quality (Cuthbertson, 1974; Timon, 1968).

Yield of Commercial Cuts

One simple, apparently useful, method of estimating carcass value is to cut the carcass up into the commercial joints and to apply an economic value to the weight of each joint in the carcass. The economic value of a joint can be based on a comparative price assessed over several years. The method suffers from the difficulty of standardizing the commercial cuts and because variation in the distribution of cuts in lambs of similar carcass weight is low, compared with the variation in total lean and total fat content of the carcass (Cuthbertson, 1974).

Taking the various methods together it appears that lamb carcasses at present can be economically described in terms of carcass weight and of fat cover and that, within the limits imposed by fat requirements, the carcass should be as large as possible.

Estimation of Carcass Quality in Live Animals

For breeding purposes the most useful estimates of carcass attributes would be those applicable to the live lamb. This would allow the selection and culling of breeding stock for carcass quality and could be particularly useful for the development of performance testing for meat rams.

Several methods have been proposed for this purpose but none, as yet, has proved suitable for practical application in the field. The possibilities include the ultrasonic scanning of back fat, which has found some application with pigs, and dilution techniques which depend on the assessment of total body water. The use of tritiated water for this purpose has not given promising results when applied to lambs killed at the same estimated carcass weight (Cuthbertson et al., 1973).

COMMERCIAL EVALUATION OF LAMB CARCASSES

For commercial evaluation, lamb carcasses can be graded according to weight, fatness and conformation into distinct identifiable categories readily recognized in the meat trade. Three examples of carcass classification or grading schemes for lambs are given:

NEW ZEALAND

The New Zealand export trade to the UK depends on selling a uniform product. Sheep meat is first differentiated into classes.

1. Lamb—Under 12 months of age at slaughter—mostly 4–6 months.

2. Hogget—Maiden ewes or wethers showing not more than 2 permanent incisor teeth at the date of slaughter (maximum dressed carcass weight 56 lb (25.4 kg)).

3. Wether mutton—The class of meat derived from sheep which are either wethers or maiden ewes.

4. Ewe mutton—Derived from female sheep which have lambed.

Within these classes the carcasses are graded to assist buyers in specifying their requirements. For exported lamb, for instance, there are three major grade classes which are further subdivided and marked according to specified carcass weight ranges as shown in Table 2.10.

The separation into the three main grade classes prime or GAQ (good average quality), Omega and Y or FAQ (fair average quality) is made subjectively, according to conformation and fat cover, the primes being higher conformation and greater fat cover than the Y's. Omega carcasses are similar to primes but leggier.

Familiarity, within the trade, with these specifications considerably facilitates trading transactions.

Table 2.10. *Description of grades applied to NZ lamb carcasses.*

Grade class	Grade mark	Weight range (kg)	Colour of mark
Prime or GAQ	D	9.1/12.7	Blue
Prime or GAQ	2	13.2/16.3	Blue
Prime or GAQ	8	16.8/19.0	Blue
Prime or GAQ	4	19.5/24.4	Blue
Omega	D	12.7/under	Brown
Omega	2	13.2/16.3	Brown
Y or FAQ	YL	9.1/12.7	Red
Y or FAQ	YM	13.2/16.3	Red
Y or FAQ	YH	16.8/over	Red

UNITED KINGDOM

The Meat and Livestock Commission of the UK introduced a pilot classification scheme for lamb carcasses in 1973 (MLC, 1973). The scheme was finalized after informal meetings held with eleven industry organizations to discuss possible methods of sheep carcass classification.

It was considered that the sheep carcass could be described with sufficient accuracy for commercial purposes, bearing in mind the practical problems, by carcass weight, category, fatness and conformation.

Carcass Weight

It was proposed that the existing UK definition of cold carcass weight should continue to apply. Removal of the kidney and kidney fat, as now practised in New Zealand, was considered but was not recommended at that stage. It was *not* proposed that, for classification purposes, carcass weight should be expressed in terms of a weight range; although the ability to order by numbered or named weight ranges might, in certain circumstances, be an advantage, the difficulties of agreeing common ranges at that stage were considered to be too great in relation to the benefits.

Category

The following categories were initially approved: lamb, hogget (from January the first except for out-of-season lambs), ewe and ram. There was considered no need to differentiate the sex of lambs or hoggets.

Fatness

Organizations were virtually unanimous in agreeing that five levels of fatness were needed to describe existing variations and to make commercial distinctions. Of these, the first would be for the very plainest lambs and the last for the very fattest—both would be rarely needed, the bulk of lambs would fall into the central three classes.

It was for further discussion whether carcasses with unusually large kidney fat development for their general level of fatness needed to be identified as such.

Conformation

It was proposed that three levels of conformation be distinguished among carcasses in the three central fatness classes to provide the scheme shown in Table 2.11.

This provided for nine class combinations, of which three

Table 2.11. *Classification of lamb carcasses in UK (Meat & Livestock Commission)*

		Fat Class		
I	2	3	4	5
Very plain	Excellent conformation			Very fat
	Average conformation			

would be rarely used. It was proposed that a lettering or numbering system be adopted so that a single letter or number applied to each class combination. In due course, carcasses would be identified by tag. Table 2.12 shows the proportion of lambs following into the various categories during a pilot period in 1973 (Cuthbertson, 1974). Of the 328 000 carcasses classified it can be seen that almost a half were in one category— the medium conformation and fat class.

Table 2.12. *Preliminary results from experimental sheep carcass classification scheme. Percentages falling into each combination (based on a sample of 382 000 carcasses classified between October 1973 and February, 1974).*

Conformation Class	Fat class				
	1 (very lean)	2	3	4	5 (very fat)
Extra (E)		1.0	14.8	7.7	
	0.2				1.2
Average		15.6	46.1	9.8	
Poor (C)			3.2		
Very poor (Z)			0.4		

UNITED STATES OF AMERICA

Sheep carcasses in the USA can be graded under the United States Department of Agriculture scheme according to two criteria.

USDA Quality Grades

Lamb carcasses have long been graded under a voluntary scheme into various quality grades to facilitate communication in the meat trade (Acker, 1971). These quality grade designations have become accepted and well known throughout the United States.

Lambs and yearlings are divided into five possible grades of which the extremes of the range of grades can be briefly described as follows:

Prime carcass moderately wide and thick in relation to length; moderately plump and full legs; moderately wide and thick backs; moderately thick and full shoulders.

Cull carcass extremely angular; extremely thin flesh with legs extremely thin and concave; flesh soft and watery.

The three intermediate ranges fit into the list of grades as follows: Prime, Choice, Good, Utility, Cull.

USDA Yield Grades

Since 1969 USDA yield grades have been available to the US industry to provide a nationally uniform method of identifying carcasses for differences in "cutability"—specifically the yields of closely trimmed, boneless, retail cuts from the leg, loin, 'hotel rack' and shoulder.

Five USDA yield grades are used (USDA, 1970). These vary from Grade 1 with the highest yield of retail cuts to Grade 5 with the lowest.

A carcass typical of its yield grade would be expected to yield 3.5 per cent more in total retail cuts than the next lower yield grade when USDA cutting and trimming methods are followed.

Yield grades of carcasses are based on the examination of (a) the amount of external fat; (b) the amount of kidney and pelvic fat; (c) the conformation grade of the legs.

(a) is evaluated in terms of its thickness over the twelfth and thirteenth ribs subjectively or by measurement. A change of 0.15 in. (4 mm) in fat thickness over the rib eye makes a full yield grade change.

(b) is measured subjectively. A change of 4 per cent of the carcass weight makes a full yield grade change.

(c) the leg is evaluated on the quality grade basis, described above. A change of one-third of a quality grade alters yield grade by 5 per cent of a yield grade.

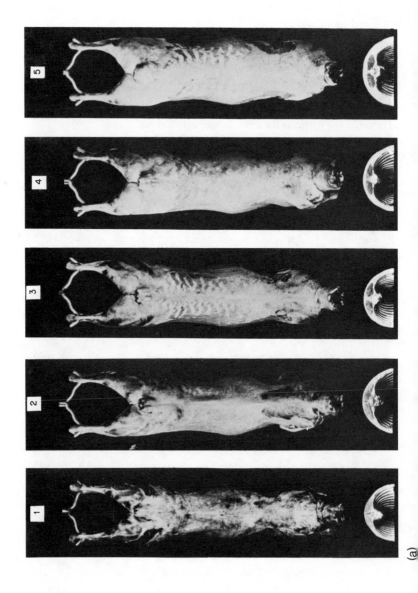

(a)

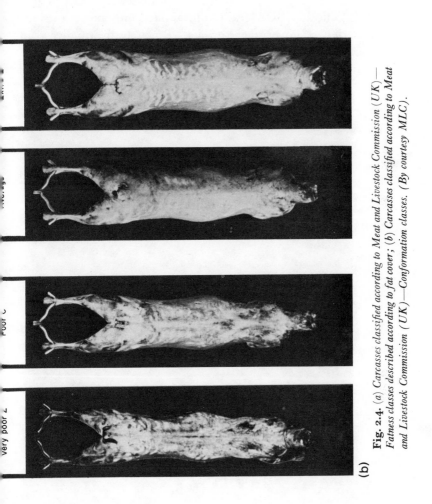

(b)

Fig. 2.4. (*a*) *Carcasses classified according to Meat and Livestock Commission (UK)—Fatness classes described according to fat cover; (b) Carcasses classified according to Meat and Livestock Commission (UK)—Conformation classes. (By courtesy MLC).*

The familiarity developed in the US meat trade has resulted in these USDA grades becoming meaningful and well recognized criteria by which marketing transactions can be carried out. Official USDA grades are applied only on carcasses, by experienced government graders. Privately the quality grades can also be used to grade live lambs before slaughter.

Wool Production 3

Historical Development

Wool has played an important rôle in the development of human society. In many ways the growth of the wool industry was a prelude to the full Industrial Revolution in Western Europe when the long held predominance of wool in world trade was eclipsed. Even before the sheep was fully domesticated (about 10 000 B.C.) the sheep's wool and skin were probably important items of human clothing but it was much later, with the development of the art of weaving, that woollen cloth became an important trading commodity.

Ormerod (1918) in describing the development of the wool manufacturing industry emphasized the importance of the immigration of Flemish weavers in developing the trade in Britain. The woollen industry was the premier English industry from the twelfth to the nineteenth century. In the initial part of this period trade consisted largely of exports of wool to the woollen industries overseas, primarily those of the Flemish in the Low Countries and of Florence in Italy. British wool was at this time the finest wool produced anywhere. Coinciding with religious persecution in the Low Countries, the sixteenth century saw a marked turning point in the British wool industry. The expansion of the manufacturing industry at home, fostered by the expertise of the refugee Flemish weavers, caused an increasing diversion of wool from

D

export to home manufacture and the consequent rise of Britain as the major exporter of woollen cloth at the expense of Flanders and Florence. In the seventeenth century an Act of Parliament was passed prohibiting the export of wool, although there had been several previous measures to this end.

Bowden (1971) has reported that prior to 1660 wool and wool cloth accounted for more than three-quarters of the export trade of Tudor and Stuart England.

It was with the start of the industrial revolution and the establishment of the British cotton industry that the long dominance of wool in the British economy ceased.

The development of the wool industry had a major influence on the agriculture and agrarian society of many countries. In Britain, wool production and processing was a widespread activity. Clapham (1966) shows that not only did the large manors and religious institutions own substantial flocks of sheep but peasants and small holders of various kinds owned small numbers of sheep, all primarily kept for wool production. Until the sixteenth century, wool production did not compete with arable cropping, and expansion of flocks took place in hilly uncultivatable areas or in a scavenger capacity in conjunction with arable cropping. In the sixteenth century, however, the greatly increased demand for wool provided an impetus to the Enclosure movement and a great social upheaval took place whereby much arable cropping was replaced by sheep keeping on a large scale with consequent depopulation of the rural villages by eviction of the peasants and the annexation of village commons (Lipson, 1953). The widespread unrest caused by this agrarian revolution instigated several govenment measures to restrain sheep farming although these were not very effective in achieving their aim. Measures to prohibit the conversion of arable land into pasture, for instance, were evaded by pulling a single furrow across a field.

Cloth manufacture was also very widespread at the start, with spinning and weaving being carried on by women and children in the homes, and only gradually was woollen manufacture on a large scale confined to specialized areas.

Spain is another country in which wool production played an important part in the foundation of its wealth and influence as a world power.

The origin of the Spanish Merino is subject to some debate but finewooled sheep were known in the Mediterranean area, from Greece to North Africa, during Roman times. It was during the Moorish occupation of Spain that these sheep were concentrated and developed in Spain as the Merino sheep (Austin, 1944). The Merino flocks were part of the transhumant movement of many thousands of sheep from the summer grazings of the northern uplands to the southern plains for the winter, a movement which survives to this day, in modified form (see Chapter 1). During the sixteenth and seventeenth century, fine wool from these Merino flocks saw Spain supplant Britain as the chief source of the finest wool for the world woollen industry. In addition to producing fine wool, the Spanish Merino was well adapted to walking large distances under arid conditions and this probably accounts for the present day 'hardiness' of the Merino under unfavourable arid conditions with large distances between waterholes.

The migratory flocks of Merinos in Spain were largely owned by the Royal Family, rich noblemen and monastic institutions, and the organization of the transhumant movements involved much cooperation between flock owners and their shepherds. This cooperation became formalized in local gatherings called '*mestas*' which dealt with the ownership of strays, conditions of hire for shepherds and other details. These local mestas were incorporated by Alfonso the Learned in the thirteenth century into a national association endowed with a charter called the "Honourable Assembly of the Mesta of Shepherds". It was under the discipline exerted by the mesta system, over several centuries, that the Merino developed into the major fine wool breed. As in Britain, the overwhelming importance of wool had great agricultural and social consequences. There was much resentment in Spain because the migratory flocks, with much vested privilege behind them, consumed the best feed from the common lands and smaller peasant holdings as they came through on their seasonal trek. The disappearance of the peasants' arable holdings and increased grazing pressure from the sheep flocks may well have been a factor in a substantial deterioration of the land and in rural depopulation.

By the eighteenth century, a few great flocks or *'cabanas'* had established themselves as the genetic leaders, as it were, of the Spanish Merino. The most famous were the Escurial Merinos owned by the King and reputed to produce the finest wool; the Paular Merinos associated with a large monastery at Paular were the most popular; the Negrette type which was larger in body size and horn development than the others, and another—the Infantado—which was rather similar to the Negrette.

In the eighteenth century the tight embargo on the export of Merino sheep from Spain was lifted and Merinos were exported to the neighbouring European countries in the early part of the century, then to the developing colonies of South Africa and Australia, and later, to the USSR, USA and South America.

The merino was imported into Germany in 1765 (Austin, 1944) and Germany quickly became a major producer of Merino sheep and wool. The breeders of Saxony particularly, bred a very finewooled type of Merino which, although they produced finer wool than the Spanish sheep, were small and not as hardy as the Spanish sheep they were derived from. Merinos from Saxony and Silesia figured prominently in the early importations into Australia.

Merinos did not become as widespread in France as in neighbouring Germany in this early period but the distinctive type developed in France, the Rambouillet, became world famous. In 1786, Louis XV obtained a selection of superior Merino sheep from his cousin, the King of Spain, and placed them on his farm at Rambouillet near Paris. The Rambouillet developed into a large framed sheep with heavy fleeces that were coarser than that of the Merinos developed in Germany. The Rambouillet sheep later became popular overseas, particularly in the USA.

Merinos were first introduced to the USA some years earlier, but became well established with large importations from Spain around 1810. The state of Vermont became an important centre of Merino breeding and the Vermont type of Merino with its large size, very wrinkled skin and heavy, greasy, medium fine fleece enjoyed a widespread vogue in many countries, particularly in Australia in the late nineteenth century.

The great Merino flocks of Spain were largely disbanded during the Napoleonic wars in the nineteenth century and Spain is no longer pre-eminent as a fine wool producer nor as the fountain head of the Merino breed, this mantle having long since passed to breeders of the Southern Hemisphere.

The development of Australia was largely based on wool and the astonishing expansion of sheep numbers during the nineteenth and early twentieth centuries is a prime example of an ecological explosion. Sheep, particularly the Merino, are well adapted to a country, much of which is too arid for reliable crop growth, particularly since fine wool production is based on flocks with a high proportion of wether sheep which can best withstand drought conditions. The system also demands very little in the way of capital in fixed equipment and can be run with the minimum of labour. Added to this, the product is non-perishable and, although bulky, quite suitable for transport over long distances.

The development of wool production in Australia and other similar developing territories provided the raw material for a vast increase in the wool manufacturing industry of Britain and all over the world which has only abated recently with the increasing competition from artificial textile fibres.

Wool, more than any of the other textiles, has been subject

to wide fluctuations in price because of the difficulty of adjusting supply to demand in spite of the sophisticated marketing organization for wool that has developed on a world basis. One interesting example of this difficulty was that Charles II, of England, decreed that everyone should be buried in a woollen shroud—a measure calculated to help the English woollen industry during time of depression.

Wool Production and Consumption

Table 3.1 summarizes the world production of textile fibres from 1961/62 to 1971/72 (Bureau of Agricultural Economics, Canberra, 1972) and shows that in 1971/72 the following percentage share of world textile fibres by the main components: Cotton, 52.7; Non-cellulosics, 25.6; Cellulosics, 15.0; Wool, 6.7.

There was a 55 per cent increase over the decade of total textile fibre production, although clean wool production

Table 3.1. *Estimated world production of textile fibres. Source: Bureau of Agricultural Economics, Canberra, Australia (1972)*

Year	Wool (clean)*	Cotton*	Man-made fibre† Cellulosic	Non-cellulosic	Total
	m. kg	m. kg	m. kg	m. kg	m. kg
1961–62	1.488	9.819	2.690	831	14.828
1962–63	1.477	10.457	2.864	1.081	15.879
1963–64	1.506	10.957	3.059	1.334	16.856
1964–65	1.480	11.308	3.286	1.691	17.765
1965–66	1.492	11.604	3,339	2,052	18,487
1966–67	1,553	10,556	3.343	2.487	17.939
1967–68	1.574	10,411	3.315	2.878	18.178
1968–69	1,622	11,623	3.531	3.785	20.561
1969–70	1.609	11.262	3.560	4.402	20.833
1970–71‡	1.591	11.164	3.433	4.951	21.139
1971–72‡	1.547	12.145	3.442	5.895	23.029

* Wool and cotton data on a seasonal basis.
† Man-made fibre data on a calendar basis, of first year shown.
‡ Provisional.

increased by only 4 per cent as compared to an increase of 24 per cent in cotton production, 28 per cent in cellulosic fibre and a seven-fold increase in the non-cellulosic fibre sector.

In Table 3.2 the world greasy wool production is broken down into the contribution from the major producing countries over a period 1968/69–1971/72 where there has been a steady fall from the all-time peak of world wool production recorded in 1968/69. Falls in production have been recorded

Table 3.2. *Estimated world wool production. Source: Bureau of Agricultural Economics, Canberra, Australia (1972)*

Country or Region	1968–69	1969–70	1970–71	1971–72*
	m. kg	m. kg	m. kg	m. kg
			Greasy	
Australia	884	924	886	869
USSR	415	390	419	424
New Zealand	332	328	334	330
Argentine†	209	201	200	184
South Africa‡	142	145	123	112
United States	97	88	85	80
Uruguay	82	80	78	50
Eastern Europe§	93	92	90	90
China (People's Republic)¶ and Outer Mongolia	79	79	79	79
United Kingdom	54	48	47	46
Other producers	418	413	412	410
World total	2805	2788	2753	2674
			Clean	
Wool type				
Merino	618	624	600	577
Crossbred	706	694	699	680
Other	298	291	292	290
World total	1622	1609	1591	1547

* Subject to revision.
† Includes wool on sheepskins.
‡ Including Lesotho and South West Africa.
§ Albania, Bulgaria, Czechoslovakia, East Germany, Hungary, Poland and Romania.
¶ Including Manchuria, Sinkiang and Tibet.

for most of the major producers, particularly Australia, Argentina, South Africa, USA, Uruguay and UK.

Properties of Wool as a Textile

Wool has several characteristics that make it a unique fibre and account for its pre-eminence as the most important fibre of animal origin. The physical properties of wool have been described in detail by Onions (1962) and only a summary of the main outstanding properties are given here.

Strength and Elasticity

Although there is much variation in wool fibres, particularly according to their fineness, some useful general comparisons can be made between wool as a fibre and other competitive textile fibres.

When a load is applied wool fibres are not notable for their strength when compared with other fibres; wool fibres tend to have a low breaking stress. This is particularly true if wool is wet.

In terms of elasticity, i.e., ability to extend and to recover after extension, the wool fibre is much better than most other fibres and its extensibility is increased at higher temperatures and when wet. This property is most important and accounts for the resilience of wool, giving an ability to retain their shape to woollen garments and a resistance to creases. It is also an essential property for the resilience necessary in carpets and in blankets. Woollen blankets maintain their thickness, retaining entrapped air within the fibres to give them their excellent insulation properties.

The effect of moisture

Wool absorbs moisture from the atmosphere to a greater extent than other fibres and in the process of doing so, liberates heat in a complex exothermic reaction. A woollen garment varies normally from about 16 per cent to 35 per cent moisture content without feeling wet (Ryder & Stephenson, 1968) and in its gradual absorption of water and liberation of heat helps to buffer the skin from marked fluctuation in moisture and temperature both from the surrounding atmosphere and from exertion and perspiration from within. Many of these properties are those for which wool was developed as the natural fleece cover on the living sheep.

Synthetic fibres and garments made from them do not have this complex property and therefore are often not so suitable as clothing.

In contrast to its ability to absorb moisture from the atmosphere, wool is resistant to liquid water so that it has good waterproofing qualities.

DURABILITY AND SHRINKING

Although wool fibres are not particularly strong under tension, they are tough, i.e., resistant to abrasion (although not so tough as nylon and terylene) and also very resistant to breaking when repeatedly flexed. This makes wool garments, or garments made from a mixture of wool with terylene or nylon, very hard wearing. Cotton is much less durable than wool in these respects.

Another property of wool which is distinctive and in many aspects useful, is the felting property which is discussed below. A less desirable consequence of felting, however, is that it is responsible for shrinkage in knitted woollen garments that are washed, and therefore inimicable to long wearing. Various processes, such as chlorination, have been successfully employed to produce non-shrinkable wool.

FELTING AND FRICTION

Wool fibres demonstrate an important property, that when subjected to pressure combined with movement creating friction, they form a denser matted mass that subsequently holds together as a fabric. This property has a complex causation which has been subject to some debate but it is agreed that it is brought about by the differential friction generated along a wool fibre according to the direction in which it points. Greater frictional resistance is generated when a wool fibre is pulled along by its tip than when pulled along by its root. This has obvious advantages in the fleece of the live sheep in that there is a tendency for all foreign matter or exudation to move from the skin of the sheep to the outside of the fleece. The cortical scales of the fibre overlap each other so that the projecting edges point towards the tip. This suggests a relationship between the scaliness of the fibre with consequent interlocking between fibres lying in opposed direction and the felting process. However, the absence of such interlocking under microscopic examination and the fact that the same property is shown when wool is rubbed against other material such as nylon, suggests that the phenomenon is a more complex consequence of the differential friction effect.

Shrink proofing treatments, mentioned above, considerably modify the frictional properties of the wool fibres.

CRIMPINESS

A notable properties of wool is its crimpiness or waviness. The same pattern of crimps or waves in neighbouring fibres gives a lock or staple of wool its distinctive waviness. The causes of crimping probably lie in the growth of the fibre in the bulb of the follicle. Movement of the follicle during the growth of the fibre can result in crimp as could differences in the keratinization of different sides of the fibre cortex.

Crimp has been widely used as one basis for assessing wool quality and there is a close association between the frequency of crimps along the length of the wool staple and the fineness of the fleece.

Growth and Development of the Fleece

Wool, like hair, is derived from follicles in the skin, containing the so-called 'roots' which are downgrowths from the epidermis into the inner dermis. Primary follicles develop from about the fiftieth to the eightieth day of pregnancy (Onions, 1962) and initially give rise mainly to the coarser fibres of the fleece.

Primary follicles are associated with three features—(a) an erector muscle which enables a hair to 'stand on end'; (b) a sebaceous gland which is responsible for the grease of the sheep's fleece, giving it its lubricated glossy property, and (c) the sweat gland—which gives the dried sweat or 'suint' of the fleece. Suint from the sweat gland and grease from the sebaceous gland together give the yellow 'yolk' of the fleece. The development of the primary follicles shows a definite pattern starting on the head, continuing on the legs to the trunk and ending on the back of the sheep.

Secondary follicles begin to develop from the eighty-fifth day of pregnancy and it is thought that most secondary follicles have been initiated by the time of birth. They are much less complex structures associated usually with a simple sebaceous gland. The secondary follicles give rise mainly to true wool fibres. Many of the later formed secondary follicles, especially in the Merino breed, develop as a bud branching off from another secondary.

Once the follicle population is complete no new ones are initiated except in extreme circumstances such as following severe flystrike. Thus follicle density is very high in the young lamb; for example it can be 3000–4000 per cm² of skin surface in the Down breeds at birth and more than 10000 in the Merino (Ryder, 1965). As the sheep grows bigger, follicle density falls, and in adult sheep may vary from as little as 1000 per cm² in the Scottish Blackface to between 5000 and 10000 in the Merino.

The non-wool fibres differ from wool in their physical characters, a consequence of the fact that they are largely medullated fibres, with an inner core of different cells. This core becomes vacuolated with spaces or interstices between the cells.

Kemp fibres are the coarsest of the fibres in the fleece and originate in the primary follicles. Kemp fibres possess a wide latticed medulla, i.e., full of spaces, which give them their brittle texture and make them difficult to dye through lack of solid substance. Some kemps are chalky white in appearance whilst others, as in some Welsh Mountain sheep, are red.

Hairs, which form a large part of the coarse outer coat of primitive and mountain breeds, are intermediate between kemp and true wool and originate mainly, but not exclusively, from the primary follicles. Hairs show much variation between the extreme types and also tend to vary along their length according to the season of growth, being thicker and coarser during the summer growth.

True wool fibres derived from the soft undercoat of the wild sheep, are usually non-medullated, i.e., comprising keratinized cells. All fibres are surrounded by a cuticle with flat scale-like cells aligned towards the tip of the fibre and packed to a varying degree of tightness like slates on a roof. Keratin, the main component of wool, is largely protein containing a high proportion of the sulphur amino acid cystine. Sulphur is therefore important in the process of keratinization that takes place in the follicle.

The wool follicles are arranged in groups with three primary follicles associated with a number of secondary follicles. The ratio of secondary to primary follicles is associated with follicle density and with the fineness of the fleece. In sheep breeds that are highly developed for fine wool production, e.g., the Merino, there is a ratio of 15–25 secondaries per primary follicle as against less well developed wool breeds, e.g., the average British breed with only about 3–8 secondaries per primary. Another feature of the improved breeds is that, after birth, the medullated fibres are shed and replaced by wool fibres, although the lambs, at birth, may have a varying cover of hairy fibres. Primitive breeds of sheep retain a high proportion of kemp and hair, which forms the outer part of the fleece in adult life, often completely hiding the inner coat of short soft fine wool. The fleece fibres of these breeds show cycles in growth, including a period when the follicle's activities cease. Kemps have a short cycle of growth and are frequently shed; the hair and wool fibres normally cease growth once a year after which the fleece is shed. Domesticated sheep still show a decrease in fleece growth at this stage although in highly developed Merino type sheep wool growth appears to be continuous.

The formation of an actual break in the fleece in the spring, depends not only on this inherent feature of fibre growth but also on the occurrence of a nutritional check if severe enough. A severe check or illness at any time can lead to fleece shedding. Some breeds, such as the North Country Cheviot in Britain, are reputed to be prone to fleece shedding although it is difficult to assess accurately the extent to which it is a breed effect or due to association with systems where there is severe under-feeding in the spring.

Not only do the fleece and the underlying follicles differ as between improved and unimproved breeds; there are also differences between different parts of the body of the same sheep. These are often particularly noticeable at birth where the back and underside (posterior and ventral aspects) show a much higher proportion of coarse hairy fibres than the front and neck parts (anterior and dorsal aspects). These differences also exist in the adult sheep, with the highest proportion of kemp and hair at the posterior end or breech of the sheep, and on the belly.

The birth coat of the lamb. The coat of the newborn lamb is of interest as a guide to the development of the adult fleece but is also, as noted earlier, an important adaptation for survival in the early stage after birth. The birth coat and its properties, particularly its relation to the adult fleece, has received some study as summarized by Ryder (1965). At one to two months of age many of the juvenile fibres are shed from the birth coat so that it approximates in general features to the adult fleece.

There are three main types of fibre in the birth coat, differentiated according to length, coarseness, shape of fibre tip and according to the period over which the fibre develops. These have been called the precurly tips, curly tips and post curly tips each subdivided according to coarseness, e.g., the coarsest type of precurly tips are called the 'halo' fibres.

The coarsest birth coat fibres—the precurly tips (particularly the 'halos') are shed some weeks after birth and are replaced by hairy fibres; the halo fibres are usually replaced by kemps.

Objectives in Wool Production

The main aim of the wool producer is to maximize his revenue in relation to his resources. Where wool is the main product, achieving this aim is a matter of striking the best balance between the quantity of wool produced and the quality and price of that wool clip. For finewool production, within the limits set by genetic factors, measures taken by the producer to increase the fleece weight of his sheep will tend to reduce the quality.

Wool variability in relation to quality. Overshadowing the many simple relationships between various factors and the major components of yield and quality in wool is the fact that the fleece is a biological material with variation in individual fibres along their length, between types of fibres within a fleece, between different parts of the fleece and between fleeces. For many purposes the wool manufacturer desires uniformity within the general spectrum of requirements for particular manufacturing processes. Uniformity in wool both within the fleece and between fleeces of individual sheep is subject to genetic improvement and the best finewool Merino strains show this very clearly, the fleece being far more uniform over the body than is the case with coarser, less improved, hill sheep breeds such as the Scottish Blackface.

Within limits, the general quality of the wool, particularly as regards its length and coarseness, is affected by the level of nutrition but often of greater importance is the effect of season and nutrition on the variability along the length of the fibre.

Nutritional checks, particularly when imposed near the time of the seasonal trough of follicular activity, give rise to very thin sections of the fibre leading to 'tenderness' or liability to break at the weak point. Some of the coarser fibres can change along their length from a coarse medullated hair like section in summer to a finer non-medullated wool like section in the winter.

In addition to the genetic changes in wool uniformity wrought by the breeders, the trade, in its complex marketing procedure from the sheep's back to the finished garment, achieve further uniformity by subdivision of the world wool clip. For specific purposes fleeces and parts within fleeces are subdivided into a large number of batches or grades suitable for different purposes but uniform within themselves. These are outlined in a subsequent section.

Components of fleece weight. Before dealing in more detail with factors influencing wool production in the sheep it is useful to consider what clean fleece weight consists of. Ryder (1965) gave a concise expression of this as follows:

$$W = LANDS$$

indicating that clean fleece weight (W) is a product of mean fibre length (L), mean cross sectional area of the fibre (A), mean number of fibres per unit area of skin (N), density of wool substance (D) and the area of wool bearing skin on the sheep (S). Only the first two factors, length and thickness of the fibre, are directly affected by changes in feeding levels from year to year and it is largely to the manipulation of these that the producer must look in making short term adjustments to his wool clip.

Factors Affecting Wool Yield and Quality

Genetic factors. Considerable breed differences in fleece characters exist. These include differences in the weight of the fleece and in its composition. Differences in the ratio of secondary to primary follicles have been noted and in the occurrence and type of the various fleece fibres. These are marked both in the birth coat of the lamb and in the fleece of the adult sheep. Later it will be shown that many important fleece characters are strongly inherited and the evolution and development of the Merino breed clearly illustrate the extent to which fleece characters are subject to genetic improvement. Ryder (1965) has made the useful generalization that differences between one fibre and another are genetic in origin whereas differences along the length of the fibre tend to be due to environmental causes.

Seasonal factors. Much of the seasonal effect is mediated indirectly through its effect on the nutrition of the sheep which is dealt with later. However, season acts directly, probably through the changes in daylength, in influencing the hormonal changes associated with the seasonal cycle of fibre growth referred to earlier and in bringing about the orderly shedding or moulting of the fleece that occurs naturally. Doney (1966) showed that the direct seasonal effect is much less pronounced in the highly developed Merino breed when feed variation was minimized, than in British breeds less highly developed for wool.

Nutrition. The nutrition of the lamb during the phase of follicle initiation and development, can have a permanent effect on the fleece and the ratio of secondary to primary follicles is shown to be associated with birth weight. Ryder and Stephenson (1968), summarizing some of the evidence on this point, concluded that underfeeding of the ewe in late pregnancy and early lactation can result in a permanent reduction of the ratio of secondary to primary follicles in Merino sheep but that for other breeds, less highly developed for wool production, the effect is not permanent and the follicle pattern returns to normal after an appropriate period of adequate feeding.

In later life, chronic underfeeding can both reduce the

growth of the wool and reduce the thickness of the fibre. It is for this reason that the best Merino fine wools are produced in drier areas on relatively poor quality soils, provided the environment is reasonably uniform. The effect of under-feeding depends to a large extent on the physiological stage at which it occurs. Lactation has a high priority for the feed energy of the ewe, so that wool growth suffers during suckling, particularly if feeding is inadequate. This tendency is more marked in breeds such as the British hill breeds, which have not been highly selected for wool characters, than in the Merino, which has a greater tendency to grow wool at the expense of other activities. Depression of energy intake in the sheep affects the rate of wool growth within a few days but the maximum effect may take 9–12 weeks to be established. By this time a new equilibrium between energy intake and rate of wool growth is established (Ryder, 1965). Although under-feeding, particularly in the lambing ewe, restricts wool growth, the maximum efficiency of conversion of food into wool is obtained at much less than maximum feed intake. Langlands and Bennett (1973) have shown that stocking rates that give maximum conversion of feed into wool are higher than those which allow the maintenance of relatively good body condition. Thus, although poor feeding reduces wool growth and fibre thickness, particularly in the nursing ewe and in some breeds, wool continues to grow at levels below those optimal for high meat production (and even during starvation).

The quality of the diet. Clean dry wool is practically all high quality protein containing about 9 per cent of cystine. However, under normal circumstances, there is little response in terms of wool growth, to increases in dietary levels of crude protein above 8 per cent (Ferguson, 1969). Work on the use of formaldehyde treated 'protected' protein has indicated that protein supplements that by-pass the rumen are used more efficiently than conventional sources and can lead to increased wool production in sheep on a low quality roughage diet (Reis & Tunks, 1969). Other nutrients, notably traces of copper, are also important in wool growth, lack of which causes loss of crimp and pigment.

The Suitability of Wool for Various Uses

The economic effect of the various factors described depends largely on the use that wool is put to. For example, wool containing a significant proportion of kemp fibres would be unacceptable for the fine wool market, but in limited quantities, for the special purpose of tweed manufacture, it could be highly desirable. There are three main outlets for the world's wool:

Worsted manufacture. High quality fine wool that meets certain requirements in terms of length and strength of staple, goes in to the process, whereby the wool is teased out into roughly parallel fibres by 'combing' and spun into fine strong threads, which are woven into high quality garments and materials.

Woollen manufacture. Fine wools with variable length of staple, possibly subject to 'break' or 'tenderness', go into a process whereby wool is subjected to a less intense teasing or 'carding' process and the fibres are spun to form a thicker, softer thread which can be woven or knitted into a soft garment, which is very warm because of the trapped air space. Some finishing processes make use of the 'felting' property of wool where the fibres coalesce for strength because of the differential friction effect generated.

Carpet manufacture. Coarser wools with a moderate proportion of kemp and hair—usually with long coarse wool fibres - - are used mainly for carpet manufacture, where robustness and hard wear are the prime requirements.

The suitability of wool for these various purposes depends on several attributes. These include the length of staple, colour, fragility and many other subjective qualities expressed in terms such as 'handle' to denote softness. However, the main criterion of the value of most wool is the fineness of the fibre and recent estimates showed that fineness or mean fibre diameter of Merino wools, as measured in the laboratory, accounts for about 80 per cent of the variation in the value of wool for worsted manufacture (Turner & Young, 1969).

In view of this it is considered that most of the selection pressure for wool quality in sheep breeding schemes can be exerted by taking a mid side sample from the fleece at shearing and getting the sample assessed in the laboratory for percentage clean yield (which measures the yield of scoured wool per unit of greasy fleece as weighed) and the fibre diameter.

In the wool trade wool is assessed subjectively for fineness and given a fineness *count*. This varies from about 30–100 and was originally based on the number of yarn lengths, each of 560 yards, that could be spun from one pound weight of wool prepared for spinning. The count is usually judged subjectively taking account of the degree of 'crimpiness' or waviness of the fibres. The wool produced over the world can be classified on the basis of its fineness count into three main categories.

'Merino' wool with quality number 60s and over.

'Crossbred' wool 44s–58s.

'Carpet' wool 44s and below.

'Merino' wool is usually destined for the best quality light worsted and woollen garment manufacture. 'Crossbred' wool (not necessarily produced from crossbreds) is used for a wide range of material including the finest tweeds, lower quality worsted material and a wide range of knitting yarns.

'Carpet' wool is used mainly for carpets and for mattress filling although the finest wools in this category may be used for tweeds.

The Commercial Evaluation and Processing of Wool

The complex chain of processing and marketing of wool starts with shearing at the farm of origin, although a significant proportion of wool—in the UK about one-third—is skin wool obtained from the skins of slaughtered sheep, primarily lambs and hoggets.

SHEARING.

A sheep is usually shorn for the first time at about 14–15 months of age and only a small proportion of sheep—in the UK about 3 per cent—are sheared as lambs when they are five or six months old.

Shearing normally takes place once a year in late spring, often some two to three months after lambing. However, in some of the Scandinavian countries, where ewes are wintered indoors, it is customary to shear twice, once in early winter when the sheep go into the house and then in spring. There are some advantages in this procedure and recent trials at Aberdeen (Rutter *et al.*, 1972) have shown that where sheep are housed in winter the extra cost of shearing twice may be justified. Other situations in which more frequent shearing takes place have been noted in Chapter 1.

Shearing itself can take many forms. The most primitive, applicable to some unimproved sheep, is to remove the fleece by plucking by hand. This is possible because the natural break in the staple is pronounced enough so that the fleece is ready to be shed naturally.

The bulk of the world's sheep are, however, sheared by cutting the wool just above skin level using a pair of shears. Hand shears have been traditionally employed for this purpose but the use of mechanically operated shears, particularly those powered by electricity, is becoming widespread. A skilful operator can shear more than one hundred sheep per day depending on the type of sheep and on whether he has assistance for catching the sheep and wrapping the wool. It is widely recognized that it is important to leave some wool on the sheep, according to conditions, to provide protection against chilling and losses after shearing.

Chemical Shearing

One development of recent years, germane to the discussion of the growth of wool fibres, is the use of drugs for so-called chemical shearing. This technique, developed by Terrill et al.,

(1970) at the USDA station, Beltsville, USA, depends on the action of the drug cyclophosphamide (CPA) administerea by mouth at the rate of 24 mg/kg body weight. Its action is thought to be that it arrests cell division in the follicle just long enought to give an effect on the fleece analogous to a severe check, causing a break in the wool. Given a short time to allow some new wool to grow, the old fleece can be 'sheared' by hand, analogous to the primitive hand plucking method. The adoption of such a drastic procedure clearly requires the most stringent testing before it can be advocated as a practicable alternative to normal shearing.

CLASSIFICATION AND SORTING OF WOOL

The process of producing batches of wool of uniform description for the varied needs of the processing industry, commences on the shearing floor. It is customary to separate at shearing the soiled wool and the floor sweepings, from the main fleece, and in some areas of the world to subdivide even further the belly wool and other lower quality wool from the best part of the fleece.

The fleece may be rolled into a bundle with the outside of the fleece forming the inside of the bundle, fastened by using the twisted neck wool and packed into large hessian bags. Alternatively, a large number of fleeces are pressed into compact bales using a mechanical press.

The wool then leaves the farm and eventually arrives at a grading centre. In the UK a producer Wool Marketing Board is responsible for collecting, grading and selling almost all wool produced. Wool merchants, acting as agents of the board, collect the wool into large warehouses where each fleece is handled and graded into many grades or classes upon which payment to the individual producer is based.

Subsequently, in the wool mill the fleeces are broken up and sorted into uniform lots each with a description including its fineness count.

Table 3.3. *Wool characteristics of some major British sheep breeds**

	Mean autumn body weight of ewes (kg)	Wool classification	Mean fleece weight (kg)	Mean staple length (cm)	Fineness count
Scottish Blackface	55	Mountain and hill	2.5	27	28–32
Welsh Mountain	38	Mountain and hill	1.5	8	36–50
Swaledale	48	Mountain and hill	2.0	25	28–32
North Country Cheviot	77	Mountain and hill	2.0	7	50–56
South Country Cheviot	50	Mountain and hill	2.0	10	50–56
Clun Forest	63	Shortwool and Down	2.5	9	56–58
Dorset Horn	74	Shortwool and Down	2.5	9	54–58
Romney Marsh	68	Longwool and lustre	4.0	16	48–56
Devon Longwool	78	Longwool and lustre	6.0	30	32–36
Border Leicester	84	Longwool and lustre	3.5	20	40–46
Teeswater	84	Longwool and lustre	6.0	30	40–48
Suffolk	84	Shortwool and Down	3.0	6	54–58
Dorset Down	74	Shortwool and Down	2.5	6	56–58

* Body weight data: MLC, 1974. Fleece data: BWMB (*British sheep breeds—their wool and its uses*)

Wool contains several impurities which must be removed. Much of the 'suint' and grease is removed by the process of scouring and much of the vegetable matter in subsequent combing or carding processes. Producers themselves can minimize such contamination of the wool by ensuring clean conditions during the process of shearing by providing a clean floor or tarpaulin. In some parts, particularly in Wales, it is traditional to wash sheep before shearing by making them swim through clean stream water and allowing several days for the fleece to be thoroughly dry for shearing. This process does not remove the need for subsequent scouring and although the price per kilo of fleece is higher for washed wool, this hardly compensates for the reduced weight of fleece and the trouble and expense involved in organizing washing on a large scale. However, in some of the hill areas of the UK for example, the washed sheep is considered easier to shear than the unwashed sheep.

Table 3.3 gives some information on the wool characteristics of several important sheep breeds.

Wool Production Systems

An account of wool production and its various facets is not complete without looking more closely at the problems of wool production systems in two selected examples. The first example is the pastoral wool production sector in Australia; Australia is not only the major contributor to the world supply of wool but it represents the wider system of large scale fine wool production in difficult, mainly semi-arid, environments. Wool production in the UK is taken as the other example as a major representative of countries with substantial sheep industries where meat is the major product and a very variable, coarser wool crop is an important by-product.

AUSTRALIA

Reference has already been made to the development and regional distribution of sheep keeping in Australia. A major segment of the wool producing industry is based upon Merino flocks run in large units or stations ranging in size up to about 25 000 sheep, with a mean from 3000–9500 in the various states in the drier areas between the wheat/sheep zone and the arid interior. Rainfall is commonly under 400 mm per annum in such areas, although it may be higher in the summer rainfall areas of northern New South Wales and Queensland. However, rainfall figures mean little in such areas, there being wide fluctuations within and between seasons and little benefit from summer rain falling largely at a time of high evaporation rate. Stocking rates are very low but extremely variable with 1–3 ha per sheep in the better areas bordering the wheat zone, to as many as 20–30 ha per sheep on some of the poorest land in Western Australia. The fact that some rain falls over the area, however little, aids the maintenance of some vegetation cover and prevents the formation of drifting sand dunes. The natural vegetation contains many useful, drought resistant, plants such as the saltbush (*Atriplex* spp) common in Western New South Wales and Mitchell grass (*Astrebla* spp) common in Queensland. Only a very small proportion of land on these pastoral stations is capable of being improved into grass/clover pasture without irrigation.

Due to the remarkable association of finewool production with drought resistance and mobility, developed in the Merino, a sheep system with a valuable cash output can be set up in these areas with a small degree of human intervention. The minimum requisites are sources of drinking water, protection from predators and labour for shearing the sheep.

Water has to be provided so that sheep do not have to travel more than a few miles to water. This is obtained from excavated reservoirs to store rainwater, and from bores into underground water often pumped up by windmills.

The chief predators are the dingoes (wild dogs), blowfly, foxes, crows and eagles. It is important that flocks at risk are fenced against the dingoes to prevent widespread devastation in lambs. These dingo fences are commonly about 160 cm high and have to be well bedded into the ground to prevent the dogs digging beneath them. Kangaroos, which are also found over much of the pastoral areas, can usually clear the dog fences without difficulty although they may cause occasional damage. In some cases the property is sub-divided into about four paddocks.

Labour for shearing is mainly provided by migratory contract teams of shearers who move from the earliest to the later shearing areas as the season progresses very much as has been the tradition of hired harvesters for centuries in many areas of the world.

It is difficult to get a detailed objective picture of the time of shearing in various parts of Australia because of the great variation due to climate, particularly rainfall pattern and the consequent repercussions on lambing date.

Meadley (1952) examined the seasonal pattern of receivals of new-clip wool into brokers' stores in the various Australian states from 1936–1937 to 1950–1951. Since it is not common practice for wool to be held by the producer for any length of time the pattern reported is mainly a reflection of shearing times. There is no evidence to suggest that the pattern reported be Meadley, shown in Fig. 3.1, has altered significantly since that time.

As a general rule shearing tends to take place towards the end of the pasture growing season, i.e., in the spring in the southern winter rainfall areas with some tendency for some flocks to be shorn at the end of summer in the northern summer rainfall areas.

The peak month for wool to be received into store is in October except in Tasmania where the peak is in December. In Queensland, April and May figures approach the highest levels shown in the spring months.

P. E. Geytenbeek (1975, private communication) lists three major considerations in the time of shearing.

(1) As pastures mature the seed heads of pasture grasses and weed species become an objectionable contaminant of heavy

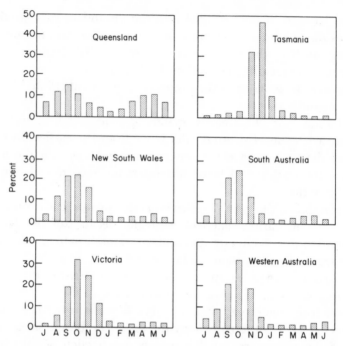

Fig. 3.1. *Average percentage receivals of new seasons wool into brokers stores: Australian states (based on Meadley, 1952).*

fleeces; the aim is therefore to shear before these plants are fully mature.

(2) Spring shearing means that sheep do not carry a heavy fleece through the summer, an important consideration in the control of flystrike.

(3) Shearing is usually timed about 5–6 months after lambing so that in an autumn lambing flock, for instance, the lambs/weaners can be shorn in the spring at the same time as the adult sheep.

The shearing season usually starts in the interior pastoral stations and ends in the wetter areas of the seaboard. Contract teams may often include 10–15 shearers at the start of the season for the larger pastoral stations but as the season progresses may split up into groups of about three men shearing the smaller properties in the higher rainfall areas.

Wether Flocks

A notable feature of the pastoral wool production system is the use of wether (castrated male) sheep.

Table 3.4 shows the classification of sheep in the whole of Australia according to age and sex. Of the 126.5 million sheep older than 1 year in 1972 more than 40 per cent were not breeding ewes and of these nearly 40 million (78 per cent) were wether sheep.

Wether sheep are stronger and hardier than ewes, particularly since they are not subject to the strain of pregnancy and lactation. They produce somewhat more wool than ewes (Turner & Young, 1969) and are not subject, under the same conditions, to the tenderness or breaks in the wool that are associated with stress around lambing time in the ewe. In the pastoral zone in 1971/72, 90 per cent of the income from sheep was derived from wool and skins (Hoogvliet, 1973) indicating a very low proportion of sales from lambs or culled sheep. Under some of the more extreme conditions of Western Australia and South Australia, where remoteness and location preclude availability of labour for managing breeding ewes, a few all wether flocks are kept. These flocks are replenished by purchasing replacements, usually as yearlings, and the wethers may later be sold at four and a half to five and a half years old for further fattening and one or two more wool crops, on better land. In extreme cases very little culling is carried out so that purchase of replacements is minimized, although the quality of the wool crop is lowered by the presence of old and poor sheep. Under most pastoral conditions it is much more common to keep a flock consisting of both breeding ewes and wethers which is self replenishing. The proportion of wethers varies according to conditions but is commonly about one half of the flock. In these part-wether flocks the ewes are generally kept to much older ages than the wethers before culling.

Table 3.4. *Sheep, by age and sex: Australia, 31 March 1968–1972. (thousands) Source: Commonwealth Year Book of Australia No. 59; 1973*

Description	1968	1969	1970	1971	1972
Rams (1 year and over)	2 079	2 184	2 200	2 177	2 060
Breeding ewes (1 year and over)	77 872	83 607	85 474	84 381	75 611
Other ewes (1 year and over)	6 700	6 424	6 483	7 521	9 089
Wethers (1 year and over)	42 512	45 178	45 441	45 269	39 777
Lambs and hoggets (under 1 year)	37 750	37 212	40 482	38 443	36 374
Total sheep and lambs	166 912	174 605	180 080	177 792	162 910

The great drawback of the pastoral wool production system, apart from its heavy dependence on wool prices, is the occurrence of unpredictable drought periods which may involve heavy losses of sheep or the necessity for the physical removal of sheep at much expense to areas less affected by drought. In certain areas there may also be problems with fleece contamination with vegetable matter (burrs) that is not easy to remove mechanically and with dust that rises from the arid land surface. Another serious problem of extensive wool growing is that of flystrike; an affected sheep often dies if untended. The 'mules' operation (described in Chapter 8) is now extensively employed and applied either when the lambs are marked or later at the hogget stage.

The development of the Merino into distinct types in Australia has markedly affected its suitability as a wool producer for the pastoral areas. As far as the most arid pastoral areas are concerned the sheep most favoured nowadays are a plainer more robust, stronger woolled sheep than in the past and the really fine-woolled strains of Merino are found mostly in the New South Wales table lands and in Tasmania. These very fine-woolled Merinos are mainly descended from the fine-woolled Saxony and Silesian strains from Germany.

A bigger, less fine-woolled, type of Merino developed by the Peppin family (called the Medium Merino Peppin) has become a popular sheep over a large part of Australia, particularly in the East. These sheep are reputed to be derived from Saxon and from Rambouillet stock. There are also some non-Peppin medium-woolled sheep.

A strong Merino is popular in areas of South Australia and Western Australia developed from popular studs such as the Bungaree and Colinsville types. The strong Merino is larger than the other types and produces a heavier less fine fleece; these sheep are particularly suitable for areas where pasture improvement has been carried out.

Another means of adapting Merinos to more fertile conditions has involved crossing with English longwool breeds, such as the Lincoln, Leicester and Romney, and then backcrossing to the Merino to produce the so-called Comeback sheep with seven-eights or more Merino.

Shearing has already been referred to and on the large pastoral stations of inland Australia it is a large scale operation with shearing sheds with as many as 20 shearing stands. In all, on the larger properties there may be 50–60 people involved.

Table 3.5. *Number and proportion of properties in Australia by flock size (adapted from Hoogvliet, 1973)*

Flock size	1960 (per cent)	1969 (per cent)	1970 (per cent)	1971 (per cent)	Estimated number of shearers per flock
200 and under 500	23.5	18.1	16.6	15.9	1
500 and under 2000	56.3	52.5	53.0	51.4	2
2000 and under 5000	15.5	22.5	23.8	25.3	3–5
5000 and over	4.7	6.9	6.6	7.4	6–10+
Total	100.0	100.0	100.0	100.0	
Total number of properties	92 907	88 193	87 632	85 011	

The organization of shearing gangs is largely dependent on the size of the flock being dealt with. Table 3.5 shows the number and proportion of producers in various flock size groups in various years. The average size of the Australian sheep flock has increased since 1960. At that time 52 per cent of producers had flocks less than 1000 whilst by 1971 the figure had dropped to 38.7 per cent. Taking the estimate of 85 000 producers in 1971 and an estimate of 188 482 of sheep shearing machine stands for the same period (Commonwealth Year Book, 1973) gives a mean figure of 2.22 shearing stands per property. This mean figure can be distributed amongst the various property sizes as shown in the last column of Table 3.5 (P. E. Geytenbeek (1975); private communication). The number of shearers appropriate to the various flock sizes has been estimated roughly on the basis that one man shearing 100+ sheep per day would complete the task on a flock below 500 sheep within a 5-day week. The owner and an assistant would handle the wool. With flock sizes 500–2000 one man would take too long to complete the task expeditiously whereas two shearers would handle all the flocks in this group within two working weeks i.e., ten days. In the 2000–5000 flock size similar considerations would apply but the number of shearers would be governed by shed size which is a maximum of 3 shearing stands in most of the non-pastoral areas of Australia. In the largest flock size, which includes many of the pastoral zone flocks, the aim is to restrict total shearing time within a maximum of 3–4 weeks. A large team can gain some of the benefits of scale, e.g., can afford to hire a cook on a weekly wage basis. The shearing of the sheep flock in such circumstances is the responsibility of a contractor who is responsible for finding shearers, shed hands, wool classer (sometimes classing is done by the contractor himself), cook, and is paid a fixed sum per hundred sheep sheared. The contractor himself bears the loss due to stoppages for wet weather or due to industrial disputes.

In some areas of Australia several adjacent properties combine to set up a Community Shed where all the sheep are sheared. This entails a saving of capital for flock owners but imposes the discipline of a local schedule for shearing.

In Australia belly wool and soiled crutchings are sheared first and kept separate; the shorn fleece is then laid on a skirting table and short wool around the edges removed. In these large stations the wool is classed on the farm rather than centralized at a warehouse as in the case of smaller units. The difference in size of operation between Australia and the UK is apparent if it is considered that whilst 90 000 producers in the UK produced about 77 million lb of wool in 1974, a smaller number of Australian producers (about 80 000) had an output of 2200 million lb.

Australian wool is baled for transport in hessian bags, using a mechanical press, into packs of about 330 lb of greasy wool. The Australian marketing system is a mixed system where wool is collected and put up for sale by merchants and brokers but the Australian Wool Corporation, on behalf of the Australian Government, engages in support buying. This means that in periods of low prices the Corporation buys up much of the wool, stores it and subsequently releases it on the market in periods of greater scarcity. Marketing arrangements in Australia and many other countries are under review at present with the intention of developing a more rational system to cope with a difficult market situation.

UNITED KINGDOM

Wool growing has long since taken second place to meat production as a prime aim of the British sheep industry although the trend for wool to be more important as conditions become more unfavourable, evident on a world wide basis, is also true of Britain (Table 3.6).

Even so, over many decades there has been a marked fall in the proportion of income from wool in the hill farming sector. As in the arid regions of Australia, the former heavy depend-

Table 3.6. *Sale products from typical Scottish sheep flocks in June, 1974. Source: Scottish Agricultural Colleges (1975)*

| | £ per 100 ewes tupped | |
| | Type of enterprise | |
	Blackface hill flock in the North West and West Highlands	Low ground flock producing fat and store lambs off grass
Fat lambs	30	1613
Store lambs	335	992
Cast ewes	190	345
Wool	125	170
Total Sales	680	3120
Wool as percentage of total sales	18.4	5.5

ence of the hill areas of Britain on wool was associated with a high proportion of wether sheep in hill flocks. There are now very few hill sheep flocks in Britain with an appreciable number of wether sheep, although it is a practice in parts of the North of Scotland to delay the mating of ewes until they are two and a half years old so that a high proportion of the flock consists of non-breeding sheep.

In spite of its relatively high sheep population, Britain is small in area compared with Australia and there are therefore not the marked differences in latitude and longitude. As a whole, Britain is much farther from the equator with a high rainfall and, in contrast to Australia, winters are long and cold. Within the country, however, conditions are very varied mainly as a consequence of altitude and the high mountain farms are, in their own way, a severe environmental test for sheep.

Shearing in the UK is concentrated into a much shorter period than in Australia, commencing mostly in early June on the most favoured lowland farms with the hill flocks being sheared in July. In many hill flocks the dry yearling ewes (the 'eild' sheep) are sheared in late June before the main flock; this allows an earlier start to shearing than is possible with the breeding ewes where the 'rise' in the fleece is delayed. Unlike New Zealand and Australia, the migratory shearing gang was not an important traditional feature of the British scene, although in the last few years, since the advent of mechanical shearing, contract shearing by small teams is rapidly increasing in many parts of Britain.

Shearing in Britain has been associated with a tradition of cooperation amongst groups of small producers. In some of the hill areas of Scotland a number of flocks (called 'hirsels') each under the care of one hired shepherd, may be part of a large multihirsel property and the shepherds get together to shear each hirsel in turn. In Wales and in other areas of the North of England and Scotland, with smaller sized flocks, it was common for several farmers to combine to gather their sheep

E

from the open or common hill grazing and to continue their cooperation for shearing their flocks. This practice still continues in some of the hill areas, but the contract shearer has largely replaced the cooperative shearing of small flocks in lowland areas as well as on the smaller farms in many of the hill areas.

The British contract shearer usually operates on a small scale, often two or three farmers' sons getting together and shearing by means of a fuel driven motor.

A special problem of shearing under British weather conditions is the delay often entailed due to rainy weather since it is essential that the sheep are sheared with a dry fleece. This was even more difficult when the practice of washing sheep prior to shearing was widespread; it meant that after a thorough soaking in a mountain stream, the sheep had to be left for several days before they were fit for shearing.

The provision of some roofed space where sheep can be kept dry overnight helps to avoid delays in shearing due to the weather.

The main characteristics of the fleece are determined before shearing and the British wools include long coarse wool such as from the Scottish Blackface, wools with a high incidence of white and sometimes red kemp as in some of the Welsh sheep and short relatively fine wool as from the Down breeds. Superimposed upon this variety are other factors such as the presence of contamination from vegetable matter and peat.

Shearing and on-farm treatment of the wool in themselves also have a bearing on the quality of the wool. British breeds of sheep, when in good condition, are relatively easy to shear, being plain bodied and often clean at the extremities, as compared with some of the finewoolled, wrinkled, extensively wool covered Merino strains. However, many of the hill ewes can be in poor condition in some seasons, thus presenting an irregular shearing surface and a fleece that is difficult to shear uniformly. This is one of the main reasons why the practice of washing sheep before shearing persisted so long in Welsh hill flocks and is still carried on in a few places. Competence in shearing involves correct positioning of the sheep, whether on the floor or on a bench to achieve high speed of operation. It also involves avoiding cutting the sheep's skin, keeping the whole fleece as a unit (and avoiding 'double-cutting'), with soiled bits or daggings separate and leaving sufficient wool on the sheep to avoid post shearing chilling. Shearing on a clean floor, frequently brushed, or on tarpaulin sheets helps prevent further contamination. In the British system the fleece is rolled into a bundle with the outside of the fleece (as it was on the sheep) on the inside of the bundle and the whole tied with a twisted strand of neck wool. Rolled fleeces are packed into hessian bags most commonly containing about 90 kg of wool and the soiled wool bagged separately. The wool is packed tight into the bag which is open along its length, without the aid of mechanical presses.

British wool is collected, graded and sold through the British Wool Marketing Board, set up by Act of Parliament in 1950. All producers with more than four sheep, with the exception of producers in Shetland and the Outer Hebrides have to register with the Wool Marketing Board for the sale of their wool clip. The Wool Board through the wool merchants, who act as its agents, is responsible for the whole process of marketing after shearing. Wool is collected from the producers into central warehouses where it is graded in its separate fleeces into 300 or more grades. The Board maintain staff in each area of the country who act as a supervising body to cooperate with the contracting merchants to ensure uniform standards of grading. The merchants advise the board of the grading for each producer's clip and the Board then make payment direct to the producer. At the collecting warehouses wool grades are combined into several lots uniform within themselves each containing about 1000–5500 kg of wool. The British wool clip is finally sold by auction at three major centres—Edinburgh, Bradford and Exeter. The lots are represented at the auction by a sample weighing 90–115 kg and by description, guaranteed by the board as a fair representation of the lot in question.

Wool at the auction is bought by international wool merchants and a substantial proportion (about 50 per cent in the early 1970s) of British wool is exported. The major importers are from Western Europe, particularly Italy for its mattress manufacture, although some is exported to Australasia to form blends with home produced wool for specialist purposes.

The United States used to be a substantial importer of British wool but this trade has largely disappeared.

Milk Production 4

Lactation is a most important function in the sheep: not only because the ewe remains an important dairy animal in many parts of the world, but because efficient lactation is the foundation for good lamb performance, necessary in any system of production.

The Process of Lactation

Lactation is a complex process, whereby various precursor nutrients, absorbed from the blood stream, are synthesised into milk, which is then released to the suckling lamb or in the process of milking. Milk is synthesised in the mammary glands contained in the udder; the sheep possesses two glands, each drained by one functional teat. The mammary glands are well supplied with blood vessels whose capillaries supply the cluster of secretory cells known as alveoli, each enveloping a duct. The duct acts as a milk channel and progressively combines with other ducts to open out eventually into the larger cistern or sinus, which drains into the teat canal as shown diagrammatically in Fig. 4.1.

Considerable advances have been made in elucidating the biochemical basis of the process of milk secretion, starting from the circulating blood precursors (Kon & Cowie, 1961; Schmidt, 1971).

The development of the udder is part of the process of growth and development of the body as a whole, described earlier, and lactation, as part of the reproductive process, is very much under hormonal control and closely synchronized with the other events of the reproductive cycle. At birth, both ram and ewe lamb have rudimentary mammary glands and teats. In the ewe lamb there is further active development of the secretory tissue of the udder at puberty and considerable changes preparatory to lactation during the first pregnancy.

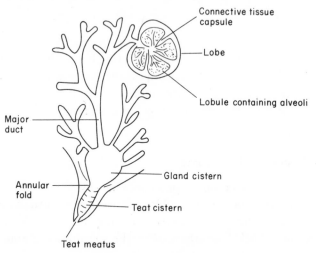

Fig. 4.1. *Ovine mammary gland.*

Hormonal Influences on Lactation

Hormones play a part in the three important stages of lactation: the development of mammary tissue, the initiation and maintenance of active milk secretion and the final phase of ejection of milk into the cistern and teats.

The ovarian steroids are involved in the development of mammary tissue in the young ewe and during pregnancy the increasing secretion of oestrogen and progesterone and the balance between the two, govern the rate and extent of development of the ducts and alveoli. Some influence on mammary development is also exerted by the complex of hormones that are secreted by the anterior pituitary and have a direct effect on lactation—the lactogenic complex of hormones—particularly prolactin. During pregnancy the influence of the ovarian hormones makes the mammary gland resistant to the stimulatory effects of the lactogenic complex, as well as inhibiting the secretion of prolactin and the other lactogenic hormones.

The hormonal mechanisms that control the initiation of milk secretion at lambing are complex and not completely understood (Denamur, 1971) but changes in the ovarian steroids are involved, particularly the increase in oestrogen in relation to progesterone, the considerable release of oxytocin at lambing and the increase in the secretion of adrenal steroids. The correct hormone balance not only stimulates increased secretion of lactogenic hormones but also makes the udder sensitive to the lactogenic influence. After lambing, suckling by the lamb further stimulates synthesis and release of pituitary hormones.

THE RELEASE OF MILK FROM THE UDDER

Apart from the secretory function of the udder there is the important physiological process of milk release. This process has received considerable attention in the cow because of its relevance to the process of efficient milking. The newly secreted milk occupies the higher reaches of the extensive network of ducts and only slowly drains into the larger branches and eventually into the cistern. Since the fat globules are a distinct phase, with different physical properties, including a lower density, there is a tendency for the seepage of milk from the secretory sites to show a differential effect, with the fat phase being more slowly mobilized, so that the higher ducts have a higher concentration of fat.

When the ewe is subjected to the correct stimuli a process of milk release or let-down is initiated. This consists of the nervous transference of the stimuli to the pituitary, which releases the hormone oxytocin into the bloodstream. Oxytocin causes the milk to be released from the ducts and expressed into the larger ducts and sinus and thence to the suckling lamb, milker or milking machine. The process of release is accomplished by a combination of duct dilation and increased blood pressure, which operates for a period of a minute or two. During the process of milk release and extraction, the composition of the milk changes from the low fat secretion present in the cistern after a period without suckling, through low pressure seepage, to the higher fat secretion in the latter stages of expulsion, where the milk from the higher reaches of the duct system is released.

The Milk Yield of Suckling Ewes

The main difference in lamb growth arising from lactation, are due to differences in the yield of milk by the ewe and several studies have reported a close association between the yield of milk by the ewe in early lactation and the growth of the lamb. One of the difficulties of these studies has been the method of measuring milk yield in the normal suckling situation.

Three main methods have been used to estimate milk yield. These include the lamb suckling technique. The basis of which is to allow normal suckling and to estimate the yield of the ewe over short periods at intervals during the lactation (Owen, 1957). The yield of milk on these occasions is estimated by preventing the lamb from suckling, except where the operator can weigh the lamb before and after suckling. In most studies estimates have been made for periods of 24 hours, at intervals of about one week. Commonly, controlled suckling has been allowed every 3–4 hours during the observation period. The controlled suckling can be achieved by separating the lamb from the ewe or by fitting the ewe with an udder cover, so that both ewe and lamb can run about normally between suckling sessions. The advantages of this method are that long term effects on normal lactation are minimized by making the measurements only at intervals, and short term upsets in secretion and let-down are minimized by allowing reasonably frequent suckling, during

Fig. 4.2. *A Clun Forest ewe fitted with an udder cover for milk yield estimates in Aberystwyth, Wales.*

the short period of actual recording. Frequency of suckling has to be a compromise between the high level of suckling, needed to simulate natural frequency and the lower frequency, dictated by the need to cut down disturbance and to ensure prompt and vigorous suckling during the recording period. This technique has provided useful information on lactation in the non-dairy ewe.

Another method used for sheep lactation studies is the oxytocin technique where the milk secreted during the recording period is obtained by hand or machine milking preceded by oxytocin injection to ensure efficient let-down (Coombe et al., 1960). Since the lamb is denied milk during the recording session this method commonly involves a shorter period of recording including two or three periods of three hours each.

Both the above methods have been operated using recording periods of less than 24 hours and because there seem to be small diurnal differences in milk secretion (Robinson et al., 1968) it is important to standardize the procedure, within any experiment, to report the timing of recording adopted. Both these methods can be used to study a wide range of factors affecting ewe lactation under suckling conditions.

Another source of lactation data for ewes is the information obtained for dairy ewes where milk is removed artificially as a routine procedure. Ewes can be used solely as dairy animals like cows, if the lambs are completely weaned at some stage and all the milk removed artificially. At the Grassland Research Institute in the UK this procedure has been used to study factors affecting the lactation of the non-dairy ewe (Treacher, 1971). Such findings need careful interpretation since the mode of evacuation has such a profound influence on the course of lactation. A high proportion of dairy ewes are subjected to a regime of milking combined with suckling. In some areas, such as the Roquefort area in the south of France, the traditional practice is to wean the lambs completely after an initial suckling period of about 30 days, and to milk the ewe for several months subsequently. It is often difficult to compare results on ewe lactation obtained under a variety of conditions including suckling only, part suckling/part milking and milking only.

THE EFFECT OF EWE MILK PRODUCTION ON LAMB GROWTH

Information is available from studies employing the above methods on the effects of lactation on lamb growth. Most reported studies show that variations in milk yield rather than milk quality have the major influence on lamb growth. There seems to be no evidence that the effect of any factor, such as feeding treatment, sheep genotype or even stage of lactation, is mediated through an effect on milk quality rather than quantity. During the first month of life, under natural suckling conditions, more than 75 per cent of the variation in lamb growth is associated with variation in the level of milk consumption. An approximate estimate of this association is that, during this first month of virtually complete dependence on milk, one unit of lamb live weight gain results from five units of ewe's milk consumed or from 0.9 units of milk solids. This estimate agrees closely with the results for artificially reared lambs where ewe's milk has been given to lambs under controlled conditions and with the finding that good ewe milk replacers used for artificial rearing consistently show conversion rates, for milk solids into lamb gain of about 1:1 (Owen, 1974). The rate of conversion of milk into lamb growth varies about the approximate mean value of 5:1 according to the weight of the lamb and the level of milk consumption (Robinson et al., 1969) as well as with other genetic and non-genetic factors.

After the first month the lamb becomes progressively less dependent on the ewe's milk, as its consumption of grass and other solid food increases. The close association between milk consumed and the growth of the lamb declines accordingly, although the overall effect of milk consumption on lamb gain to weaning is usually considerable. In the grazing situation, there can be an added significance to the ewe's milk yield during the declining phase of lactation because of the positive effect on the lamb's resistance to parasites (Spedding, 1965). This may be partly an effect of good nutrition per se and partly the result of a more gradual attainment of full grass intake allowing the lamb, whilst still well nourished, to be slowly accustomed to parasitic infestation. Lambs with a high milk intake, such as the single lambs slaughtered early in the season, often show no ill effects from parasites, where lambs with lower milk intake are badly infested later in the year. The ewe's milk yield is also of vital importance where the herbage available to the flock is of poor quality as in the hill environment. Complete dependence on such herbage, from an early stage, would result in much reduced performance because of the effect on voluntary intake of specific nutrient deficiencies. A small supplement of good quality protein as contained in suckled milk taken direct into the abomasum has been shown to have a beneficial effect on the intake of poor quality roughage (Weston, 1971).

In dealing with the growth of the lamb of the dairy ewe, it is difficult to estimate the actual milk consumption of the lamb suckled by a ewe that is also being milked. Israeli work (Folman et al., 1966; Morag et al., 1970) has demonstrated that the lamb is sustained on additional milk secreted as a direct result of suckling, supplemented by its consumption of solid feed. This additional milk, secreted as a result of the removal of what would otherwise be the residual milk fraction, influence the feed intake of the ewe and the maintenance of its body reserves, but otherwise seems to have little influence on the amount of milk obtained by milking.

Factors influencing Lactation in the Ewe

Information is available on a number of important factors that influence lactation in the ewe.

The stage of lactation

As in other mammals the yield and composition of milk varies considerably with the stage of lactation.

Non-dairy Ewes

Lactation curves for suckling ewes (Fig. 4.3) typically show an early peak of milk yield reached within the first 2 or 3 weeks, followed by a gradual decline, although milk yield is still about 50–60 per cent of the peak at 10–12 weeks after lambing. The suckling ewe continues to milk for several months, although, if there is no human intervention, the lamb is eventually weaned, partly because the ewe will seldom stand still to be suckled.

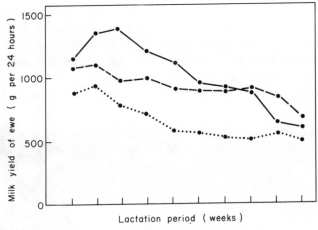

Fig. 4.3. *Lactation curves for suckling ewes.*

Dairy Ewes

Knowledge of the effect of stage of lactation on the milk yield of the dairy ewe is rather fragmentary, because of the variety of milking practices, particularly as regards the stage of lamb weaning. Another complication is that ewe milking is a complicated procedure with several distinct phases. Labussière and Ricordeau (1970), in a study involving 302 Prèalpes and Friesian × Prèalpes, showed that the dairy ewe releases its milk in two stages. The first flow of milk which reaches its peak some 8–10 seconds following the start of milking is thought to be the cisternal milk. A second flow starting about 32 seconds, and reaching a peak about 40 seconds, after the start of milking, is alveolar milk expelled under the influence of the let down mechanism. The second release of milk was not apparent at the start of the lactation but appeared in 70 per cent of the ewes between the fourth and thirty-second day. The development of milk ejection reflex is an indication of the suitability of the ewe for milking and depends on the breed and age of the ewes as well as a number of other factors.

The results of this study demonstrate that the milk obtained in the first emission decreases progressively during the course of lactation but that the milk obtained in the second emission increases to a peak between 18 and 32 days after lambing and then declines. In this study the ewes were milked by machine and both machine stripping and hand stripping was employed.

Fig. 4.4. *Awassi ewes being milked in the middle east. (By courtesy of Dr E. Chovieri)*

In ewes with a well developed ejection reflex the amount of milk obtained by hand stripping decreases to a constant level after about one month of lactation.

Milk Composition

The stage of lactation affects several aspects of the composition of the ewe's milk. The first secretion or the colostrum, differs markedly from the milk produced after the first few days although gradual changes in composition continue during the

Fig. 4.5. *Sardinian sheep—a breed noted for their amenability to milking. (By courtesy of the Italian Embassy, London).*

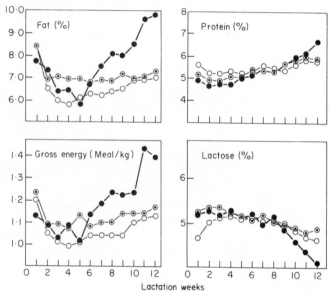

Fig. 4.6. *Effect of stage lactation on milk composition:* ●, *Triplet suckled* ⊙, *Twin-suckled;* ○, *Single-suckled.*

course of the lactation. The gross changes in milk composition that occur in suckled ewes are illustrated in Fig. 4.6 (after Peart 1972).

Taking this and other studies, reviewed by Ashton et al. (1964), into account the main changes in milk quality during lactation can be summarized as follows:

The content of fat, protein, solids not fat and ash, after initial falls from the high level found in colostrum, tend to increase with the advance of lactation. Lactose content, on the other hand, after some initial increase tends to fall throughout lactation.

More detailed studies of the mineral constituents of ewe's milk by Ashton and Yousef (1966) have shown that calcium tends to increase sharply to a stable level, magnesium is relatively constant but with a slight increase with the advance of lactation. Sodium increases and potassium falls progressively with the advance of lactation.

AGE OF THE EWE

In common with many other characteristics, milk yield increases with age up to 5–6 years and then declines. In the case of the ewe the normal senile decline is exacerbated by failing dental efficiency. Lactation performance improves rapidly in the first two or three lactations depending on whether the ewe is mated to lamb at one or at two years of age. The lower yield of the yearling ewe is a function of immaturity and lower size whilst the immaturity of the two year old ewe is coupled with the difficulty of dental inefficiency in the changeover from a complete set of primary incisors to the first pair of permanent ones. This difficulty is only apparent when feed supplies are short or reliance is made on feedstuffs which require good teeth, e.g., roots.

Milk quality also changes with age and the evidence for dairy ewes shows that milk quality, particularly the content of fat and protein, is higher in the second than in the first lactation (Ricordeau & Flamant, 1969); this is contrary to the situation for most dairy cattle breeds.

In spite of the potentially marked effect of age on milk yield and other characteristics of the ewe, reasonable production can be maintained even when there is complete loss of the incisors, provided that a high level of supplementary concentrate feeding is given. Under normal circumstances, healthy ewes that have avoided damage to the udder can continue to produce and rear lambs for 12–15 years.

BODY WEIGHT OF THE EWE

Several studies have confirmed that the milk yield of the ewe is associated with body size. The precise form of this association is difficult to establish because the effect of size is overshadowed by the many other factors influencing lactation. A reasonable supposition is that within breed the trend is for most aspects of input and output in the ewe to be scaled up in accordance with size so that the basic efficiency of conversion of feed is little different according to size. Between breeds, however, there are

obvious divergencies from a simple milk yield/weight relationship in dairy sheep although for non-dairy breeds there is little
evidence available.

There is an important distinction between size—largely a
reflection of skeletal size—and weight which is a reflection both
of the size and of the 'condition' of the ewe.

METHOD OF EVACUATION

Substantial effects on lactation result from variations in the
method of removal of milk from the udder.

The Effect of the Suckling Lambs

It is well established that the milk yield of the ewe depends on
the number of lambs suckled. Many workers have shown that
well nourished ewes suckling twins give about 40 per cent more
milk than those suckling singles (MLC, 1973). This would
result in twins obtaining about 70 per cent of the milk available
to the single lamb. Further increases in the number suckled lead
to smaller increases in the milk secreted (Peart et al., 1972).
This suggests that near maximal suckling stimulus is achieved
by two lambs.

The effect of numbers of lambs suckled on the ewe could arise
in several ways. The effect of a multiple pregnancy on subsequent
lactation would be more likely to depress rather than augment
milk yield. The fact that twin lambs reared as singles have been
shown to grow more like singles and to obtain a similar amount
of milk suggests that the effect is one associated with the act of
suckling. Two lambs have a higher requirement for milk than
one and no doubt stimulate higher milk yield by more frequent
suckling. Munro (1957) did not find that twin suckling for the
first 10 days stimulated higher milk yield in the remainder of
lactation. Peart's work has confirmed that much of the increased
yield is shown in the first three weeks of lactation and that the
milk yield in later lactation is little different. More vigorous
stimulation and removal of residual milk has a similar effect to

that reported by Eyal (1972) where suckling and machine milking were compared in the dairy ewe.

Another interesting facet of this phenomenon is the report that lambs of different genotype can also exert a sufficiently variable stimulus to the ewe to produce significant effects on milk yield. In one experiment (Moore, 1965) Merino ewes suckling pure bred Merino lambs produced less milk than Merino ewes suckling cross bred lambs. The effect of number of lambs suckled, litter size at birth, and age of ewe, on the 100 day weight of the lamb has also been studied in the Aberdeen breeding project and Table 4.1 shows the data obtained in the years 1970, 1971, 1972.

Table 4.1. *Adjusted 100 day weights of lambs according to number born, number reared and age of ewe.*

Number suckled	Age of ewe	Number of lambs born 1970, 1971, 1972		
		1	2	3
1	2	30.1	27.7	25.3
	3+	31.3	28.9	26.5
2	2	28.8	26.4	24.0
	3+	30.0	27.6	25.2

These data show a much smaller effect of number suckled than many other studies reported and it may well be a reflection of the relatively good feeding conditions and freedom from parasites in this particular flock.

Milking and Suckling

Reference has already been made to the effect of artificial versus natural withdrawal of milk from the ewe. The Israeli work with Awassi ewes referred to, indicated that, where ewes were allowed to suckle their lambs after milking, the total milked yield of the ewes was very little different to that obtained where the lambs were completely weaned at various stages, in spite of the fact that the lambs still obtained sufficient milk to make reasonable progress. The extra milk obtained, due to the lamb being suckled, is a direct consequence of the stimulus of suckling and in its turn seems to lead to some increase in the ewe's voluntary feed intake and of depletion of body reserves. The removal of the lamb as soon as possible after birth prevents the establishment of the ewe/lamb relationship and hastens the establishment of good milk let down.

It is difficult to assess the effect on total milk production of the traditional stripping used in many dairy ewe flocks. The ewe is first milked by hand or by machine and then, after the lapse of several minutes, hand stripped to obtain a further small amount of milk. It is inconceivable that such a labour consuming process can in future be justified in any part of the world since the experience with dairy cows was that stripping did not lead to any economic increase in the yield of milk.

The effect of nutrition on lactation

Lactation is a highly exhaustive process and the ewe can only cope with its demands by maintaining a high level of feed intake. Because of limitations on intake the ewe runs into deficit in terms of body reserves in early lactation, even when the best diet is freely available.

A number of studies have been carried out since the classic experiment of Wallace (1948) which give a reasonable picture upon which to base sound recommendations for feeding ewes to best advantage. These are dealt with in detail in Chapter 5. Wallace's work indicated that the milk yield of the ewe could be affected by substantial differences in the level of feeding in the last two months of pregnancy. Subsequent field studies in New Zealand by Coop (1950) failed to support this finding and it is now accepted that substantial effects on lactation due to pregnancy feeding can only result where the feed deficit is very large. Single bearing ewes only suffer such underfeeding where extreme weather conditions such as drought or hard winters lead to a prolonged period of semi-starvation. Under temperate lowland conditions, underfeeding during pregnancy is only likely to be evident with ewes giving birth to more than one lamb. Even for ewes with twins the evidence suggests that under commercial conditions, good feeding after lambing leads to a recovery of milk yield such that the effects on total yield are small. However, the milk yield of the ewe depends so much on the number and vigour of the lambs suckling, any effect of pregnancy feeding on the survival and vigour of the lambs, would in turn be reflected in the subsequent lactation.

Lactation can be severely affected by the level of feeding after lambing although the ewe, to some extent, is capable of buffering lactation against the effects of underfeeding, by drawing on body reserves. Under most practical conditions ewes are usually grazing on good pasture during lactation and seldom suffer from a lack of protein in relation to the energy supplied.

Feeding is known to affect the quality as well as the yield of milk. Ashton et al., (1964) showed that ewes receiving supplementary concentrates in addition to grazing, during lactation gave milk with significantly higher levels of calcium and phosphorus than the ewes receiving no supplementary food. Several workers have found that ewes given a high plane of nutrition produce milk higher in solids–not–fat, protein and ash constituents than ewes fed on a low plane, although observations regarding the effect of feeding on fat content are conflicting.

GENOTYPE

There are relatively few reports of within flock comparisons of breeds and crosses in relation to their milk yield. The few reports available, e.g., Salerno and Malossini (1968) and Ricordeau and Flamant (1969) for dairy ewes and Glen et al., (1963) for non-dairy ewes, confirm that genotypic differences exist. Some of these differences are associated with differences in body weight and there are several reports of a within breed association of milk yield with the ewe's body weight.

Within breeds there is a considerable variation in milk yield with a coefficient of variation of 20–30 per cent.

The estimates of heritability (see Chapter 9) are variable and there is insufficient evidence to assert that it is higher than for dairy cows, where about 25 per cent of the variation in milk yield is due to genetic causes.

Reproduction 5

Breeding efficiency is an important aspect of both natural and man-controlled animal systems. Even where most of the emphasis is on the production of wool or milk, high reproductive efficiency is a desirable attribute, but where meat production from young animals is the chief aim breeding efficiency is a major component of overall efficiency. As a rule, the more intensive the meat production process, the more advantageous is the production of large numbers of young per breeding female. Under harsher, more extensive conditions, long term breeding efficiency is achieved at a lower reproduction rate, consistent with achieving a reasonable level of performance in the young and limiting the drain on the resources of the breeding female. The optimum may thus vary from about one lamb per breeding ewe in a year under unfavourable conditions, up to four lambs per ewe per annum under the most intensive conditions. The considerations discussed later in the Chapter show that under commercial flock conditions, the optimum mean level of reproduction is restricted to a limit of about $2\frac{3}{4}$ lambs at any lambing and a mean flock lambing interval of about 8 months. The former limit is set by the difficulty of coping with a significant proportion of really large litters of small lambs and the latter by the difficulty of consistently reducing the interval from lambing to successful remating, even where the problem of seasonal anoestrus has been overcome.

In the present chapter the components of breeding efficiency in sheep are analysed and discussed as they relate to different systems of sheep production. These components are:

Breeding frequency or lambing interval—the frequency of lambing over a defined interval or the interval between two successive lambings expressed either for an individual ewe or as a flock average.

The lambing to conception interval. Breeding frequency is limited in many circumstances by the length of the breeding season and in all circumstances by the length of post-partum anoestrus which is the period following lambing where the ewe cannot be successfully remated.

Barrenness. A common cause of reduced breeding frequency, barrenness is the term applied when a ewe fails to get in lamb after exposure to the ram; it is often difficult in practice to ascertain the precise stage at which the early failure of reproduction has occurred.

Prolificacy. Another component of breeding efficiency which relates to the numbers of lambs resulting from any one mating. This can be expressed in a variety of ways—litter size at birth or at weaning for the individual ewe or the average for the flock, based on the ewes actually lambing. A useful practical term in common use is 'lambing percentage' which expresses the number of lambs weaned on a group basis, as a percentage of the ewes exposed to the ram, so that account is taken of all ewes including those barren or those that die before lambing.

Prolificacy can be seen as the end result of the progressive erosion of potential litter size from the number of ova shed by the ewe at oestrus. This potential may be nipped in the bud at some early unknown stage resulting in barrenness, or it may be a stepwise process of reduction occurring at significant hurdles in the race from the starting point to the finish at the weaned lamb stage. The first hurdle is fertilization, the second occurs after fertilization during the hazardous free living and early implantation stage, the third, more recently suspected may occur after implantation but still early in pregnancy, the fourth in late pregnancy, manifested in stillbirth and abortions. Parturition itself is a fifth traumatic hurdle which brings down many lambs, followed closely by the sixth stage of establishing a good mother–offspring relationship, essential for the young lamb. The seventh and final hurdle comes in the growing period where some proportion of lambs may still succumb.

The Breeding Process in Sheep

ANATOMICAL FEATURES

The reproductive organs of the sheep are basically similar to those of the majority of mammals and the intention in this section is to give only an overall summary, giving emphasis to any special features relating to the sheep.

The Ram

The main reproductive organs of the ram are the pair of testes suspended outside the abdominal cavity in the sac-like scrotum. It is within the testes that the important process of spermatogenesis—the development and maturation of the male gametes or spermatozoa—is carried out. The testes are also the site of synthesis and release of important hormones described later. Several ducts within each testis open into a single convoluted tube at the posterior end of the testis—the epididymis. This serves as a store for spermatozoa prior to the act of mating. Leading from each epididymis is the vas deferens tube which transports the spermatozoa to the penis. Into this tube several other important diluents are introduced to produce the final semen. The penis of the ram is the organ adapted to achieve successful deposition of the semen within the ewe's reproductive tract.

Of special note as far as the ram is concerned, is the relatively large size of testes relative to many other species—a ram of 100 kg live weight has a pair of testes weighing 250 g (0.25 per cent of body weight) whereas the bull's testes, about 300 g in weight, are less than 0.05 per cent of its body weight, and the boar's testes at 350 g, only about 0.1 per cent. This is probably a reflection of the small body size and the very seasonal mating activity of the sheep necessitating a considerable semen output over a relatively short space of time. The ram, like the bull, is also well adapted to protect spermatogenesis from variation in outside temperature, having a scrotum which allows considerable buffering of temperature, by varying the proximity of the testes to the abdomen. The structure of the penis in the ram is modified in a particalar way to achieve insertion of semen into the cervix of the ewe. The modified penis has an erectile appendage which forms a continuation of the main penis.

The Ewe

The ewe's reproductive organs are not very different, in general structure, from those of the cow, although much reduced in scale. This gives rise to a modification of the methods of artificial insemination as compared to the cow and the sow (described later). The pair of ovaries are the site of oogenesis or development of the female gametes or ova; the size and appearance of the ovaries vary according to the stage of reproduction and the number of ova shed at any one time. The presence of ovarian follicles and subsequently of the purplish coloured corpora lutea, substantially increases the mass of the ovary. Ovarian follicles can develop in both ovaries and will rupture at oestrus to give ovulation or release of the ova.

HORMONAL CONTROL OF REPRODUCTION

Reproduction in the ewe is controlled by a number of hormonal systems coordinated in a complex way to give the desired result. Full details of the mechanism are still being elaborated, although some simple components of the whole system can be manipulated to give striking results.

The process of spermatogenesis in the ram is also subject to similar hormonal influence although the act of mating and the ejaculation of semen is more a complex neural reflex influence, largely dictated by the presence of a ewe on heat.

Several hormones, controlled by the central nervous system, through the hypothalamus, influence the occurrence of oestrus during the breeding season of the ewe. The anterior pituitary gland situated at the base of the brain, the ovaries, and the uterus, are all directly involved in control of the oestrus cycle. In very simple terms the processes can be summarized as follows: Secretion of follicular stimulating hormone (FSH) by the pituitary gland, is associated with the development of follicles in the ovary. The cells of the ripe follicle produce the hormone oestrogen; the occurrence of heat or oestrus is associated with high levels of oestrogen secretion. When oestrogen activity is at its peak and the ewe is showing full signs of heat, the levels of luteinizing hormone (LH) in the blood, secreted by the pituitary gland, increase, and those of FSH decrease. At this stage the ripe follicle bursts and the ovum is shed into the abdomen. The empty follicle forms the site of a new gland—the corpus luteum—which secretes the hormone progesterone which inhibits the scretion of FSH and prevents further follicle development. If the ewe is pregnant the corpus luteum (or several corpora lutea if it was a multiple ovulation) persists, whereas if the ewe does not conceive the corpora lutea regress and the process is repeated all over again.

Recently, it has been shown that substances called prostaglandins, specifically prostaglandin F2α, are present in the uterine wall in the sheep. The prostaglandins have several powerful effects on physiological processes in animals. It is now known that the uterine prostaglandins are associated with the regression of the corpus luteum and therefore with the control of the ovarian cycle in the ewe (Inskeep, 1973).

MATING BEHAVIOUR

The outcome of the processes described is that the unmated ewe, during its breeding season, comes on heat at intervals of 17 days on average. Cycle lengths vary for any one ewe and some ewes consistently tend to have longer cycle lengths than others.

The length of the heat period is also variable and is to some extent related to the age of the ewe. Ewe lambs have relatively short heat periods (Hafez, 1952) and maiden $1\frac{1}{2}$ year old ewes have been shown to have shorter heat periods than mature ewes (Blockey & Cumming, 1970). Depending on breed and individual, heat lasts for an average of 30–36 hours in mature ewes (Hafez, 1969). It is at least 10 hours shorter in immature ewes.

When the ewe is on heat she becomes agitated, seeks out the ram and may form a 'harem' of ewes following one ram. In full heat the ewe will stand still when the ram approaches, raising and wagging its tail when the ram prepares to mount. There is often during heat a discharge of clear mucus from the vagina.

Tomkins and Bryant (1972) have described the typical behaviour of the ram during mating. This includes the approach where the ram seeks out the ewe on heat, pawing with one of the fore feet alongside the ewe and rubbing the head along the side of the ewe, licking and biting the wool. The mount involves jumping the ewe and making a series of exploratory thrusts. There may be several mounts before successful intromission is achieved. The serve includes mounting the ewe, achieving successful intromission, and ejaculation, characterized by a deep pelvic thrust.

There have been several interesting studies of flock mating behaviour in sheep. These have shown several consistent features:

Diurnal Variation

It has been shown (Blockey & Cumming, 1970) that during the breeding period mating activity is very low after nightfall when the flock rests in its night camp with little grazing or sexual activity. At dawn grazing and sexual exploration commences and there is often a high proportion of matings at 06.30–07.30 hours. Activity subsides to a low point at mid-day and increases again in afternoon and evening.

Ram Interaction

When several rams run with one flock of ewes a hierarchy is established amongst the rams, the older, heavier rams usually being dominant to the smaller rams. In some cases, dominance has a marked effect on the pattern of mating—the dominant ram claiming most ewes for his harem (Bourke, 1967). Subservient rams may, therefore, only have an opportunity to mate when several ewes are on heat. Others, like Tomkins and Bryant (1972) have observed little effect of ram dominance on the frequency of services by various rams.

Ewe Preferences

When several rams are present a high proportion of ewes are mated with more than one ram. Lees and Weatherhead (1970) have reported preferences by Clun Forest ewes for rams of their own breed and it is a general finding that groups of sheep from different origin remain segregated from other groups for long after they have been allowed to run together. The preference of ewes for rams of their own breed may be partly visual, as in dark headed breeds, or it may be a more subtle attraction associated with the sense of smell or presence of pheromones, substances which are known to be implicated in various aspects of sexual attraction in animals (Whitten, 1966; Morgan et al., 1972).

Frequency of Mating

The number of services by a ram in any day of the mating season depends on the number of ewes on heat, although as the number increases the services per ewe falls. In Merino rams, Mattner et al., (1967) recorded between 8 and 38 services by individual rams during the hours of daylight. The number of services per mature ewe during a heat period has been reported to average just over 4 in several studies, but maiden ewes, particularly ewe lambs, tend to be served less often, partly due to the decreased length of oestrus. Rams will mount the ewe on average 3–4 times for any successful mating, although there is some variation in this respect between different rams. The number of times a ewe is served during heat seems to have an effect on the establishment of successful pregnancy; Mattner and Braden (1967) showed higher recoveries of sperm from the genital tract and a higher proportion pregnant at 20–60 days post mating, in ewes served three times or more as compared to those served only once.

One difficulty in sheep breeding is encountered with the fat tailed breeds. Fat tailed rams are adept at displacing the fat tail of the ewe so that they can mate successfully. However, rams from thin tailed breeds seem unable to perform this displacement, thus leading to difficulties where it is desired to cross rams from thin tailed breeds with fat tailed ewes such as the Middle Eastern Awassi sheep. Where crosses need to be made between such incompatible sheep, artificial insemination may be employed.

Parturition

The lambing process is a most complex one, in which hormonal and nervous reflex influences are delicately coordinated to achieve the desired end. Pregnancy in the ewe lasts for about five months. The mean gestation length in 13 breeds of sheep varied from 144 days for Dorset Horn and Southdown to 151 days for Karakul (Clegg, 1959). The Finnish breed has a very short gestation length of little more than 140 days. Within breed, gestation length shows low variation (Forbes, 1967), although consistent small variations have been reported according to the litter size and sex. Singles tend to have slightly longer gestation than multiples and single ram lambs longer than ewe lambs. Age of ewe has also been shown to have some effect on length of gestation; usually there is some slight increase with age.

The initiation of parturition is not yet completely understood, although parturition can be induced by artificial means such as the administration of corticosteroid analogues such as dexamethazone or of prostaglandins.

Just before lambing there is a decline in progesterone and a rapid rise in the corticoids and in oestrogen, but neither the fall in progesterone nor the rise in oestrogen appear to be absolute requirements for lambing (Liggins et al., 1972). It has been established that the unborn lamb initiates parturition in the sheep and that an intact hypothalamic-pituitary-adrenal axis in the fetus is essential. Transfer of the active agents from the lamb across the placenta to the ewe sets in train the hormonal changes referred to earlier. The action of these culminates in the dilatation of the cervix and lead on to the uterine and abdominal contractions required to expel the lamb or lambs (as well as affecting the lactation process).

LAMBING BEHAVIOUR

During the early stages of cervical dilatation and uterine contraction the ewe shows visible signs of lambing—seeking a sheltered spot and restlessness. When the lamb is far enough advanced in the pelvic channel the ewe goes into the final stage of powerful contractions—usually lying on her side and raising her head skywards as each involuntary contraction exerts heavy pressure to expel the lamb.

Some detailed objective studies of lambing behaviour in ewes have been reported (Sharafeldin et al., 1971). They showed that in mature Barki ewes a mean of 46 minutes elapsed between the first sign of uneasiness to completed lambing. In two-year-old ewes the interval was longer. From lambing to the expulsion of the afterbirth (placenta) took a mean of 143 minutes. Practical observers often claim that there is a distinct diurnal pattern of lambing and this was the case in Sharafeldin's observations; of the lambings observed between 06.00 and 18.00 hours, 54 per cent occurred between 06.00 and 11.00 hours. It is not known how general this diurnal variation is nor what factors may influence it. From the mechanism of the initiation of parturition it is difficult to account for the occurrence of such a lambing pattern.

Dystocia, or difficut lambing, is a relatively frequent occurrence in the most developed sheep breeds, partly because of the better feeding and also, presumably, because a long association with man, giving intensive shepherding care at lambing, has removed some of the natural selection against factors that pre-dispose to lambing difficulty. Breeds developed without inten-sive lambing care, like the Shetland breed, are claimed to need little shepherding and to be 'easy-care' sheep, but there is little objective data to go on. Some of the factors essential to high production, such as better feeding to increase prolificacy, or heavy feeding in late pregnancy, may increase the likelihood of lambing difficulty and it is not yet known to what extent highly productive sheep can be successfully selected for easier lambing.

Gunn (1968) in a study of difficult births in Scottish hill flocks showed that of 15 584 recorded ewe lambings 3.1 per cent were classed as 'difficult' and that 44 per cent of 'difficult' lambings were considered to be normally presented lambs and of these about 60 per cent received assistance. More than 60 per cent of all lambings that received assistance involved mal-presentations. Of these, head alone presentation comprised 42 per cent, head and one leg only 29 per cent, breech 17 per cent, and forelegs only 6 per cent. Overall in this study 3.5 per cent of single and 1.3 per cent of twin births were classed as difficult. Difficult birth was considered to be responsible for about 12 per cent of all lamb deaths and it was concluded that assistance at lambing in such flocks was not economic.

An Australian study (Winfield et al., 1972) showed that ewes that had to be assisted at birth had larger lambs and tended to show abnormal behaviour and to desert their lambs more frequently.

POST LAMBING BEHAVIOUR

After lambing, the new born lamb quickly struggles to rid itself of enveloping mucus and to start breathing. The ewe us-ually shows a maternal interest and, even before she gets up she may lick the lamb vigorously around the head and body helping to dry the lamb's fleece thus helping to avoid rapid evaporative heat transfer. If the ewe carries another lamb she withdraws from the first lamb during the final stages of lambing but may continue to give the first intermittent attention.

Fig. 5.1. *A Merino ewe with its new born lamb adopting a helpful posture to ease suckling. (By courtesy of Prof. H. Ll. Davies, University of New South Wales, Australia).*

By a series of inborn reflexes the lamb gains its feet within minutes of being born and begins an active teat seeking reflex in which it explores its mother's body. The ewe generally adopts a helpful posture and as soon as the lamb is nudging near the udder she presents the udder as far as possible. The lamb soon fastens on to the teat and sucks vigorously showing the excited tail wagging characteristic of the older experienced lamb. Sharafeldin and Kandell (1971) showed that in their Barki ewes

F

the average time interval from lambing until the ewe stood up was 2.9 minutes. The interval from lambing until the ewes started licking their lambs was 4.0 minutes and from lambing until the lambs sucked 20.5 minutes. These intervals were somewhat longer in 2-year-old and in lighter ewes. However, it must be borne in mind that there is a great deal of individual variation in all of these intervals.

Once the lamb has sucked it lies down to rest, oblivious of the ewe and a ewe will graze some little distance from her lamb. During the first day or so the ewe keeps close to the lamb, but as the lamb's mobility increases the ewe is content to go greater distances from the lamb for grazing.

Lamb Wastage

ESTIMATES OF FLOCK WASTAGE

There are a number of scattered reports of detailed studies of the extent of lamb wastage in various flocks and in some of these the causes of loss have been ascertained in some detail. There is much variation in wastage according to flock and season. In a survey of UK sheep flocks, losses of total lambs born were in the region of 10 per cent but a range between flocks from 1–21 per cent (Wiener et al., 1973). Mortality rates of 19.1 per cent for Blackface and 12.1 per cent for Welsh single lambs born have been reported in UK hill flocks (Purser & Young, 1959). Overall lamb mortality from birth to marking for Cheviot sheep were 16 per cent and for Blackface sheep 9–17 per cent in several Scottish hill flocks (Gunn & Robinson, 1963). An overall loss of 17.8 per cent in over seven thousand lambs born was reported in New Zealand hill country flocks (Hight & Jury, 1969).

Losses of 14 per cent for upland and 11 per cent for lowland flocks, in numbers of lambs born in 504 commercial flocks in the UK, were reported in 1970 and 1971 (MLC, 1972). Vetter et al., (1960) reporting mortality rates in over four thousand, lowland lambs in the USA, gave a figure of 15 per cent for singles and 23 per cent for twins (overall 18 per cent).

CAUSES OF WASTAGE

It is sometimes difficult to assess the proportion of deaths due to various causes because a number of studies show a high proportion of deaths due to unknown causes. In a recent study of mortality in North Country Cheviot flocks in the North of Scotland, virtually all the lambs were examined for causes of death (NOSCA, 1974). In the ten flocks studied 12.5 per cent of lambs born died before castration time in May. Still births and a small proportion of abortions accounted for 32 per cent of all deaths, 10.5 per cent were due to dystocia and 26 per cent due to starvation.

Vetter et al., (1969) in their study had a high proportion (50 per cent) of deaths where the cause was unknown, but of the deaths where the cause was known 37 per cent were lambs born dead and the remainder were attributed to pneumonia (10 per cent), weak at birth (13 per cent), abnormal (7 per cent), overlaid (11 per cent), bumped (11 per cent), and starved (10 per cent).

Hight and Jury (1969) carried out detailed examination of a 60 per cent sample of all dead lambs in several NZ hill country flocks and ascribed the main causes of death to dystocia (32 per cent), starvation (26 per cent), infections (12 per cent) and pre-natal deaths (10 per cent). They also showed that of the mortality of all lambs born, 57 per cent of singles and 52 per cent of multiples had occurred by 3 days after birth.

A study of causes of death in the lambs of the prolific ewe project at Aberdeen in 1974 are shown in Table 5.1.

It is evident from these studies that a high proportion of deaths in lambs, under a variety of conditions and management systems, stem from lambs born dead, either stillbirths or due to dystocia and that a further significant proportion is due to starvation. Most of these losses have occurred by 2–3 days after the ewe has lambed.

Table 5.1. *Causes of death in all lambs that died up to 150 days of age in the Aberdeen flock (prolific ewe project) in 1974, classified by age of ewe and litter size at birth*

Age of ewe	One year old			Two years and older						Total	per cent of all lamb deaths
Litter size	1	2	3	1	2	3	4	5	6		
Before 2 days of age											
Stillbirths	1					3	7	3	6	20	20.8
Positive *Vibrio foetus*		1	1							2	2.1
Toxoplasmosis		1								1	1.0
Lung anoxia	3	1	2			1				7	7.3
Lung mucous congestion			1			2		2	1	6	6.3
Peritonitis							1			1	1.0
Abdominal haemorrhage		2		1		2				5	5.2
E. coli infection		3				1		1		5	5.2
Non viable									6	6	6.3
Inconclusive diagnosis			1		1					2	2.1
Total	4	8	5	1	1	9	8	6	13	55	57.3
As per cent of lambs born in category	19.1	13.8	33.3	12.5	2.5	7.0	16.7	24.0	72.2	20.5	

After 2 days of age										Total	Per cent
Toxoplasmosis	1									1	1.0
Lung congestion		3					3			6	6.3
Enteritis		1				1				2	2.1
Haemorrhage		1								1	1.0
E. coli septicaemia		2				1	1			4	4.2
E. coli enterotoxaemia			2			1				3	3.1
Pasteurella	2	2	1				1			6	6.3
Acidosis		4				1	2			7	7.3
Liver abcesses								1		1	1.0
Coccidiosis		1								1	1.0
Lack of colostrum	1					1				2	2.1
Inconclusive diagnosis	1	1		1		1	1		2	7	7.3
Total	5	15	3	1	0	6	8	1	2	41	42.7
As per cent of lambs born in category	23.8	25.9	20.0	12.5	0	4.6	16.7	4.0	11.1	15.3	
Total lamb deaths	9	23	8	2	1	15	16	7	15	96	
As per cent of all lambs born	42.9	39.7	53.3	25.0	2.5	11.6	33.4	28.0	83.3	35.8	100.0

FACTORS INFLUENCING WASTAGE IN LAMBS

Lambing Management

Where other feeding and management factors are optimal it has already been suggested that intensive lambing care in hill flocks may be uneconomic. In lowland flocks with higher lambing rates the analysis of wastage suggests otherwise. Level of husbandary at lambing can have a large effect on the quantity of immune globulin absorbed by lambs and thus reduce the lamb's susceptibility to disease (Ducker & Fraser, 1973). Lambing management, therefore, operates not only on the losses due to dystocia but it should cut down losses from starvation and from infections, resulting from mis-mothering.

Ewe and Lamb Genotype

Many of the studies already mentioned have shown clear differences in mortality rate between ewes of different breeds and crosses kept together in the same flock. Many of the results suggest that heterosis in the dam contributes to good mothering ability. Variation in lamb mortality, is also due to the sire of the lamb, particularly from dystocia where large mutton breed sires are mated with smaller ewes for lamb production.

Birthweight

Birthweight of the lamb is consistently associated with lamb mortality. Mortality decreases sharply as birthweight increases from very low levels but reaches an optimum, particularly for single lambs, above which mortality increases again, largely due to lambing difficulties. Fig. 5.2 based on the data of Hight and Jury (1969) illustrates this relationship.

Type of Birth

All the studies reveal the consistent increase in mortality rate from singles to twins, and Table 5.1 gives data for lambs from higher litter sizes. This is partly a reflection of the smaller

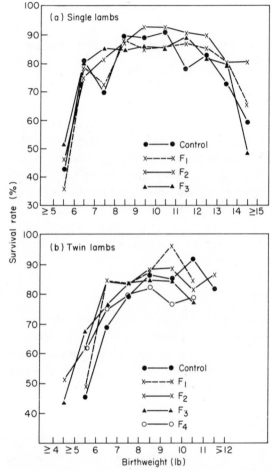

Fig. 5.2. *Effect of birthweight on lamb survival (from Hight & Jury, 1969).*

size of lambs born as multiples but also reflects the increasing susceptibility to starvation particularly, due to the increased competition involved.

Sex of Lamb

Where sex differences in lamb mortality have been reported (Vetter et al., 1960) ram lambs tend to show higher mortality than ewe lambs in spite of their slightly higher birthweight. It appears that a higher incidence of difficult births may be one of the factors involved in the higher death rate of male lambs (Gunn & Robinson, 1963).

Age of Ewe

Higher mortality in lambs from young ewes, particularly those lambing for the first time, is a consistent finding of mortality studies. After the first lambing, differences due to age of ewe are less marked. The higher mortality in lambs of inexperienced ewes is consistent with the finding that most stages of lambing and mothering activities are delayed in the ewe lambing for the first time. The high wastage from lambs born to ewe lambs, particularly when they have twins, calls for further investigation.

Cross-fostering

An age-old practice by shepherds is to foster lambs that have been orphaned, or from twins and triplets, on to ewes that have lost their lambs, or on to those with only a single lamb. There are no objective data available by which the value of the practice can be assessed, although it seems likely that in flocks where there is a significant proportion of triplets born, it should prove valuable.

Various methods have been used to achieve adoption and it is normally easier if attempted as near to lambing time as possible. Where the prospective adopted lamb can be well covered in the maternal mucus and fluid, a high proportion of ewes will accept a strange lamb. Another ploy is to skin the ewe's own dead lamb, if available, and to fasten the skin around the lamb to be adopted.

A reliable method of achieving adoption is by close confinement of the ewe and lamb for 24 hours or more, soon after the ewe has lambed. This method has long been used and has been further developed by the invention of a "lamb adopter" which

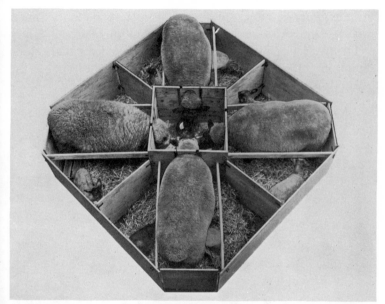

Fig. 5.3. *A lamb adopter, available commercially, in action. (By courtesy of R. L. Farmer Ltd., Doncaster).*

ensures close access of ewe and lamb with safety and freedom from bullying for the adopted lamb.

Another complementary method is the use of aerosol sprays based on benzocaine to inactivate the ewe's sense of smell temporarily so that she more readily gets accustomed to the lamb (L. G. Donald, 1974; private communication).

Artificial Insemination

The development of artificial means of synchronizing heat in ewes has increased the practicability of artificial insemination in sheep. The technique of insemination is well developed and, provided the ewe is at the right stage and the semen of good quality, results have been near to those achieved with natural mating. Because of the small size of the ewe which precludes palpation of the reproductive organs through the rectum, as in the cow, insemination is performed using a speculum so that a small volume of semen can be placed into the cervix.

The speculum is used in conjunction with a light that can be shone up the vagina to illuminate the cervix, to enable the correct placement of the semen (Terrill, 1968).

Fig. 5.4. *Collecting semen from a Pecti ram in South Africa. (By courtesy of the Republic of South Africa Embassy, London).*

Poor results in the field, from the use of A.I. in sheep, often reflect a failure to pinpoint the right stage of oestrus, infertility associated with the use of vaginal sponges, poor quality semen or inexperience on the part of the operator.

One particular difficulty, especially for small scale trials, is the necessity to use relatively fresh semen; results using frozen semen have been far poorer in the sheep than with other species like cattle. Recent work on diluents and freezing technique has improved the conception rate from using stored semen but the efficiency achieved with frozen semen is still too low for widespread commercial use. Semen from rams is usually

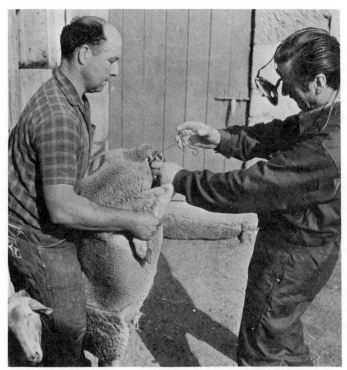

Fig. 5.5. *Insemination of ewe in France. (By courtesy of Farmer's Weekly.)*

collected by artificial vagina since electro-ejaculation tends to result in poorer quality semen.

The main attraction of artificial insemination at the present time is that it could prevent the need for large numbers of rams where many ewes have synchronized heats. In really large flocks insemination could substantially reduce the number of rams required and consequently allow a considerable increase of selection pressure for desired traits (Salamon, 1972).

A semen dose containing 110–125 million normal spermatozoa is necessary for full fertility (Salamon, 1962). A well trained viable ram can provide an ejaculate of 1 ml of semen containing 3 billion spermatozoa. If this is diluted 1 : 1.5 with a suitable diluent, 25 ewes can be inseminated using 0.1 ml placed directly in the cervix (Terrill, 1968). Theoretically, therefore, one ram should be capable of inseminating several thousand ewes with the efficient use of A.I. In practice, such large numbers that can justify the use of several sires in A.I., are not often available. Also, results have so far been poorer where the ewes are synchronized and mated to a fixed time without individual heat detection (Gordon, 1969). In the USSR and other Eastern European countries, A.I. has been widely used on collective and State farms, and Ozin (1966) reported that 36 million ewes were artificially inseminated in the Soviet Union in 1965. Semen is supplied from the 1500 State stud farms, and in one of these, for example, stud rams were used on an average of 1372 ewes per ram and superior rams on 8000 ewes per ram.

A calculation of the costs of artificial insemination (MLC, 1972) showed that, compared with natural mating without the use of synchronization, it cost more than twice as much to mate one ewe by this method, assuming that 20 000 ewes were inseminated annually.

When synchronization is adopted for its own sake then the relative cost of A.I. decreases. Also, in cases where individual pen or hand mating is the normal procedure, as in some large dairy flocks, the relative benefit of the availability of A.I. would be greater.

ASSESSMENT OF RAM FERTILITY

It would be advantageous if potential rams could be reliably assessed for their fertility and libido at an early stage. The ultimate test is the ability to get ewes in-lamb and no other test can fully match this.

However, there are several guides by which rams can be classed on potential fertility (Fraser, 1970).

1. The ram should be checked for general health—lameness and general unthriftiness often seriously reduce the efficiency of a breeding ram.

2. Physical examination of the external reproductive organs particularly the testes, which should be well developed, free from obvious abnormalities and hardness. When the testes are pulled down into the scrotum parts of the epididymis can be felt to check for normality.

3. Examination of the semen, particularly under the microscope, to determine the presence and concentration of spermatozoa and to evaluate their motility and freedom from abnormality. Semen samples are most conveniently taken by electro-ejaculation.

The tests depend on the interpretation of largely subjective attributes and experience is required to give a reasonable guide.

None of these tests directly evaluate another essential of the fertile ram—its libido. Rams, apparently normal in other respects, usually work, although there are rare exceptions. However, as in most attributes, there is a variation in working performance, some rams being much more active and assiduous in searching out ewes on heat. This behavioural difference between rams may outweigh other differences, particularly where the ewe:ram ratio is high or where a number of ewe lambs are concerned.

Temporarily reduced activity and impotence are more common in ram lambs and there is some evidence that the problem may be worse in rams reared artificially from birth, particularly in certain breeds (J. L. Read, private communication). If this finding is confirmed, the reason may be due to psychological deprivation of the mother at the suckling stage, or the fact that the rams are reared in groups without contact with ewes.

The Control of the Breeding Season

Most sheep are seasonal breeders and the ewe's annual breeding pattern usually involves a period during which there are regular oestrus cycles followed abruptly by a period of anoestrus when cycling virtually ceases. The ram may also exhibit seasonal variations in activity, particularly in libido, although such seasonal activity can only be observed where ewes are induced to show oestrus during the normal anoestrus period. Most other domesticated species, which in their wild state probably showed some seasonality of breeding behaviour, have tended to lose this seasonality, so that they breed at any time of year. Even in these species, such as cattle, there may still be some seasonality in fertility. The sheep since domestication has often benefited less from better nutrition and management than the other species; this may account for the greater retention of seasonal breeding in the sheep, particularly in mountain sheep where spring lambing is such an advantage.

The Pattern of Breeding Activity in Sheep

There is wide variation in the breeding activity reported for ewes of various genotypes in various locations but the extent of the data on this important subject is limited because of the difficulty of measurement. Even a record of the date of onset of oestrus involves running a harnessed teaser with the ewes and observing and recording individual ewes as they are marked. Measuring the duration of the breeding season involves not only the complicated process of recording repeated matings, but of keeping ewes unmated for a season. Hafez (1952) and Yeates (1949) reviewed the known observations, then available, of the breeding activity of sheep in different parts of the world. Table 5.2 summarizes Hafez's own findings on small samples of several important British breeds. Subsequent reports have added to, but not radically changed, the main outline of the pattern set out in detail by Hafez. One important finding is that on the effects of origin and environment (Hulet et al., 1974) on reproductive phenomena in Rambouillet ewes. In a two year experiment they assessed the effect of location (Dubois, Idaho and McGregor, Texas) and source of ewe (Texas or North West). The locations are both in the Northern hemisphere.

They found the commonly observed seasonal pattern of

Table 5.2. *Onset and Cessation of Oestrus. (from Hafez, 1952).*

Breed	No. animals	Onset range	Onset Mean ± SE	Cessation range	Cessation Mean ± SE	Mid-breeding season
Blackface	17	26 Sep.–10 Nov.	25 Oct. 298 ± 2.6	17 Jan.–3 Apr.	19 Feb. 50 ± 5.2	23 Dec.
Border Leicester	9	24 Sep.–13 Oct.	9 Oct. 282 ± 3.2	18 Dec.–11 Mar.	10 Feb. 39 ± 5.4	10 Dec.
Dorset Horn	12	15 Jun.–21 Aug.	24 Jul. 205 ± 6.8	22 Jan.–22 Apr.	2 Mar. 61 ± 7.4	12 Nov.
Romney Marsh	11	16 Sep.–19 Oct.	4 Oct. 277 ± 3.1	20 Jan.–23 Mar.	2 Mar. 61 ± 9.1	18 Dec.
Suffolk	12	12 Sep.–23 Oct.	3 Oct. 276 ± 3.6	7 Feb.–20 Apr.	17 Mar. 76 ± 5.7	25 Dec.
Welsh Mountain	9	15 Oct.–11 Nov.	15 Oct. 298 ± 3.3	1 Feb.–25 Feb.	17 Feb. 48 ± 3.7	22 Dec.
Welsh Mountain × Dorset Horn	10	12 Sep.–22 Oct.	1 Oct. 274 ± 3.7	21 Feb.–3 Apr.	10 Mar. 69 ± 7.1	20 Dec.
Combined Data	80	15 Jun.–11 Nov.	30 Sep.	18 Dec.–22 Apr.	27 Feb.	14 Dec.

oestrus at both locations and showed that it was closely associated with ovulation rate—peak oestrus activity coinciding
with highest ovulation rates. However, they found a striking
difference in the seasonal breeding pattern between the two
locations for both types of ewe. In Texas the ewes went into
anoestrus about 2 months earlier than in Idaho and also came
out of anoestrus 2–3 months earlier. The authors could find no
ready explanation for this shift of approximately two months
in the breeding season between the two locations.

Another modification of the conclusions of Hafez (1952)
which were based on small scale observations, is that on a large
flock basis the breeding season is usually less clear cut. A small
proportion of individual ewes (a proportion that increases at
lower latitudes) have aberrant breeding behaviour, so that for
a whole flock anoestrus may not be complete. Lees (1969) in a
study of breeding behaviour in a Clun Forest flock in Wales has
shown that provided non-pregnant ewes are exposed to the ram
some sporadic successful matings occurred in virtually every
month of the year.

In spite of the paucity of evidence and the questions that
remain unanswered, some general conclusions can be drawn, the
most obvious being that, for most sheep, the breeding season
starts in late summer or early autumn and continues until the
late winter. The breeding season tends to be more distinct
and shorter, the higher the latitude and the more distinct the
natural seasonal variations. At the equator, where seasonal
differences are less marked and less consistent, there often
remains, although to a lesser extent, some seasonality to the
breeding season in sheep, whilst in northern latitudes, with the
wide differences in winter and summer seasons, the restricted
breeding season is most in evidence. However, at the same
latitude, there is much variation in the date of onset and length
of the breeding season between different ewes within flocks of
any one breed, and also between the mean date of onset and
length of breeding season of different breeds. The Finnish sheep,
for instance, appears to have a longer breeding season than

many breeds found in lower latitudes (Majala & Kangasniemi, 1969). In Britain, the Dorset Horn breed has a distinctly longer mean breeding season than other breeds; this may be associated with the contribution of its presumed ancestor, the Merino, a breed evolved in lower latitudes.

Evidence from contemporary comparisons, made under the same conditions, also indicates that hill and mountain breeds tend to have a later onset and more restricted breeding season than lowland breeds. There is too little evidence available, however, to be able to place all breeds in any confident order of breeding season length.

Although in some cases the breeding season appears to centre about the shortest day, this is by no means the rule, and it is common for the mid point between recorded onset and recorded cessation of breeding activity, to occur before the shortest day. A breed with an early onset of the breeding season, such as the Dorset Horn, may go into anoestrus before another breed that commenced its breeding season later. At the equator, where the light rhythm does not vary, there are reports of adverse effects on the prolificacy of breeds introduced from other latitudes; there seem to be differences between breeds in this respect. However, breeds can be subjected to very different latitudes from those of their origin and, after a period of adaptation, will show normal breeding behaviour and prolificacy, provided there is some fluctuation in the light rhythm (Williams & Thwaites, 1974).

Evidence for seasonal breeding activity in the ram is less clear cut, but coinciding with the ewe's anoestrus period, there is an ebb in the ram's activity (Lees, 1969). In addition to a lowering of semen quality there may be a diminution or complete absence of libido. Distinct ram differences are apparent in this respect and there appears to be a breed difference (Lees, 1969). Although Finnish and Kerry Hill rams appear to be more active than the Suffolk during the summer, these observations are not on such a scale that generalization about breeds is possible. It is important to find out more about these differences, so that breeds best suited to frequent breeding programmes can be selected.

Factors Influencing Breeding Activity in the Sheep

Several factors have been suggested as the cause of the seasonal breeding activity in the sheep, and there is some evidence that the following factors are involved:

THE INHERENT RHYTHM

There are a number of complex biological phenomena in living organisms whereby there is an orderly ebb and flow of activity on a cyclical basis. Although the rhythm may be modified and chronologically displaced by various factors, it is seldom completely over-ridden. Such appears to be the case with the sheep's breeding season. There seems to be no report of ewes having been maintained in continuous breeding activity or in continuous anoestrus for an extended period of a year or more. It seems logical to propose, therefore, that there is an inherent physiological mechanism which creates a rhythmical pattern and that no external factor yet known can completely control breeding activity, without some alternation of activity and inactivity. This places some limitation on the degree of manipulation of breeding activity that can be exercised in controlled breeding programmes. It has been pointed out (Speedy, 1973) that at the Cambridge latitude (52°N) no experiment, in which a treatment consisting of one period of increase and one of decrease in daylength, had resulted in oestrus activity earlier than May the twenty-first, even when a pattern of daylength, completely the reverse of the natural for that latitude, was applied.

The phenomenon of overt cyclical oestrus activity, with its regular occurrences of ovulation and mating behaviour, is only a manifestation of deeper seated control at the hormonal and central nervous level, and although breeding activity in the sheep is exhibited in an 'all or none' fashion, such a pattern reflects an underlying level of circulating hormones which varies in a systematic cycle over the year (Hafez, 1952) as shown diagramatically in Fig. 5.6.

A certain intensity of breeding activity as determined by these underlying mechanisms, is manifested by regular oestrus

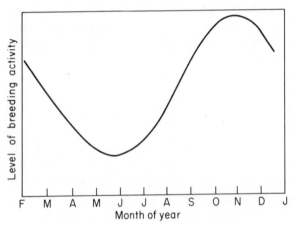

Fig. 5.6. *Hypothetical curve of seasonal change in breeding activity.*

cycling, which continues until the intensity falls again and the ewe goes into anoestrus.

In this light, factors influencing the breeding season in sheep can be seen either as somewhat superficial influences which can temporarily overcome the basic rhythm, particularly in the zone around the beginning and end of the breeding season, or as more profound influences which can shift and buckle the inherent wave pattern but without obliterating it. On the basis of this hypothesis, where the breeding season is the outward manifestation of a deep seated, orderly, cycle of events, it would be expected that other aspects of the intensity of breeding activity, such as ovulation rate, would vary within the overt breeding season. Evidence for this is presented later.

AGE OF EWE

Ewe lambs born in the spring have a much shorter breeding season than adult ewes. Hafez (1952) for example, recorded the mean number of heats per sheep per season as 1.5 and 3.6 respectively for Blackface and Suffolk ewe lambs, as compared to 6.9 and 10.2 for the corresponding adults. Yearling ewes also tend to have a shorter breeding season and a somewhat later onset than older ewes, although the difference is much less marked. The interaction of age with nutrition and other factors in determining the length of the breeding season in sheep, is discussed later.

In general, considering a number of breeds, ewe lambs experience their first oestrus when they are 40–70 per cent of the mean adult body weight (Dýrmundsson, 1973) although in a study of Clun Forest ewes the range was narrower (50–60 per cent). Ewe lambs born early in the season show earlier breeding activity but at higher body weight and age than later born lambs. Age, body weight and stage of the season all, therefore, have some influence on the date of onset of oestrus in ewe lambs of any genotype but there is insufficient data with which to apportion variation in the start of breeding activity between these three components. Ewe lambs show a higher number of silent heats and a lower level of efficiency in most aspects of reproductive performance.

THE MAJOR MODIFYING FACTOR—DAY LENGTH

The evidence available from numerous studies indicates that the major factor modifying any inherent breeding periodicity is the seasonal change in day length, which occurs with increasing intensity as latitude increases from the equator. Evidence from the study of sheep which have been transported from one hemisphere to another shows that after a period of irregular breeding activity the sheep eventually adopts a breeding pattern corresponding to that of its previous environment, but chronologically reversed (Yeates, 1949). This shows that day length, in concert with all the other external influences, can completely reverse the normal pattern of breeding. Reported attempts to modify the breeding season by manipulating day length artificially, at the same location, have not succeeded in such complete reversal.

Although day length change appears to be the major operative mechanism in modifying the initiation of the breeding season, there is less evidence to indicate its role in the cessation of the breeding season. However, manipulation of day length change between wide limits in the autumn and early winter has been shown to hasten the cessation of the breeding season (Ducker & Bowman, 1970). However, in an experiment carried out at Cambridge (Speedy, 1973) ewes that were maintained at a constant 8 hour day from December the twenty-first onwards, ceased breeding activity no later than ewes exposed to the normal increase of day length.

The Nature of the Light Stimulus

Several detailed aspects of the operation of photoperiodic control of breeding activity in the sheep are still unclear. The mechanism is unlike a simple reflex because of the long period that elapses between the apparent stimulus and the resulting change in overt breeding activity and the pathway from the eye to the hypothalamus is not yet fully understood.

The actual stimulus appears to be the change in the daylength rather than any particular level of daylength. The change may be from a long daylength to a gradually decreasing daylength as occurs naturally or it may be an abrupt change from a constant high level to a constant lower level (Ducker & Bowman, 1972). There is also some evidence (Ducker et al., 1970; Newton & Betts, 1972) that the onset of the breeding season may be earlier following a greater abrupt drop in daylength or steeper progressive decrease, than it is when less extreme changes are involved. Little information is available on any critical values of light and dark intensities, or the contrast between them, that are necessary for effective stimulus. It is also not clear how long the lower, or decreasing, level of daylength has to be maintained to ensure that the eventual effect is irreversible.

The Reaction Interval

Time elapses between the change in daylength and the response in terms of overt breeding activity which has been termed 'reaction interval'. Under natural conditions it is conveniently calculated from the longest day (the twenty-first of June in the Northern hemisphere) as far as the onset of the breeding season is concerned, although this interval may not have any biological significance. It has already been shown that this interval is short in breeds like the Dorset Horn and long in many of the British hill breeds. Under artificial lighting regimes the reaction interval depends on the stage of the season at which the light stimulus is applied (Newton & Betts, 1972). However, strangely as it may seem, a light stimulus applied in late pregnancy seems to be as effective as in the non-pregnant ewe, in that the reaction interval has been observed to be unaffected, provided the change in daylength occurred no more than 50 days prepartum (Speedy, 1973; Newton, 1969; Moseley & Lamming, 1969).

THE MINOR MODIFYING FACTORS

Several factors have been shown to modify the pattern of seasonal breeding activity, whose major characteristics are set by the internal rhythm and the effect of daylength. Most of the other minor modifying factors have been shown to operate by their effect on the ewe in the period just prior to the onset of the breeding season. Whatever the basic factors that control onset, it appears that for a short period just prior to this, the ewe is on the verge of oestrus activity and in such a state several factors can push the ewe into overt activity. Breeding activity in the ewe, as depicted in Fig. 5.2, can be likened to sleep in humans—deep anoestrus corresponding to deep sleep and full breeding activity to full waking activity. Various stimuli such as noise are much more likely to awake a person when it occurs near to his normal waking time.

Temperature

Lowered ambient temperature, occurring within a short period before onset, may advance the breeding season by several days (Lees, 1969).

Presence of the Ram

The sudden introduction of rams to a flock of ewes during this pre-onset period has been widely shown to precipitate the onset of breeding, the ewes first exhibiting the usual silent first heat, within about 6 days (Moule, 1970). The work of Morgan et al., (1972) suggests that the rams affect the sense of smell through olfactory receptors in the ewe. This suggestion is supported by the fact that there is some doubt as to whether vasectomized rams retain this stimulating effect after a lapse of time although their libido is unimpaired (Edgar & Bilkey, 1963).

Stress

The stress of movement or transport in lorries has also been shown to precipitate ovulation (Braden & Moule, 1964).

One consequence of the precipitation of the onset of the breeding season in this manner is that cycling, in a group of ewes exposed to such factors, may be substantially synchronized and use can be made of this to achieve synchronization of mating and therefore of lambing. The development of sponges impregnated with progestagens for intra-vaginal insertion, has given a potentially powerful tool to give planned synchronization and can be thought of as another method of precipitating breeding activity. When these sponges are inserted intra-vaginally into a group of ewes in the pre-onset period and PMS injected at sponge withdrawal, a useful degree of synchronization together with some advancement of the breeding season can be achieved (Robinson, 1967; Gordon, 1971).

Nutrition

In spite of the known effects of a high plane of feeding in the few weeks prior to mating on ovulation rate, there is little firm evidence in the many trials reported on this phenomenon, of any appreciable change in the date of onset of breeding by such feeding. It must be acknowledged, however, that there is high individual variation involved and many of the trials are small-scale. Nutrition in the longer term can have such an effect, particularly in the case of ewe lambs, where sexual maturity is advanced by good feeding, resulting in higher weight for age in the ewe lamb (Dýrmundsson, 1973). There is also evidence (Hunter, 1968) which shows that a high level of nutrition several months previously can advance the onset of breeding in the ewe. This is consistent with the observation that draft hill ewes after a season under good lowland conditions tend to breed early.

It is not easy to reconcile such an effect of long term nutrition with the finding (Lees, 1969) that ewes previously barren have a delayed breeding season. Lees also found that ewes that lamb early in the year tend to breed early in the subsequent season; it is questionable how much of this effect is environmental.

Lambing to Conception Interval

Most ewes breed only once a year either through design, in that they are not exposed to the ram or, where given the opportunity to mate after the first lambing, because the breeding season has ceased. Even in ewes with a long breeding season, mated early enough to allow a long period of potential breeding activity after lambing, there is a period during which successful mating cannot be achieved. This includes the post partum anoestrus period and occurs in many species that are not seasonal breeders (rats, pigs, humans, etc.). The factors that influence it are difficult to study in the sheep because of the variability and the shortness of the period of potential breeding activity, but Hunter (1968) has written a full review of observations recorded to that time. The post partum anoestrus is a phenomenon distinct from the seasonal anoestrus and controlled by different factors. There are only isolated reports of ewes that have conceived before 30 days have elapsed but, depending on the circumstances, from 30 days onwards increasing proportions of ewes can be successfully mated and the reports on rate of return to oestrus following lambing show that normal proportions of ewes showing oestrus have been achieved 70–120 days post partum. These intervals cannot be regarded as true post partum anoestrus since the effect is confounded with that of breeding season. There is limited evidence that the true interval from lambing to conception, where breeding season effects are removed, is much shorter; 42 days has been a mean interval reported for a small number of Clun Forest ewes (Lees, 1969). Information on this aspect of ewe reproductive behaviour is important in the development of frequent breeding systems, because of the possibilities for two successful matings within the same breeding season at an interval of 6–8 months.

Ewes have often been observed on heat within the two or three days following lambing due, it is thought, to the high level of oestrogen circulating at this time. This is purely a behavioural oestrus, unaccompanied by ovulation, and no ewes have been reported as pregnant from such a heat. In addition to the lack of ovulation in the ewe in the period after lambing, there is also a period of low fertility in ewes that do mate. After lambing, the ewe's uterus goes through a period of involution and cleansing so that physical conditions again become ready for further breeding. Difficult births, retention of afterbirth and damage to, or infection of, the uterus and reproductive tract inevitably delay the process of recovery, but the commencement of oestrus cycling are accompanied by a marked improvement in uterine conditions (Heap et al., 1963).

Several factors can affect the length of the anoestrus period at this stage.

GENETIC EFFECTS

So far, little is known about the genetic basis of the length of the lambing to conception interval, although there is some evidence which suggests that it may be shorter in breeds like the Dorset Horn and the Finnsheep which exhibit other aspects of intense reproductive activity (Speedy, 1973). Little is known either about the effect of age, although normally the breeding season of ewe lambs tends to be too short to allow sufficient estimation of their potential in this respect.

LACTATION

Lactation is one of the factors that can affect the length of the rebreeding interval, although several studies have failed to show any effect (Hunter, 1968). The release of oxytocin through the stimulation of sucking is known to hasten the involution of the uterus but its seems probable that the other hormonal accompaniments of lactation, possibly the presence of prolactin, may be a factor depressing breeding activity. Evidence for ewes lambing in the autumn shows that at the height of the normal breeding season, ewes can become pregnant in full lactation. It is in the early or waning stages of the breeding season that the effect of lactation may be sufficient to depress breeding activity, particularly the occurrence of ovulation in normal oestrus. It has been observed that ewes that lamb early but which lose their lambs are more likely to become pregnant again during the same breeding season, although Hunter (1968) has pointed out that this is an unsatisfactory basis for comparison.

In an experiment at Cambridge, forty early lambing, 3-year-old, ewes were put to the ram (Speedy, 1973). Of these, twenty had their lambs removed at birth for artificial rearing, whilst the other twenty suckled lambs. None of the suckling ewes showed oestrus after lambing whilst nine out of the non-suckling ewes showed oestrus and five were successfully remated.

There may be a complex interaction of the genotype, stage

of the breeding season, and lactation which may make lactation a decisive factor in the remating of ewes otherwise about to cease breeding activity. Much more information, however, is needed before it can be stated with confidence what role, if any, early weaning may have in frequent breeding systems for sheep.

NUTRITION

Part of any inhibiting effect of lactation may be its role in promoting undernourishment of the ewe and thus depressing reproductive activity. The evidence available on the effect of different levels of feeding on the length of the lambing to conception interval is not conclusive, although even where a low level of nutrition has not prevented oestrus, it is likely that the successful establishment of successful multiple pregnancy would be affected. The long term success of any frequent breeding system must depend on adequate feeding levels and it seems sensible to ensure that the extra feeding is given at crucial stages such as between lambing and remating.

It may be possible for the recommencement of breeding activity in the waning phase of the breeding season to be induced by precipitating factors such as those discussed in relation to the onset of the breeding season.

RAM EFFECT

There is some evidence of the effect of sudden introduction of the ram shortly after lambing, and Hunter (1968) suggests, from the limited available evidence, that the ram stimulus may be effective provided the rams are introduced no earlier than about 3 weeks after lambing.

INTRAVAGINAL SPONGES

There are a number of reports (Hunter, 1968a) of ewes treated four or more weeks after lambing with intravaginal sponges combined with PMS injection but response has been variable.

It seems likely that such a technique is best employed as a precipitating and synchronizing agent in a situation where ewes have been brought near to correct breeding conditions by manipulating all the other important factors involved.

Prolificacy

Any development of sheep systems from the low input/low output philosophy of the semi-natural conditions of extensive mountain and range environments, depends largely on being able to finance greater inputs. Simple calculations can show that under a wide range of economic circumstances increasing prolificacy, in terms of weaned lamb output per ewe, is a potent method of improving the economic performance of an enterprise (Table 9.3, page 359).

At low average levels of lamb production (e.g., recorded lowland sheep in Britain show an average lambing percentage little more than 130) an increase of 10 per cent in weaned lambs from the same ewes could increase gross margin per ewe by between 7.5 and 10 per cent (MLC, 1972). Investment in such improvements could, therefore, be well worthwhile. At the other end of the scale there are the possibilities of producing very high output systems based on frequent breeding. In these cases, higher costs are incurred and a really high level of prolificacy is desirable.

The major components of prolificacy have been defined in the introduction to the chapter and they can now be elaborated, having dealt in the previous section with the factors influencing the presence or absence of breeding activity.

Ovulation Rate

The number of ova or eggs shed at a normal heat in the ewe can vary from one to as many as 9 or 10, judging from the numbers of lambs that have been recorded as being born. With hormonal induction, many more ovulations can occur; over

30 having been recorded on occasion (Robinson, 1951). Several factors are involved:

THE GENOTYPE

The genotype of the ewe is a major influence on ovulation rates, for example when comparing groups of ewes of the Romney Marsh, Suffolk and Finnish breeds, Heaton Harris (1970) reported ovulation rates of 1.3, 1.8 and 2.5 respectively. Taking lambing results as a guide to ovulation rate it can be seen that much potential between breed variation exists, from the high levels exhibited by prolific breeds like the Finnish, Romanov, Dahman, East Friesian and Chios to the low levels characteristic of most of the mountain breeds. As mean ovulation rates increase, so does individual variation in potential litter sizes. Where mean ovulation rate is 1 ovum per oestrus there is no variation in ovulation rate but at the highest mean breed levels of $2\frac{1}{2}$ to 3 ovulations, ovulation rate may vary in individuals from 1 to a small proportion with 5 or 6. Making various assumptions of mean ovulation rate and assuming a maximum potential ovulation rate of 6, the distribution of mean ovulation rates corresponding to each mean have been calculated using the well known binominal theorem (Fig. 5.7).

When allowance is made for markedly increased embryo losses associated with increased numbers of ova shed, these distributions broadly correspond with data on distribution of litter size at birth recorded for different breeds, suggesting that although purely hypothetical they can give a useful guide to probable distribution of ovulation rates at various mean values. Although ovulation rate is manifested in discrete units each being one egg, there is no reason to suppose that the basic underlying factor which affects ovulation is not a continuous variable with the normal distribution common to many other biological phenomena.

The fact that as mean ovulation rates increase the variation in litter size also increases, has several important practical

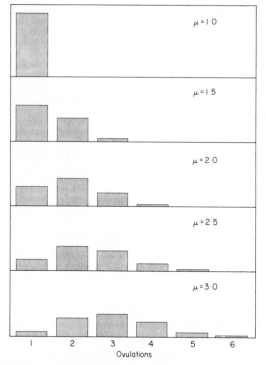

Fig. 5.7. *Proportion of ewes having various numbers of ovulations at various mean values for ovulation rate (μ).*

repercussions. It has to be accounted for in calculating future rates of progress in selection for prolificacy in ewes and in estimating the optimum prolificacy likely to be supportable in commercial systems. Since it is not known to what extent, if any, it will be possible to reduce this variation, the use of prolific breeds for some time, is likely to be accompanied by the problems of varying numbers of lambs born in a flock. Selection for prolificacy is discussed in Chapter 9.

THE AGE OF THE EWE

Just as age affects the properties of the breeding season in sheep it also has an influence on ovulation rates and consequent reproductive rates. Ewe lambs and to a lesser extent ewes in their second year of life, have lower ovulation rates than more mature ewes, as well as poorer conception rates. Peak ovulation rates, at least as judged by number of lambs born, are not achieved until the ewe is about four years old and seem to be maintained for several years thereafter before senile

Fig. 5.8. *Quintuplets obtained by natural mating from a three year old Cambridge ewe in the Aberdeen prolific ewe project. (By courtesy of Aberdeen Journals Ltd.)*

decline sets in. Turner (1969) has suggested that in flocks with a higher average level of reproduction rate ewes reach their peak and start to decline earlier than in lower producing flocks. If this is so, it is not clear to what extent it is a reflection of differences in patterns of ovulation rates or of other components of reproductive rate.

Even though the performance of ewe lambs is much poorer than that of adult sheep it seems that, provided they are well nourished and well managed, subsequent productivity and length of productive life is not reduced (Keane, 1974).

BODY SIZE AND CONDITION

Between breeds there is much variation in the relation of body size to ovulation rates; some of the most prolific breeds are of relatively small size like the Finnsheep, the Romanov and the Llanwenog. Within breeds a positive association between bodyweight and ovulation rate has been reported (Coop, 1966). The relative contribution of body condition and skeletal size is not fully quantified. Coop has shown that in Merino and Romney ewes an increase of 5 kg in body weight is accompanied by a 6 per cent increase in lambing rate based on lambs born. The effect of body condition on ovulation rates has been clearly shown (Gunn & Doney, 1973) (Table 5.3).

Table 5.3. *The lambing performance of Scottish Blackface ewes classified according to body condition score at 6 weeks before mating and at mating. (Based on Gunn et al., 1969).*

	Body condition score at 6 weeks before mating						Body condition at mating	
	$3\frac{1}{2}$	3	$2\frac{1}{2}$	2	$1\frac{1}{2}$	1	3	$1\frac{1}{2}$
per cent lambs born	158	150	177	86	93	62	162	79
per cent ewes barren	11	9	0	24	20	47	6	32
per cent multiple births	76	64	74	13	17	17	71	16

FLUSHING OF EWES

Body condition at mating is one facet of the important general effect of nutrition on ovulation rate and prolificacy in sheep, a subject of some controversy and much research. 'Flushing', the practice of giving ewes good feeding in the 3–4 weeks prior to turning in the rams, is an old practice, it being claimed that ewes in rising condition at mating produced more lambs. Subsequent research has confirmed the value of the practice in many respects even though the physiological basis for the effect is still not clearly understood. Coop (1966) summarized the previous work on the value of flushing ewes and reported on an extensive series of field trials carried out in New Zealand. He demonstrated that there were, in effect, two components of the benefits to be obtained by good nutrition. One, which he called the dynamic effect, was due to increased feed level and an actively improving body condition in the 2 or 3 weeks prior to mating, which resulted in an increase of up to 10 per cent in multiple births, with no discernible effect on barrenness. The other component of the effect of nutrition was a longer term one, or the static effect, reflected in the actual body condition of the ewe at mating and referred to previously. This improvement in body condition, achieved over a long period prior to mating, resulted not only in an increase in multiple births, over and above that achievable by any short term flushing, but also reduced the incidence of barrenness. For maximum ovulation rates it is recommended that ewes should be managed so as to regain body condition progressively from the time the lambs are weaned, so that they are in high condition at mating and under good conditions at the time of mating. The notion of severe restriction of feed intake in ewes from weaning, to prevent undue improvement in condition before flushing, may be justifiable in some circumstances but it will be achieved only at a cost to prolificacy. Ewes of many productive breeds that have suckled lambs do not easily become over fat under normal conditions and in such cases maximum prolificacy involves a dry period of at least two months under good grazing conditions.

Work with Panama ewes in the USA (Hulet et al., 1974) indicates that the effect of flushing is greatest early and late in the breeding season and unimportant at the peak of breeding activity.

THE STAGE OF THE BREEDING SEASON

It has been suggested earlier that an underlying cyclic influence, controlling breeding activity, exists, which has to reach a certain level of intensity before actual oestrus cycling is established. It is therefore reasonable to expect various degrees

G

of anoestrus and conversely of breeding activity. Thus, just as there seems to be deep anoestrus with a shallower phase at the beginning and end of the anoestrus period such a gradation also appears to occur during the breeding season, manifested in variation in ovulation rate. The evidence available confirms that ovulation rates tend to be lowest at the start and at the end of the season and at their highest at an intermediate stage (Fig. 5.9), (Hulet et al., 1974; Lees, 1969; Hulet et al., 1974b). Such a variation in ovulation rates is an important consideration in judging the economic effect of different mating practices. For instance, mating early in the season has to be judged not only in its effect on costs and on market return from an early lamb,

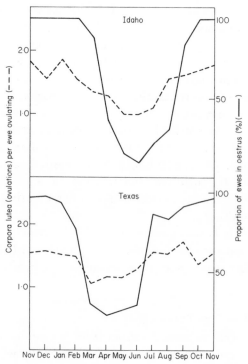

Fig. 5.9. *Proportion of ewes on heat and their ovulation rate (based on Hulet et al., 1974).*

but also in its possible consequences in lower prolificacy. More precise information is needed on this effect since economic circumstances may well dictate a much more flexible approach to lambing dates whether or not any actual increase in breeding frequency is envisaged.

ARTIFICIAL INDUCTION OF BREEDING

The results obtained when the breeding season is artificially manipulated can be seen as another aspect of the effect of breeding stage on ovulation rates. It is important to determine what level of ovulation and successful conception occurs when breeding activity is induced. There are many isolated reports of ovulation rates and lambing rates resulting from both hormone therapy and from artificial light treatment or from a combination of the two (Speedy, 1973). These vary from a level of performance as high as expected under natural mating conditions to a much lower level. The results obtained from the hormonal induction of breeding in the deep anoestrus period (April/May normally in the Northern Hemisphere) have been poor, particularly as regards the occurrence of oestrus and in the conception rates and lambing rates attained. Recent reports indicate that with the use of intravaginal sponges and good mating management (involving a high ram:ewe ratio) most ewes can be induced to come on heat but that conception to first oestrus is below normal. For example, Gordon (1971) in a study involving 584 ewes in 24 flocks in Ireland reported that 98 per cent of the ewes bred and 68.5 per cent conceived after treatment in June/July. Thus, treatments applied nearer the normal breeding season have been more uniformly successful but there still remains a substantial problem of lowered fertility in the first induced oestrus when progestogen sponges are used. Results from early breeding following light treatments (photo-stimulation) are also variable but conception appears to be somewhat higher than that achieved after hormone induction.

SUPEROVULATION WITHIN THE NORMAL BREEDING SEASON

Several workers have studied the possible use of hormone therapy to boost ovulation rates during the breeding season. The treatment consists of a synchronizing treatment, normally intravaginal sponges, combined with an injection of PMS 48 hours prior to expected heat.

Actual lambing resulting from the first mating of treated ewes may not be much more than 60 per cent of ewes even in the breeding season (Newton, 1969). The maximum response to superovulation in Scottish halfbred ewes was obtained with 1500 I.U. of PMS. and resulted in an increase in lambs born from 1.9 to 2.8. Response varies according to breed and even after treatment there remain substantial breed differences in numbers of lambs born per ewe (Newton, 1969).

One major problem with regard to superovulation is that there may be pronounced individual and seasonal variation in response, so that although mean prolificacy is only slightly improved there may be a significant incidence of very high litter sizes.

WASTAGE FROM OVULATION TO WEANING

Conception

Conception in mammals involves several elements of chance and reliable fertilization of several ova depends upon the correct placement of a high concentration of active spermatozoa at the right time. A degree of mis-timing or misplacement may mean that there is total failure of conception although the result may also be partial fertilization with consequent lowered lambing performance. In some cases ewes with access to more than one ram have been known to give birth to twins fathered by different rams. The role of the ram in influencing conception rates directly has often been discounted but there is increasing evidence of significant effects of the mating ram (Turner, 1969). Mention has already been made of a variety of factors that influence conception rate. However, there are no known specific venereal diseases, either bacterial or viral, affecting the conception of sheep.

PRENATAL MORTALITY

Prenatal mortality in sheep has been the subject of a review by Edey (1969) which forms the basis of much of the subsequent summary. He estimated from several reports available that 20–30 per cent of fertilized ova are usually lost during pregnancy, with most of the loss occurring in the first month. These losses are due to several causes:

Ovulation Rate

There is some evidence that prenatal mortality is higher, the higher the ovulation rate, although the effect may be confounded with the possibility that the more prolific genotypes not only have higher ovulation rate but also provide a better maternal environment.

In an experiment at Cambridge, groups of ewes from three breeds—Romney, Suffolk and Finnish—were implanted with 5 fertilized ova per ewe, from a separate source (Lawson & Rowson, 1972). The natural ovulation rate as estimated from the numbers of corpora lutea and the numbers of lambs born to the ewes which lambed are shown in Table 5.4. Although the numbers are too small to generalise, the results suggest that the Finnish sheep not only had high ovulation rates but were also

Table 5.4. *The distribution of litter size and mean litter size after transfer of five eggs, relative to the mean natural ovulation rate of recipient ewes which lambed. (based on Lawson & Rowson, 1972)*

Breed of recipient ewe	no of ewes	1	2	3	4	5	Mean litter size	Mean ovulation rate
Romney Marsh	13	–	5	7	1	–	2.69	1.46
Suffolk	12	1	4	4	2	1	2.83	2.08
Finn sheep	14	1	2	4	5	2	3.36	2.71

capable of supporting a greater number of viable lambs than were the ewes of the less prolific breeds.

Genetic Defects

Genetic defects in the embryo are now thought to be an important cause of early embryonic death; these may stem partly from the parents but also from mutations and chromosomal abnormalities in the embryo itself.

Age of Ewe

Edey could find no clear-cut effect of age on prenatal mortality and it is difficult to separate the effect of age per se from the many other factors usually associated with it. However, prenatal mortality may be one of the factors associated with the poor reproductive performance of ewe lambs.

Nutrition

Although it has been demonstrated that both very low and very high levels of nutrition in early pregnancy can increase fetal mortality, some of these effects are difficult to separate from effects of higher levels of nutrition on ovulation rate. Within more normal limits there is little evidence that variation in nutritional level, in the period about mating time and early pregnancy, is an important cause of prenatal mortality.

Season and Temperature

Although seasonal differences in prenatal mortality have been reported, it is difficult to discern a consistent pattern, partly because of the confounding with the effect of season on ovulation rates. High temperature in early pregnancy is known to increase fetal mortality and there are reports from hot countries that indicate that this may be important under field conditions.

Work at the British experimental husbandry farms (Bastiman & Williams, 1972; Kneale & Bastiman, 1974) has indicated that ewes that are housed at 35–40 days of pregnancy and wintered indoors have higher prolificacy than outwintered ewes. It is suggested that some early mortality in one of a pair of twin lambs had occurred possibly due to the effect of low temperatures on ewes on low feed levels.

LATE PREGNANCY AND THE PERIOD AROUND LAMBING (THE PERINATAL PERIOD)

These two periods together account for major loss in lambs (page 155)

Several disease conditions are implicated in high pre-natal mortality in sheep, particularly as a cause of abortion. These include disease associated with the organisms of the *Vibrio, Toxoplasma, Brucella, Salmonella, Listeria, Pasteurella, Rickettsia, Psittacosis* and *Bedsonia* groups as well as the infections that specifically affect the lamb after birth.

Many of these problems may be averted by a vaccination programme, where the ewe itself is protected, or where protection is passed on to the lamb via colostrum. In certain circumstances the lamb itself may be immediately protected from pulpy kidney and lamb dysentry by injecting the appropriate antiserum shortly after birth. Some of the infectious agents such as enzootic abortion, toxoplasmosis and listeriosis can also lead to the birth of live but weakly lambs.

The Development of Frequent Breeding Systems

Knowledge by itself is of little use to the sheep industry if it cannot be applied to improve existing systems or to create new systems. The development of systems involving breeding at a higher frequency than one in 12 months is aimed not only at gaining the benefits of increased annual lamb production, but also at getting a less seasonal drop of lambs to allow more flexible marketing time. The ultimate that can be envisaged in frequent breeding systems is a frequency of two lambings in a year requiring post partum anoestrus of less than 35 days but, as noted earlier, the evidence available on observed length of anoestrus makes it necessary to accept that a more immediate practical aim is to achieve an 8 month mean lambing interval for a flock, i.e., 3 lambings in two years. It is not sensible to aim for a constant frequency but rather to aim for two lambings in the one breeding season and to be content with one lambing in the following breeding season. This is because ewes mated early in the breeding season can, in certain conditions, be mated again before the end of the same season. To repeat this the following season is more difficult. By splitting the flock into two sections a rational programme of lambing can be devised to produce lambs at several times of the year.

The success of the practice depends on both the genotype of the sheep, with respect to breeding season length, and the extent of the lambing-conception interval. Usually, the higher the latitude at which frequent breeding is attempted, the more important becomes the use of a sheep with a long breeding season and a short post partum anoestrus period. In lower latitudes it appears that many of the available sheep breeds could be induced to breed at high frequency given appropriate management.

Some Dorset Horn breeders in Britain have long practised frequent breeding. Three lambings in two years is achieved by mating the ewe in July to lamb in December. A February/ March mating then results in July/August lambing, too late to be able to repeat the same process in the following breeding season so that the next lambing occurs in March/April following an October/November mating. In the following season the whole process can be repeated to achieve an average lambing frequency of 3 in 2 years. Such a pattern can be achieved with a wider range of breeds in southern latitudes. In Britain, other genotypes such as the Finn/Dorset cross, have also been used in frequent breeding systems. Some ewes of many more breeds, are capable of frequent breeding activity and examples are known where unorthodox lambing performance has been achieved more or less by accident. Where ewes have lost their lamb at birth, remating after an early lambing often occurs. More experience is required before we have the knowledge upon which to choose the genotype of sheep and the practice to adopt, in order to ensure a high proportion of double matings within a season. So far, results under farm conditions indicate that it is difficult to achieve results for February matings and to a lesser extent for July matings, in the Northern hemisphere, that compare consistently with matings in the Semptember-December period (NOSCA, 1974)

Frequent breeding systems have been based on the use of photostimulation or of exogenous hormones and in some cases such as that of Robinson et al., (1972), on a combination of the two methods.

The usual practice with hormones in the practical situation is to insert intravaginal pessaries and to withdraw them 10–14 days later and at the same time to inject PMS (500–1000 I.U.). Much stress has been placed on the provision of sufficient ram power for synchronized matings and a ratio of 1 ram to 10 ewes or fewer is the usal aim. Workers in the USA (Hulet & Stormshank, 1972) have used subcutaneous implants of plastic, containing natural progesterone, for oestrus induction, but the method of administration is more difficult than for the intravaginal sponge and there is no clear evidence of how much better, if any, the response is.

The techniques now available for manipulating the breeding activity of ewes can be put into very simple use in the case of older ewes ready for culling. These can be treated to lamb early enough, either to be sold fat with their lambs at times of high price or so that a further crop of lambs can be obtained, out of normal season, before the ewes are disposed of.

All of the systems of increased breeding frequency that have been tried in practice, particularly those that employ artificial lighting or hormone therapy, involve increased costs which can only be recouped by achieving a combination of increased lambing frequency with a high natural prolificacy. Only with prolific ewes can increased frequency of breeding bring substantial commercial rewards to its user. This was brought out in a report on the development of frequent breeding systems in Northern Ireland (Northern Ireland Agricultural Trust, 1974). A total of 200 ewes in several flocks were included in a scheme where 2 lamb crops were produced in a 12–14 month cycle. Annual lamb production ranged from 180–230 per 100 ewes mated and it was estimated that an annual lamb production of 250 was necessary to make the system more profitable than the traditional method of lamb production off grass.

There must obviously be a limit to the level of prolificacy that is desirable and the earlier discussion on the variation in litter size indicates that when litter size in the mature ewes reaches a mean of 3.0 a few litters of six lambs are born. The small size and low viability of lambs at this level indicates that the proportion should be minimal and it is unlikely, therefore, that optimum prolificacy will exceed a level of about 2.7 lambs reared on a flock basis.

Nutrition 6

Feeding has long been the most potent tool by which man manipulates productivity in his domestic animals, and the sheep is no exception. The cost of feed in some way accounts for the major cost of sheep enterprises, although in more extensive systems this is often indirectly reflected through the cost of labour, rent and wintering. The sheep has a fascinating ability to survive and produce under a surprising range of conditions and in respect of winter survival on poor mountain herbage sheep far excel cattle. This accounts for the association of the sheep on a worldwide basis with mountainous regions (Chapter 1).

The Sheep's Digestive System

It is not the intention to repeat detailed descriptions of the anatomy, physiology and biochemistry of animal digestion that can be found in standard texts, but to outline very briefly the main relevant features and to deal more particularly with aspects where the sheep differs from other species.

The most outstanding feature of digestion in the adult sheep is that it is a ruminant, possessing an enlarged sac-like rumen between the oesophagus or gullet and the true stomach or abomasum. The rumen is an active site for the fermentation and breakdown of food by a variety of micro-organisms, including bacteria and protozoa. The main end products of fermentation, the volatile fatty acids, are absorbed into the blood stream through the rumen wall. The possession of a rumen has far-reaching consequences for the sheep, mediated not only through the ability it confers to digest and utilize low quality roughage, but also because of the effects that it has on the capacity for food intake.

THE MOUTH AND DENTITION OF SHEEP

The sheep is a lip browser using the lips to manipulate the food that it grasps between the lips and between the lower incisors and the upper bare gum; unlike cattle, sheep and goats have a split upper lip which may partly account for their greater ability to select herbage and to graze close to the ground.

The lamb starts off with a set of temporary teeth. These are similar to the permanent teeth in form and placement but smaller in size and fewer in number. There are twenty teeth in the temporary set, eight incisors at the front of the lower jaw and twelve molars and premolars at the back of both jaws. The permanent set of the normal adult contains eight incisors and six pairs of molar and premolar teeth in the upper and lower jaws, a total of thirty-two. The lamb is born either without incisor teeth or with one or two just erupting and usually has a full set of eight incisors by the time it is one to four months of age. The permanent incisors erupt in pairs—the central pair, then those on each side and so on until the full set of incisors is present and the sheep is 'full mouth'. The state of the incisors is used as a rough guide to the age of a sheep, although there is much variation, genetic and non-genetic, in the precise age at which each pair of incisors erupt.

The first, central, pair of incisors erupt between twelve and eighteen months in most sheep and the sheep at this stage is often described as a 'two-tooth' equivalent to a 'shearling' or 'gimmer'. The second pair of incisors erupt between $1\frac{1}{2}$ and 2 years old, the third between 2 and 3 years, and the final pair between 3 and 4 years (Ryder & Stephenson, 1968; Belschner,

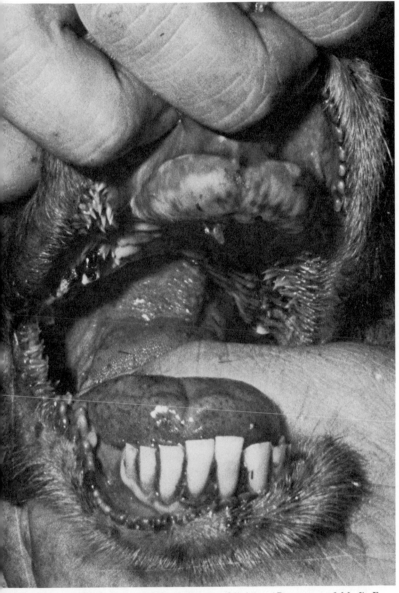

Fig. 6.1. *A full mouth ewe with her four pairs of incisors. (By courtesy of Mr J. F. Reaper, School of Agriculture, Aberdeen).*

1959). Because of the variation involved the teeth are only a limited guide to age and mostly of value to distinguish shearling ewes at their first mating from older ewes.

The permanent molar teeth first appear as the fourth pair in the existing set of a sheep at 3–5 months of age. The other molars and premolars appear progressively in pairs until the full complement is usually present at two years of age.

Effects of Incisor Dentition on Sheep Production

At varying intervals after becoming 'full mouth', the normal ewe begins to suffer from a loosening of incisor teeth and some may be lost. The ewe is then 'broken mouthed' and for many sheep owners this is a major criterion for culling. Some sheep retain their incisors for much longer than others and in these cases the incisors wear down evenly almost to gum level.

Although it seems logical to expect that a broken mouth is likely to reduce the ewe's efficiency, particularly under mountain conditions, there have been few objective observations on this aspect. In a comparison between broken mouthed and sound mouthed Blackface ewes of $6\frac{1}{2}$ years of age, it was shown that there were few differences between the two groups in early pregnancy but there was evidence of greater weight loss in late pregnancy and some indication that lactation performance was poorer (Sykes et al., 1974a). Under lowland conditions, particularly where ewes are given supplementary feed or are housed in the winter, broken mouthed ewes and ewes that have lost all their incisors can continue to produce even if their efficiency is somewhat impaired.

There is much variation between individuals and between flocks in the age of development of permanent incisor loss but the clinical observations have failed to demonstrate the basic cause of the condition. Physical factors such as eating turnips are thought to be secondary and only aggravate an underlying tendency to broken mouth (Gunn, 1969).

One possible cause is the deficiency of minerals such as calcium and phosphorus and there is evidence that low level supplementation with either calcium or phosphorus can affect the incidence of broken mouth (Gunn, 1969). Some observations of broken and sound mouth sheep that are age contemporaries have failed to establish that broken mouth is associated with a generalized or permanent impoverishment of the skeleton as a whole. However the depletion of the skeleton during late pregnancy and lactation, resulting in the weakening of the tooth socket, and the delay in the repletion of the skeleton in older ewes could be important factors in premature incisor loss (Field et al., 1974b).

The rumen

A brief outline of the rumen of the sheep is given before going on to deal with the applied aspects of nutrition in sheep. The rumen itself is a large muscular organ with a capacity of 4–10 l in the sheep (Ryder & Stephenson, 1968). It is characterized by the presence of a mixture of food and rumen fluid in which a variety of micro-organisms can flourish. The conditions in the rumen, particularly the acidity (pH), and the fluid content, depend on feed intake, the secretion of saliva, and the ingestion of water both directly and from the moisture content of the food. According to the type of fermentation and the resultant pH level in the rumen, a varied spectrum of micro-organism species exist including bacteria and protozoa. The task of individual identification of the various organisms is formidable, because of the large number present. Species and varieties of micro-organisms differ in the substrates that they live on, e.g., the cellulolytic bacteria that break down cellulose and release material protected by cellulose tissues. Several micro-organisms utilize ammonia, dissolved in the rumen fluid, to synthesize amino acids for the proteins in their bodies. These proteins are subsequently used by the host sheep when the bacteria are washed out of the rumen into the rest of the digestive tract. Similarly, micro-organisms synthesize some of the vitamins such as Vitamin B_{12} normally essential in the diet of non-ruminants.

Unfortunately the rumen micro-organisms are indiscriminate in their activities, so that even the proteins and carbohydrates of good diets are degraded in the rumen and less efficiently used than if they had been passed straight on to the true stomach or abomasum. In the younger suckler lamb this undesirable process is avoided because of a highly developed reflex, whereby a groove, called the oesophageal groove, acts as a continuation of the oesophagus directly into the abomasum. The rumen is thus by-passed, allowing efficient use of the high quality nutrients in the milk from the ewe.

THE ABOMASUM AND INTESTINES

In addition to the absorption of volatile fatty acids and water through the rumen wall, the rumen contents are also progressively evacuated through the ruminal/omasal orifice and pass on to the abomasum, which is like the true stomach of non-ruminants. In the abomasum and intestines carbohydrates, fats and proteins, either from food left undigested in the rumen or from the micro-organisms themselves, that are washed through from the rumen, are digested and absorbed. The abomasum and the small intestine are the chief sites for protein digestion and absorption in the sheep. Much of the residual water is removed from the digesta in the large intestine and this process is carried out very efficiently in the sheep resulting in a relatively small loss of water in the faeces as compared to cattle.

Voluntary Feed Intake in the Sheep

The approach to the feeding of sheep, described later in this section, is largely based on the integration of knowledge about the sheep's feed intake and on the efficiency of feed utilization, when allowed access to a variety of different diets. The whole of the sheep's diet is seldom fully controlled by the feeder and he usually has an inadequate knowledge of the composition of a major proportion of the whole diet. Decisions on a feeding policy for sheep, therefore, depend upon: (a) a knowledge of the voluntary intake of feedstuffs and diets based upon them; (b) the nutrient content of the diet and the likely efficiency of nutrient utilization. Before discussing the problem of designing feeding programmes for sheep, a discussion of factors influencing intake is necessary as a prelude to examining the feed requirements of sheep. The factors influencing voluntary food intake are twofold:

Physical Factors

Voluntary feed intake in sheep is limited by various physical barriers. On the one extreme, if the sheep is offered a diet of very low quality, like low grade wood shavings, it would have to consume for its daily energy needs (let alone other nutrients) a quantity well beyond the limit of what can be broken down and processed daily within the animal body. Many diets therefore containing a low proportion of useful energy to indigestible material, cannot be consumed at a level sufficient for various objectives, be this full growth, lactation of even maintenance of body weight. Improvement in the rate of production is therefore limited, not by the quantity of feed available, but by the quality of the diet and the amount consumed.

Such physical limitation of intake can occur in all animals if the diet offered is of sufficiently low quality due to the limitation on the rate at which the food once swallowed can pass along the digestive tract. Normally the most limiting sector of the digestive tract in non-ruminants seems to be the intestines rather than the oesophagus and the stomach (Cole et al., 1971). In ruminants on the other hand the main limiting factor to the rate of passage of most low quality diets is the rate of passage of digesta from the rumen except where low quality feeds are very finely ground (Balch & Campling, 1962; Ben Saud, 1972).

Physiological Factors

This category can best be explained by stating that these factors control intake when it is not limited by the physical factors. As the physical restriction to intake decreases, the animal, if it continued to eat more, would reach a stage where it could no longer metabolize all the energy consumed so that there are physiological limits to the energy that can be successfully utilized in the various body processes including growth, lactation and fat deposition. In the normal healthy sheep, gradually accustomed to a diet, these limits are not exceeded because of the control of feed intake exercised involuntarily through the central nervous system.

Physical factors influencing the feed intake

The concentrate/roughage ratio. The concept of the sheep's diet as a mixture of two components—'roughage' and 'concentrate' —in varying proportions, is useful in practice, but it can only be used quantitatively in relation to a particular diet combination such as barley straw and barley, because of the difficulty of defining precisely the terms 'roughage' and 'concentrate'. In many senses the two terms signify the two extremes of a continuous transition:

roughage ──────────────→ concentrate	
high crude fibre	low crude fibre
large particle size	small particle size
low digestibility	high digestibility
low content of digestible energy	high content of digestible energy
low density	high density

A roughage has the characteristics that favour the physical limitation of intake (Balch & Campling, 1962) so that the sheep, allowed to eat ad libitum, still fails to consume the maximum amount of energy. On the other hand, for the sheep allowed to eat a concentrate ad libitum, intake is limited by other factors.

Foodstuffs classed as 'roughages' span a range at the roughage end of the above spectrum; concentrate feeds also vary in their properties. High quality roughages merge into low quality concentrates.

Sheep exist on a wider range of diets than almost any of man's animals, varying from poor quality roughage that hardly provides for body maintenance, to a diet, largely composed of cereals, used for the most intensive form of lamb fattening. Ben Saud (1971) observed the results of feeding young wether sheep on diets varying from all straw to all concentrates. These diets were given in the form of pelleted, coarsely milled, ingredients.

The results (Fig. 6.2) illustrate the control of intake changing from the 'physiological' to the 'physical'. Maximum intake of dry matter occurs at the point of transition from one form of control to the other, i.e., as the roughage/concentrate ratio decreases (diet 'quality' increasing) intake rises as the physical limitation of intake is relaxed. At the stage when this limitation is fully relaxed the sheep is consuming the maximum amount of energy and further decreases in the proportion of roughage

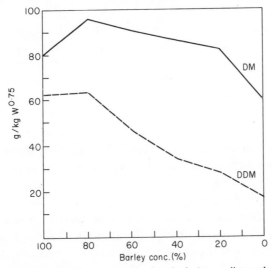

Fig. 6.2. *The effect of barley concentration in a barley/straw diet on the intake of dry matter (DM) and digestible dry matter (DDM) by sheep.*

or indigestible fibre results in a lower feed intake. Eventually the sheep suffers from lack of 'roughage' giving an undesirable fermentation in the rumen and a lower energy intake. A further complication is the fact that at the very high levels of straw, protein deficiency is also affecting food intake.

This and several other studies have shown that a progressive reduction in intake occurs as the ratio of roughage or indigestible material in the diet increases.

Roughage quality. The higher the quality of the 'roughage', particularly in terms of the dry matter digestibility, the higher the intake and performance attainable with sheep on an all roughage diet, and the higher the proportion of roughage to concentrate in a mixture without lowering performance. Depending on the stage of production, good hay or artificially dried grass may give maximal performance, without concentrate addition. With cereal straw, a substantial proportion of added concentrate is required for almost any form of sheep production. The quality of the concentrate will also affect the optimum ratio of roughage to concentrates in any feeding situation.

The feeding quality of conserved foodstuffs for sheep depends on nutrient content and intake characteristics and can be determined partly subjectively, in terms of freedom from secondary biological and chemical decomposition, and objectively in terms of various laboratory analyses.

Subjective tests. The smell, colour, texture and sometimes the taste of the material is a useful guide to the absence of deterioration caused by the growth of bacterial and fungal organisms or by the leaching out of soluble materials. Such changes during preservation may give rise to toxic effects of the material and refusal by the sheep.

Objective tests. Several criteria can be used to evaluate the feeding value to sheep of feeding materials. Theoretically the most satisfactory estimates are those based on results of feeding trials involving live sheep but because of the expense and amount of material needed, other methods have to be employed.

For the content of major nutrients satisfactory laboratory methods are available which are applicable to small samples. Nutrients in this category include protein and the major mineral elements. In recent years cheaper automated analyses of an increasing number of the minor nutrients, both minerals and vitamins, have been developed. The use of these may be justified in large scale compounding and in an intensive feeding situation.

Energy content is best described by the metabolizable energy (ME) content of the material (ARC 1965) since this energy represents that available to the sheep for various functions including maintenance of body processes and body tissue, for growth and for lactation. The proportion of the ME of a material that is eventually converted into useful work, body energy storage or milk energy depends on the animal, its environment and, to some extent, on the food. Tables have been constructed which summarize the ME content of a variety of materials (MAFF, 1972).

The metabolizable energy of a feed material is estimated from equations developed relating ME (as a dependent variable) to various constituents as determined in the laboratory. These equations have included a number of characteristics sometimes estimated indirectly from the proportion of lignified structural plant material. An example is as follows:

$$ME \ (Kcal) = 3.94 \ X_1 + 9.5 \ X_2 + 3.24 \ X_3 + 3.62 \ X_4$$
$$(Hoffmann, 1969)$$

where X_1 = digestible crude protein (g), X_2 = digestible crude fat (g), X_3 = digestible crude fibre (g) and X_4 = digestible N.F.E. (g).

The extensive use of such tables as a guide to the feeding of sheep is limited because of the lack of guides to the likely voluntary intake of the diet, in particular the effect of a number of constituent materials, when combined, on the intake of the total diet. However, it is well established that the increased feed intake observed as a concentrate is added to a basal roughage (Fig. 6.2) is also apparent when roughages of different ME content are given (Balch & Campling, 1962). Although the relationship is not close, intake tends to increase as the ME content increases. This relationship is discussed in relation to grass and it is clear that roughages of the same ME content can have very different intake characteristics (Chapter 7, page 264).

As far as the adult ewe, kept indoors, is concerned, in diets based primarily on a loose mix of coarsely ground barley straw and barley, there appears to be no practical benefit in increasing the concentrate/roughage ratio beyond 60:40. (Owen, 1974). Where the diet is pelleted a ratio of 50:50 may be sufficient.

For the growing lamb the concentrate/roughage ratio of a pelleted diet needs to be increased to about 85:15 to ensure maximal growth in diets based on barley and coarsely ground roughage (Owen et al., 1969).

The form of the diet. Mention has already been made of the effect of the form of the diet on the resulting voluntary feed intake. Of particular importance is the way the roughage component has been processed since it is this component of the diet that has the greatest effect on physical limitation of intake. Since intake seems to be limited by the restriction placed upon rate of passage of food out of the rumen through the rumen/omasum orifice, then grinding the roughage should allow increased voluntary feed intake. Work at Cambridge with lambs and with yearling wethers has shown that both the grinding of the roughage and the pelleting of the diet seem to have a similar effect although varying in degree (Owen et al., 1969). Grinding and pelleting has little effect when diets have a high concentrate/roughage, either on intake or performance but as the concentrate/roughage ratio decreases both grinding and pelleting seem to delay and mitigate the operation of physical limitation. A summary of the results of an experiment in which wether sheep were given diets containing 0–75 per cent barley straw in conjunction with a basal concentrate diet is given in Table 6.1. The straw was either chopped to give a coarse roughage or finely ground and the diets were given either pelleted or as a loose mix (Owen, et al., 1972, unpublished data).

The results show that maximum dry matter intake was greater on the ground/pelleted diet and when the roughage/concentrate ratio is high. Very finely ground, highly concentrated diets provide too little roughage for the proper functioning of the rumen. This may be due partly to the difference in the volatile fatty acid proportion and low pH on such a diet and partly due to the lack of physical abrasion on the rumen wall. Ørskov and Fraser (1972) have shown that barley and other cereals are better utilized by lambs when given whole, without rolling or grinding.

Mention has previously been made of the substantial variation of the digestibility/intake relationship found in grass varieties. Workers at the Welsh Plant Breeding Station (Jones & Miles, 1967) for example showed important differences in the voluntary intake of grass species and varieties of similar digestibility. It can be postulated that these differences arise from the form of the diet, that is the physical nature of the indigestible material in the grasses, which allows a higher rate of passage through the rumen for some grasses. This finding emphasises the importance of methods to measure intake characteristics of grasses and clovers as well as the digestibility and ME, in any attempt to evaluate the crude potential of grass for animal production.

Protein Content

Very poor roughages not only place a physical limitation on intake because of the proportion of large indigestible particles, but also often because of their low protein content. It is known that animals respond to nutrient deficiencies in the diet by reducing intake (Blaxter, 1964) to avoid the danger of physiological upsets. Protein deficiency in ruminants and non-ruminants has such an effect and this phenomenon has been noted in a variety of species, including young lambs and older

Table 6.1. *Voluntary food intake and liveweight gain of wethers on diets varying in straw content and in method of processing.*

Mean dry matter intake (kg/day)

Form of: diet	straw	Level of straw (per cent)						SE
		0	15	30	45	60	75	
Pelleted	Ground	1.52	1.67	1.80	1.78	1.83	1.48	0.134
Loose	Ground	1.47	1.91	1.79	1.60	1.19	1.05	0.063
Pelleted	Chopped	1.49	1.83	2.17	1.91	1.74	1.39	0.086
Loose	Chopped	1.52	1.60	1.08	0.97	0.71	0.61	0.083

Mean liveweight gain (g/day)

Form of: diet	straw	Level of straw (per cent)						SE
		0	15	30	45	60	70	
Pelleted	Ground	208	165	175	131	82	-1	66.3
Loose	Ground	187	159	153	66	50	61	31.0
Pelleted	Chopped	244	226	195	112	84	72	35.8
Loose	Chopped	270	185	64	-17	-50	27	41.8

Composition of diets (%)

Barley straw	0	15	30	45	60	75
Barley	62.25	45.8	29.35	12.9	0	0
Sugar beet pulp	20.0	20.0	20.0	20.0	16.45	0
Ext. Soya bean meal	7.25	7.25	7.25	7.25	7.25	7.25
White fishmeal	5.0	6.45	7.9	9.35	10.8	12.25
Molasses	5.0	5.0	5.0	5.0	5.0	5.0
Sodium sulphate	0.5	0.5	0.5	0.5	0.5	0.5

To each 100 kg of diet a vitamin/mineral mix was added to supply the following ingredients:

	g	
'Advitamix' AD_3E	20	contains 50 000 I.U. per g A, 10 000 I.U. per g D, 52.5 I.U. per g E
Cobalt sulphate	1.7	
Iron sulphate	3.6	
Manganese sulphate	1.8	
Potassium iodide	0.2	
Zinc oxide	2.0	

sheep. The sheep can accommodate some lowering of the protein content of the diet by adjustment in its own body composition so that diets deficient in protein lead to fatter carcasses (Andrews & Ørskov, 1970). Beyond this level however the intake of a badly deficient diet is reduced. This voluntary reduction in feed intake is an aspect of 'physiological' control, mediated through the central nervous system. In the ruminant, however, its effect is largely overshadowed by the influence of the rumen micro-organisms. A deficiency of true protein can be made up for in the ruminant by the bacterial synthesis of protein provided there is a supply of non-protein nitrogen. When nitrogen is limiting, there is a reduction in the size and efficiency of the whole microbial population, resulting in lowered feed digestibility and a reduction in voluntary feed intake because of the reduction in fermentation and the rate of passage of food particles out of the rumen. Egan and Moir (1965) have shown that infusion of casein into the duodenum of a sheep on a low quality roughage diet can lead to a quick elevation in intake, indicating that a true protein deficiency also exists at tissue level.

In experiments where diets containing polyethylene (a plastic) were given to lambs as a substitute for low quality roughage it was demonstrated that changes in the protein content of such a diet markedly affected voluntary feed intake (Ben Saud, 1972). One experiment involved two diets—one of shredded barley straw (ground through a 19mm screen) and the other of a simulated straw, of the same gross composition, but based on semi-purified ingredients with polyethylene as a diluent. When the diets were supplemented with soya bean meal to the level of 10 per cent crude protein, voluntary intake increased by 57 per cent and 69 per cent for the straw and simulated straw respectively. The results indicate that, irrespective of any effect on the rate of cellulose digestion in the rumen, correction of the basic protein deficiency has a marked effect on feed intake.

The inference from this work is that on roughages of very

low protein content, protein deficiency is often the limiting factor to intake and processes like grinding to improve rate of passage will not lead to high intake until this deficiency is remedied.

Other essential nutrients and intake. A major deficiency of any essential nutrient will depress feed intake in a similar way. In Chapter 7 some of the factors influencing the intake of poor hill herbage are discussed and nutrient deficiencies found in such circumstances act partly through their effects on lowered feed intake.

Rumen size. It has been suggested that the physical restriction of intake in ruminants is related to rumen capacity and that the low intake associated with late pregnancy or overfatness in sheep may be due to the reduction in abdominal space brought about by the gravid uterus or internal fat, thus preventing normal distention of the rumen (Forbes, 1970).

Several subsequent findings suggest that the simple mechanical restriction of space is not the sole reason. For example, Ben Saud (1971) suspended a balloon filled with water into the rumen of each of several wether sheep and showed that, within limits, the sheep could adapt to the restriction of rumen space and maintain the same voluntary intake. When the balloons contained 2 l of water there was little effect on the sheep's intake of a pelleted coarsely ground straw or on a pelleted lucerne diet. However when three litres of water were suspended, although the intake of lucerne was unaffected, there was a reduction in the intake of straw. The adaptation to the space restriction in the rumen seemed to be partly through a change in eating behaviour of the sheep, which tended to eat smaller meals over a longer period of the day and partly because of the higher rate of passage of food through the rumen as space was restricted.

Similarly it has been shown that the voluntary feed intake of ewes drops in late pregnancy even when given complete diets with a high energy concentration (Heaton Harris, 1970). The reduction of intake in late pregnancy and in overfat ewes may therefore be due to physiological factors and not purely a physical restriction.

Physiological control of intake

Several aspects of physiological stage of the sheep have been shown to affect intake and it is now apparent that these physiological factors can override the purely physical factors associated with the rate of breakdown of feed in the rumen.

Previous Restriction

Ruminants and non-ruminants respond to ad libitum feeding following a period of restriction, by increased food intake (either in absolute terms or in relation to their size; Wilson and Osbourne, 1962). The increased intake in such realimented animals seems to be the major cause of the phenomenon of compensatory growth (Owen et al., 1971). Even sheep that are given roughage diets, normally regarded as within the range of diets where voluntary intake is limited physically, exhibit such elevated intake (R. F. Lee, 1974; private communication). This is a clear indication that the physiological factors can override the physical, at least partly.

Age

During the milk feeding stage the young lamb appears to have a very pronounced intake regulating mechanism, evident when an artificially reared lamb, on ad libitum milk replacer, is given the milk at different concentrations. The lamb adjusts its intake of liquid so that the intake of milk powder is similar, at least within a range of 15–25 per cent dilution with water (Large, 1965).

Artificially reared lambs, weaned at 4–5 weeks of age, appear to have a less well developed intake regulating mechanism in the early post-weaning phase up to 8–12 weeks old, so that there is slower and less complete response to the dilution of the diet with indigestible material (Owen et al., 1969; Andrews & Ørskov, 1970).

Physiological State of the Ewe

It has been suggested earlier in the chapter that the reduced intake of ewes in late pregnancy is due to physiological and not to purely physical factors and it is interesting to note that one detailed study showed a greater reduction in intake at a low dietary roughage/concentrate ratio than at a high ratio (Heaton Harris, 1970). Another effect of physiological stage on food intake is shown during lactation; a ewe after lambing

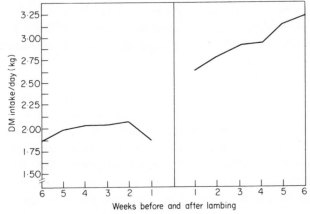

Fig. 6.3. *Dry matter intake of the ewe in the period before and after lambing (from Heaton Harris, 1970).*

shows a marked increase in intake, reaching a flat peak more than a month after lambing (Fig. 6.3). Intake appears to be 30–50 per cent higher during lactation than in late pregnancy, on a standard diet (Heaton Harris, 1970). Increased intake during lactation has been observed on high roughage as well as on highly concentrated diets (R. F. Lee, 1974, private communication) although the peak intake may be much lower on the less concentrated diet (Hadjipieris & Holmes, 1965). Work with dairy cattle has shown that the increased intake of food by the same animal at different stages is accompanied by increased rumen size (Hutton, 1963), but the precise way that physical restriction is overcome is not yet clear.

Water Intake

Water intake is closely associated with food intake because water is required not only to maintain body moisture but to process the food consumed, to enable growth to take place and, in the lactating ewe, to supply the demands of milk production. Water intake has been shown to increase linearly with increase in feed allowance (Ben Saud, 1971); wethers consumed about 2 kg of water for each extra kilogram of dry feed in addition to a predicted requirement of almost 2 kg of water when no food was eaten. Observations on ewes of different breeds on dry feed showed that, during pregnancy and lactation, ewes consume about 3·5 kg of water for each kg of dry feed consumed (Heaton Harris, 1970).

Not only can changes in food intake affect water intake but vice versa. Under cool temperate conditions, wether sheep given water once every three days, as opposed to those with free access to water, consumed less water and less food. However there was considerable adaptation to reduced water availability (for example the faeces became much drier) and sheep watered once every two days maintained their food intake in spite of lower water intake. Climate, particularly temperature, has an obvious effect on the water requirement and there must also be an upper limit, where the moisture content of the feed is so high that the body fails to get rid of sufficient water to allow a sufficient intake of feed dry matter. There seems to be little evidence as to where this limit is, although it can seldom be exceeded in practice since sheep can thrive on roots such as turnips, where the moisture content of the diet approaches 90 per cent.

Having considered the major factors influencing voluntary feed intake, it is necessary to deal with the sheep's nutritional requirements in relation to its stage of development and to available feedstuffs.

The Requirements of the Lamb

The unborn lamb as soon as it is attached to the uterine wall is nourished by its mother through the exchange of nutrients between the two blood systems (the ewe's and the lamb's) that occurs at the placenta.

The development of the unborn lamb can be influenced both by competition for nutrients and space within the uterus from other developing lambs and also by the way the pregnant ewe is fed. In general the developing fetus has a high but not absolute priority for nutrients in the ewe's body. This competition may be for specific nutrients (Twardock et al., 1973).

THE NEWBORN LAMB

At birth the lamb is born like the calf (and unlike the human baby), in having no immune antibodies in the blood to protect it from disease and it depends upon getting colostrum from the ewe and absorbing the large molecules of the gamma globulin fraction through the intestine wall.

Early ingestion of colostrum is also important from other points of view. Australian work on the energy transactions of the newborn lamb has shown how rapidly the lamb's reserves of energy are dissipated after birth in maintaining body temperature and therefore how vital the first suck of colostrum is (Alexander, 1962). The rate of heat loss in the young lamb is high because of the poor thermodynamic properties of the body—a high proportion of extremities in relation to trunk mass where most heat is generated. Under severe climatic conditions, such as driving cold rain and sleet, the birth coat of the lamb may be of some importance in insulating the lamb and allowing it an extension of activity to obtain colostrum before hypothermia sets in. The major hill breeds of Britain— Welsh Mountain, Scottish Blackface, Swaledale and North Country Cheviot are all characterized by having a high proportion of lambs with a hairy birthcoat. The extent of hairiness varies from the extreme of the lamb with a completely hairy coat to a lamb which has only a little hair on its hindquarters. One UK study has shown that survival under severe conditions

is highest in lambs of an intermediate birthcoat category
(Purser & Karam, 1967).

LIQUID FEEDING

The oesophageal groove functions from birth and, with the
maintenance of the appropriate stimuli, can persist into adult
life. Sucking from a teat is not essential to the functioning of
the groove; it has been demonstrated that lambs can display
all the attributes of the successful oesophageal reflex when
appropriately accustomed to drinking from a shallow container (Owen & Davies, 1965).

Milk Composition

Table 6.2 shows the composition of cow's milk and ewe's
milk and illustrates few differences between calves and lambs.
Apart from the obvious difference in solids concentration of
the milk both ewe and cow's milk is adapted to supplying much

Table 6.2. *Composition of Milk.* (*Source*: *Kon & Cowie, 1961*)

	Cow (*Bos Taurus*)	Ewe
g/100 g		
Total solids	12.10	18.40
Crude protein (N × 6.38)	3.25	5.60
Fat	3.50	7.50
Lactose	4.60	4.40
Ash	0.75	0.87
Calcium	0.12	0.19
Phosphorus	0.10	0.15
Sodium	0.05	0.07
Potassium	0.15	0.19
µg/100 ml		
Thiamine	40.0	70.0
Riboflavin	150.0	500.0
Nicotinic acid	80.0	500.0
Pantothenic acid	350.0	350.0
Vitamin B_{12}	0.5	0.3

the same requirements for the young of both species and the composition in terms of the major nutrients—energy and protein, reflects this similarity. There is one difference in requirement of the lamb and the calf as a consequence of growth of the fleece in the lamb. Wool is almost pure protein and contains a high proportion of the sulphur amino acids. Whole cow's milk, either fresh or reconstituted, can be used to rear lambs artificially but it is usually more expensive to use than manufactured replacers.

Immunological Status

The success of any rearing system depends on the maintenance of the lamb's immunity to disease. The effectiveness of the transfer of immunoglobulins from colostrum to the lamb is, like that for the calf, a function of antibody concentration in the milk, the level of intake by the lamb and the timing of consumption in relation to the birth. It is important that the lamb consumes a large quantity of colostrum within 6–10 hours of birth so that it acquires some immunity to pathogens experienced by the dam in the period before the birth. This immunity is soon augmented and replaced by the lamb's own antibody system. Colostrum deprivation can result in reduced performance and higher mortality, under normal conditions of husbandry (Halliday, 1968).

There are several possible substitutes for the dam's colostrum; these include frozen natural colostrum, cow's colostrum, other oral substitutes or the injection of a combination of sera giving passive immunity against the major toxins, combined with vaccination to ensure prolonged active immunity. Most management systems normally allow an adequate opportunity for the lamb to obtain colostrum but in a positive policy of artificial rearing, with removal from the ewe a short time after birth, it is desirable to adopt a routine procedure of administering a supplement of colostrum or a suitable replacement. This is particularly desirable where competition between lambs after birth is likely to occur. Colostrum can be stored

H

by deep freezing and will remain effective for long periods. Ewe's colostrum is difficult to obtain and for routine use a cheaper replacement would be attractive. The gut of the new-born lamb is permeable to bovine colostral globulin (Morris, 1968) and it should provide some protection (Faruque & Walker, 1970). Because of the specific nature of the protection and of the variation in conditions that exist, it would be wise to test the suitability of using cow colostrum under a wide range of conditions before its widespread adoption.

There appears to be no published evidence of any other substitutes for ewe's colostrum that can be given by mouth to give the immunological protection of colostrum.

The use of injected sera and vaccines have not so far proved effective in practice because of the variety of Eschericia coli (*E. coli*) serotypes which may be associated with disease.

Even with adequate colostrum intake, artificially reared lambs seem to be more susceptible to a breakdown in resistance, leading to the incidence of scouring and other digestive trouble. This can be a function of "stress" in its widest sense including nutritional stress. The composition of the milk replacer can be a predisposing factor, as lambs given ewe's milk have performed better and shown no signs of scouring as compared to those on a milk replacer. The incidence of scouring, associated with *E. coli* organisms, cannot be adequately explained purely on the basis of random infection. The concentration of an infectious agent is one possible cause of health breakdown but there appear to be many other causes, nutritional and psychological, which can cause a breakdown, forming the focus for secondary infection of *E. coli* and other organisms. Effect on abomasal motility could easily upset the delicate balance of pH in the zone of rapid change from low pH in the abomasum to high pH in the small intestine (Mylrea, 1966; White et al., 1969).

Milk replacer formulation relates directly to this health problem because the clotting characteristics of milk seem to be an important factor in its utilization.

The casein of milk forms a clot with fat in a similar manner to the formation of cheese. Whey proteins, lactose and minerals can thus leave the stomach in advance of the clotted fraction which slowly abrades releasing fat and protein and their breakdown products, at an even rate. This property of clotting may be one of the factors that causes difficulty when substitutes for casein are used in milk replacers.

Energy Requirements

The sources of energy in ewe's milk are lactose, casein and butterfat. The nutrients, primarily providing energy, are fat and lactose. There is a known specific requirement for linoleic acid and some evidence that there may also be a specific need for carbohydrate. Butterfat provides the greater part of the energy of ewe's milk and it would be difficult, without reducing the casein content of milk, to maintain the optimum protein: energy ratio if the fat content were very low. Reduction in both the casein and fat content of a milk replacer based on these three main ingredients would push the lactose above the tolerance level which seems to be little more than 20 per cent of total energy from carbohydrate (Walker & Faichney, 1964). Most suitable milk replacers for artificially rearing lambs therefore contain a proportion of fat.

It has been calculated that lambs on liquid milk replacer require 100–125 kcal ME/0.73 kg per day for maintenance and that the energy cost of growth amounted to 11 kcal ME/g fat and 8.5 kcal ME/g protein; these requirements can vary with different feeds and different lambs (Walker & Norton, 1971).

Protein Requirements

Ewe's milk supplies about 50 g of crude protein for each Mcal energy and so far no economic substitute for casein has been devised, suitable for lambs immediately after birth, in particular for its outstanding physical property of forming a curd in the abomasum. From 3–4 weeks onwards, as the lamb's enzyme systems become more varied a variety of substitutes can be given in liquid form to provide the protein needs of an artificially reared lamb (Ørskov et al., 1970).

SOLID FOOD

Given the opportunity, a young lamb, within a few days of birth will nibble at, and consume various solid objects. It is not until the third week of life that lambs have been observed to settle down to serious consumption of measurable quantities of offered dry feed and to commence rumination (Owen et al., 1969). The precise age at which measurable solid food intake occurs may vary with genotype but quite large differences in milk intake do not seem to have a marked effect on the age of initiation of concentrate consumption. Therefore the relationship between start of measurable consumption and lamb weight is not particularly strong (Owen et al., 1969).

The transition from initiation of eating to substantial consumption of solid feed is, however, strongly influenced by milk intake. Restriction of milk intake (twins versus singles under natural suckling, restricted milk allowance versus ad libitum feeding under artificial rearing) causes an early acceleration in solid feed consumption (Owen et al., 1969).

In a lamb that is still suckling, or otherwise receiving milk, solid feed forms a low level supplement to high quality milk and the composition of solid feed consumed at that stage may be of little importance provided it is a palatable formulation which fosters early feeding by the lamb.

The inclusion of roughage in weaner concentrates for lambs can have a beneficial effect on performance in the transitional and immediate post-weaning period (Davies, 1972; Poe et al., 1969). Improved performance has also been reported in lambs given whole cereals as compared to milled cereals (Ørskov & Fraser, 1972).

When the lamb is weaned and completely dependent on its own resources as a ruminant, the immediate limiting factor to performance is usually the level of feed intake. Depending on the stage at which weaning occurred and the treatment in the period before weaning, a lamb weaned before two months of age undergoes a temporary check in live-weight gain when the energy intake is well below that of lambs maintained on full liquid feeding (Ørskov et al., 1973). The diet available for early weaned lambs must therefore not only supply essential nutrients in suitable proportions, but must also ensure the maximum voluntary intake.

In this respect, the level and quality of protein is important. A variable proportion of the lamb's diet at this stage, depending on its composition, escapes breakdown in the rumen and passed on to the abomasum for digestion. The contribution of bacterial protein is not sufficient at this stage to ensure maximum growth so that the supply of amino acids from the undegraded feed is important (Miller, 1968). Nevertheless, bacterial protein does make a significant contribution to protein metabolism from an early age; on diets containing a high level of sugar beet pulp, urea can influence the growth of rumen micro-organisms and thus indirectly lead to superior performance in the young lamb (Boxall, 1972).

In terms of protein requirement, the lamb varies from a complete dependence on dietary amino acids in the first week of life, to a stage where the protein requirement is low and, on suitable basal diets, can be adequately met without any supplementary dietary protein. The requirement of the lamb for protein in crude terms can vary from about 18 per cent crude protein in the diet of the lamb newly weaned at 4–6 weeks of age to a level of 12 per cent in lambs at about 40–50 kg (Miller, 1968).

When the basal ingredients consist largely of maize or finely ground cereals, the intake and performance of ruminants may be lower without roughage than when hay or straw is available or included in the diet (Lamming et al., 1966).

Requirements for Minerals, Vitamins and other Essential Nutrients

There are few reported studies of the detailed requirements

of the lamb for minerals and vitamins and little evidence to suggest that these requirements differ markedly from those for calves. One of the major differences is that lambs are prone to retain copper in the body and it is usually difficult to avoid levels of copper in excess of requirement in diets for the artificially reared lamb (Ross, 1965).

Table 6.3. *The main constituents of ewe's milk expressed on a dry matter basis. (Source: Table 2 and Ashton & Yousef, 1966)*

Gross energy kcal/g	6.00
Fat (per cent)	40.00
Crude protein	30.00
Lactose	24.00
Calcium (Ca)	1.10
Phosphorus (P)	0.80
Sodium (Na)	0.25
Magnesium (Mg)	0.08
Chlorine (Cl)	0.40
Parts/10^6	
Copper (Cu)	1.20
Iron (Fe)	4.20
Manganese (Mn)	3.80
µg/g	
Thiamine	3.80
Riboflavin	27.00
Nicotinic acid	27.00
Pantothenic acid	19.00
Vitamin B_{12}	0.02

Until more detailed information on the lamb is available, a useful empirical guide to the requirements of the lamb during the milk feeding stage is the vitamin and mineral content of ewe's milk. Table 6.2 and Table 6.3 summarize the gross composition of the ewe's milk.

Requirements for the main nutrients in the weaned lamb are given in Table 6.4 and are based on British recommendations (ARC, 1965) used in conjunction with data from several experiments carried out at Cambridge in the '60s.

Table 6.4. *Suggested composition of the diet of weaned lambs to cover main nutrient requirements*

per kg diet dry matter	Body Weight (kg)	
	20	40
Calcium (g)	6.60	5.50
Phosphorus (g)	2.90	2.60
Magnesium (g)	0.80	0.65
Sodium (g)	0.95	0.80
Chlorine (g)	0.95	1.40
Iron (mg)	30.00	30.00
Copper (mg)	5.00	5.00
Cobalt (mg)	0.10	0.10
Zinc (mg)	50.00	50.00
Manganese (mg)	40.00	40.00
Iodine (mg)	0.12	0.12
Vitamin A (μgB carotene)	1050.00	1300.00
Vitamin D (I.U.)	105.00	130.00
Vitamin E (I.U.)	20.00	20.00
Digestible crude protein (per cent)	12.60	8.80
Crude Protein (per cent)	16.9	11.7

Another difference between lambs and calves lies in the extra requirement of the lamb for the growth of the fleece. This is practically pure protein with a significant proportion of sulphur containing amino acids.

Formulating Diets to Meet the Lamb's Requirements

Knowledge of requirements needs to be translated into appropriate diets and feeding practices in the context of the cost and availability of alternative feeds and in relation to economic and labour-saving aspects of the feeding methods used.

For the artificial rearing of lambs, milk replacers in current use are formulated mainly on the basis of dried skim milk and whey with added sources of fat and a small quantity of additives. Milk fat globule size is very small (2·5 nm diameter in cow's milk) and similar atomization of the added fat fraction is aimed at in milk replacers so that a stable liquid emulsion is produced without damage to the nutrient value, particularly to the casein fraction.

The methods of drying skim milk and producing a homogenized milk replacer powder differ in the detail of commercial preparation of milk replacers. In most cases the skim milk (or a mixture with whey or buttermilk) is first evaporated under reduced pressure, the fat added and the mixture homogenized before spray drying. The nutritive value is little different from the original liquid milk since only the vitamin C and some of the vitamin B complex are reduced—by about 20–30 per cent. In addition to correcting any small deficiencies it is usual to add some antioxidant as well as a small amount of lecithin. The net result is a smooth fine powder which will readily mix with water and remain in suspension, once mixed. During the whole process care has to be taken to avoid denaturing the casein by overheating and inactivating any required nutrients (Owen, 1974).

The fat fraction of ewe's milk is about 98 per cent digestible and the metabolizable energy of the milk is utilized with an efficiency of over 75 per cent by the young lamb. With few exceptions, a wide range of animal and vegetable oils are well utilized in milk replacers with an efficiency approaching that of the natural source, provided proper homogenization is achieved. Because of its availability and price it is usually economic to use tallow mixed with a vegetable oil such as coconut oil. The usefulness of a fat source depends on the fatty acid composition, some of the less useful fats being the more saturated fats with a high content of stearic or erucic acid (Walker & Stokes, 1970).

In practice a level of about 20–30 per cent fat in the dry matter of milk replacers is better utilized by the lamb than much lower values. Milk replacers containing low levels of fat may be poorly utilized because of their high content of carbohydrate (Owen, 1974).

At present there appears to be no practicable substitute for the protein of cow milk products in milk replacers suitable for the lamb in the first 3–4 weeks of life, although small amounts of substitutes such as soya bean and yeast protein have been used. After 3–4 weeks cheaper ingredients, based on whey and fish protein for example, can be incorporated in liquid feed but there is also the alternative of making a complete transition to simpler self-feed systems using solid food.

Tolerance of starch is low in young lambs, as in other species, and the intestinal digestion of starch must be very limited.

Where ad libitum liquid milk replacer has been offered, consumption of solid food has remained at a low level. Where early weaning systems based on restricted milk feeding are adopted, which encourage early solid food intake, the lamb shows preferences for certain feed ingredients. Soya bean meal and barley are high and maize and fish meal low on the lamb's list of preferences.

The following list (taken from Davies et al., 1974) gives the various feedstuffs given to lambs from 1 week of age to 20 kg live weight ranked in order of preference (based on relative consumption 28–56 days):

1. Soya bean meal
2. A commercial weaner pellet
3. A commercial high energy weaner pellet
4. Rolled barley
5. Molassed sugar beet pulp
6. White fishmeal
7. Flaked maize
8. Whole oats

On the basis of the available evidence there is no clear case for paying special attention to palatability, provided the other requirements of diet formulation can be met.

Feeding roughage separately is common practice for lambs, as it is for calves, although it has been shown that the animal may not consume the optimum amount of roughage. The incorporation of roughage into a complete diet gives better control of consumption as well as controlling the physical wastage commonly found with long hay.

When a number of ingredients is offered, some degree of processing is usually involved. Apart from any mixing required it is common practice for grain and other ingredients to be rolled or coarsely milled. Roughage can be incorporated into a diet in a coarsely milled form. The rolling of grain can increase its digestibility for cattle and can lead to better utilization of the grain. For sheep and calves, however, whole barley appears to be at least as well utilized possibly because the smaller size of the omasal orifice helps delay the passage of whole grain to the rest of the digestive system.

Pelleting the diet has several practical advantages but its effects are similar to that of fine grinding and it can therefore exacerbate rumen malfunction where roughage is already deficient.

Table 6.5 shows the composition of diets that have given high performance when used in ram lamb performance tests.

Table 6.5. *Composition of diets suitable for high performance in weaned lambs*

Per cent	To 70 days of age	After 70 days of age
Barley straw (ground through 15 mm screen)	20	10
Rolled barley	57	67
Fish-meal	8	8
Extracted soya-bean meal	10	10
Molasses	3	3
Vitamin/mineral mix	2	2

Composition of vitamin/mineral mix used at 20 kg per ton of diet to meet minimum requirements

Limestone flour	12.9 kg
Salt	7.0 kg
Zinc oxide	0.07 kg
Vitamin A	4 million I.U.
Vitamin D	1 million I.U.

Application of data on the composition and prices of commonly available feedstuffs is needed to allow appropriate least cost alternatives to be formulated.

The Requirements of The Ewe

Having outlined the main nutritional requirements of the lamb from conception to slaughter age, at 4–6 months, it is appropriate to deal with the main nutritional requirements of the ewe starting at about the age of six months. There is as yet little direct evidence that the level of feeding up to this stage has a bearing on the young ewe's subsequent performance although it is quite possible that such an effect exists.

In dealing with the requirements of the ewe it is assumed for convenience that the ewe is given feed ad libitum, although the poor quality of the diet on offer may at times place a severe limitation on nutrient intake. Requirements are therefore dealt with in terms of the nutrient content and the intake of a total diet consumed by the ewe.

Feed requirements in the first year of life depend largely on the policy adopted—whether the ewe lamb is mated or not.

In a system where it is the aim to breed from ewe lambs a diet designed to meet the requirements of a productive lowland ewe will usually ensure a diet adequate for the ewe lamb including the need for growth, pregnancy and lactation, but there may be several management advantages in keeping these young ewes separate, to prevent the danger of parasitism and of unfair competition from the heavier older ewes.

Where ewe lambs are not to be bred in their first autumn then requirements are much lower and little is gained by high expenditure on concentrate feeds in their first winter. Good roughage or pasture with a minimum supplementation with concentrates is usually sufficient to maintain a low growth rate. In the case of hill sheep a very poor level of growth in the first winter, even though it has little apparent effect on size by the time the ewe is 18 months old, may lead to poorer reproductive performance, particularly in terms of barrenness (Davies,

1950; Gunn, 1968). Under very adverse conditions ewes may not be mated until they are $2\frac{1}{2}$ years old, because of the poor performance from ewes mated earlier. Judicious supplementation at strategic times during the first 18 months of life should overcome the need for such a long delay in commencing production.

FEED REQUIREMENTS BEFORE MATING

In order to achieve the aim that ewes should be in good body condition when mated (Chapter 5), sheep should have access to a good quality diet during the period 6–8 weeks before mating. In most production systems the lambs are weaned from the ewe about 2 months before remating; in frequent breeding systems the interval can be considerably shorter, occasionally as little as 4–6 weeks. At weaning the ewe's body reserves are normally depleted to some degree. With the cessation of lactation requirements are substantially reduced and ewes usually improve in condition on medium quality pasture or good quality conserved roughage (7.5 MJ ME per kg). The diet should allow steady recovery of body condition with a change to higher quality feed, in the form of rested pasture regrowth or its equivalent, in the last few weeks before mating, so that the condition of the ewe is maintained or slightly improved.

PREGNANCY REQUIREMENTS

Requirements of the pregnant ewe are little more than those of the dry ewe at the end of the second month of pregnancy. By lambing time however there is an additional requirement for the growth of a lamb or lambs, together with the requirement for udder growth and initiation of milk secretion. This marked increase in requirement over the last three months starts earlier and is more pronounced the greater the number of lambs carried. There is also the complicating factor that in the last days prior to lambing the pregnant ewe may suffer a depression in food intake which increases the negative energy balance at this time.

To minimize the loss of body reserves in the ewe the diet, in late pregnancy, would have to be of maximum energy content compatible with a sufficient roughage intake to maintain healthy rumen function and with the intake of an adequate supply of essential nutrients.

In practice it is seldom economic nor practicable to meet requirements in full at peak demand periods so that the ewe normally makes use of body reserves at these periods.

Protein requirements before mating and in the first three months of pregnancy are in the region of 12.0 g crude protein per MJ ME (MLC, 1972) and medium to good quality conserved herbage or its equivalent, normally containing about 7.5 MJ per kg of dry matter, usually contains the necessary 9 per cent crude protein in the dry matter to supply these needs. From the end of the third month of pregnancy until just before lambing, requirements increase rapidly and it is important to increase feeding levels although requirements cannot be fully met. Protein levels in the diet for productive ewes should increase from about 12.0 g per MJ of energy at the end of the third month to about 14.5 g just before lambing (MLC, 1972).

It is clear that in most cases meeting the sheep's protein requirements is a matter of providing the rumen micro-organisms with sufficient nitrogen. When this is achieved only in rare cases, such as the very young lamb or the heavily lactating ewe, is extra protein in the abomasum beneficial. The actual level of crude protein in the diet will therefore be a function of the metabolizable energy content of the diet which determines the requirements of the bacteria.

REQUIREMENTS DURING LACTATION

It is normally accepted that in early lactation the full

Table 6.6. *Possible diet composition for productive ewes (60 kg liveweight) in relatie*

State of production	Approximate voluntary intake (kg DM)	ME content of diet (MJ/kg DM)	Crude protein content (percentage of I
Dry or first three months of pregnancy	1.5	7.5	9.0
Last two months of pregnancy	1.8	9.0	13.0
Lactation	2.5	9.0	13.0

nutritional requirements of productive ewes cannot be met so that there is further depletion of body reserves. The requirements of a ewe in peak lactation are approximately three times those of a dry ewe but it is normally impracticable to increase the energy concentration of the diet sufficient to match this increased demand particularly since ewes in the first 3–4 weeks of lactation have not reached maximum voluntary feed intake (Table 6.6).

Several factors that influence the level of milk yield in the ewe have been noted earlier (Chapter 4) but only the effects of a few of these factors are sufficiently well quantified to have predictable effects on feed requirements. One such factor is the suckling load and it is traditional farming practice to make cognizance of this difference in requirement by differential feeding of ewes suckling twin lambs. Since the composition of the basal diet (generally pasture) is only imperfectly known, the difference in feeding is usually implemented by prolonging the period of supplementation and reserving better pastures for the twin suckling ewes.

The breed or cross of ewe is also of importance in relation to milk yield but there is insufficient evidence of any departure from an average relation of milk yield to body weight, to enable differential requirements for lactation to be assessed.

uirements at various stages of production

Requirement to maintain body weight		Actually supplied by suggested diets	
(MJ ME/day)	(gCP/day)	(MJ ME/day)	(gCP/day)
8.5	100	11.2	135
14.5	210	16.2	234
24.0	340	22.5	325

Meeting Requirements from Available Feeds

The feed requirements of the ewe and lamb as outlined above have to be met under two situations:

1. Under most current farming conditions it is a problem of supplementing grazed herbage, which varies in quantity and quality from an ideal diet to a roughage of very little value, except as a small proportion of the diet. In practice sheep seldom suffer from sheer lack of availability of feed unless very tightly stocked or under snowy conditions. The feed available under mountain range conditions may be of very low quality so that nutrients are severely limiting at certain times of the year. This situation is explored more fully in the succeeding chapter on grass and its utilization.

2. A housed sheep flock that has no access to naturally occurring basal herbage and no straw or other edible bedding has its total diet fully controlled. Under these conditions feeding may still be on traditional lines or it can involve feeding "complete diets" where a mixture of roughage and concentrates is given ad libitum as the whole diet of the ewes (Owen, 1971).

SUPPLEMENTING PASTURE

Temperate pasture, traditionally managed, provides for the ewe, particularly in the early part of the season, an ideal diet which meets nutrient requirements as well as possible. Excessive loss of body condition in early lactation is avoided, and during late lactation and particularly after weaning, a recovery period is possible to redress the depleted balance from earlier under-feeding.

Questions as to the adequacy of pasture for the ewe during the main growing season usually only arise:

(1) Where there is overstocking and therefore severe restriction on the ewe's intake.

(2) Where the timing of lambing is changed so that peak lactation occurs towards the end of the grazing season

(3) Under hill conditions where the quality of available herbage is deficient even during the grazing season.

As regards (2) the changing of the timing of lambing there are few reported observations of the performance of ewes and lambs where the ewes have lambed in the latter half of the grazing season. It is not known if the progress of the lamb is up to the expectation for those born earlier in the season. Poorer performance could be the result of direct effects of season on the lamb's growth or it could be the indirect effect of poorer feeding resulting in poorer milk yield of the ewe, as well as lowering the quality of the lamb's own food intake, both from the point of view of nutritive quality and that of parasite infestation. On the hill, herbage is usually plentiful during the summer season but, in spite of selective grazing, the digestibility of the ewe's diet is liable to limit lactation, as well as limiting the growth of the young lamb. There may also be the carry over effect from severe under nutrition in the previous winter which puts a heavy strain on the ewe's ability to recover.

Rectifying the deficiencies of hill swards, as feed during the summer period, cannot be accomplished economically by any method of supplementation so far developed, but there are several aspects of management that can ameliorate the depressant effect of flock performance of grazing the hill sward. These may involve the earlier weaning and movement to lowland pastures of some lambs and the reservation of improved or low-ground pastures for ewes suckling twins and for weaned lambs.

Whilst pasture, during the main grazing season, often provides the sole source of feed for the ewe and lamb, this is not usually so during the winter period—at least half the year in most temperate areas—where pasture growth is poor or non-existent. In many cases the autumn is a period where there is still reasonable availability of pasture often of low quality, that has escaped grazing during the season of active growth. As far as the ewe is concerned, the only real problem set at this end of the season is that of ensuring that prolific lowland ewes, already in reasonable condition following the weaning of the lambs some two months previously, can be maintained in reasonable condition for mating, to ensure high ovulation rates and successful conception. This is best achieved by reserving some pasture for mid-summer that will have fresh growth for the ewes for some 2–3 weeks prior to mating. Only in areas where drought limits the supply of herbage, or in cases where òut of season mating occurs, will supplementary feeding be justified.

With the advance of winter and as the reserve of surplus herbage is depleted supplementation may become justifiable. In view of the uncertainty about herbage supply and quality, the most economic way to use supplementary feed is to inject it into the production cycle at a time when the ewe has its highest requirements, coinciding with the stage at which there is the greatest penalty from under-feeding. This stage extends from 6–8 weeks before lambing for some 3–4 weeks after lambing, depending on when lambing occurs in relation to the growing season. In cases where there is a restriction in the supply of grass available before this stage, the supplement, or indeed the whole diet, may be in the form of good quality roughage—either hay or silage.

'Rule of thumb' guides are generally employed to ensure adequate levels of concentrate supplementation and a farmer learns by experience as to whether the level employed matches the potential level of productivity of the flock. To assess accurately the requirements for energy and nutrients and to meet these from predetermined amounts of feedingstuffs, whose nutritive value is accurately assessed, is a task beyond our current capability. As a guide to the extent of supplementation it is useful to realize that it can vary between the limits of no supplementation at one extreme to that of supplying a mixture of roughage and concentrate feed in the ratio 40:60, at the other. Since the voluntary intake of a ewe of about 60 kg varies between 1.0 and 2.5 kg of dry matter daily, the maximum supplement of cereal based concentrate will not exceed 1.0 kg even in early lactation. The range of supplement normally varies between 0.2 and 0.7 kg of concentrate feed and 0.2 and 1.0 kg of dry roughage if no pasture is available. Increasing concentrate supplementation beyond 60 per cent of the total diet has little beneficial effect on performance, since roughage intake is simply depressed; in the extreme a low roughage diet leads to rumen malfunction and digestive upsets.

If the basal diet is good roughage (hay, silage or either of these with grazing) a reasonable supplementation scale for high production ewes would increase from 0 at 8 weeks before lambing to a maximum of 0.6 kg (DM) of a barley based concentrate at lambing and up to 1.0 kg at peak lactation if grass is not available. This level of supplementation is likely to sustain the production of a highly productive ewe without excessive loss of body reserves. Where the level of prolificacy of the ewes is low or where ewes are suckling only a single lamb, these levels would need to be substantially reduced. Ewes normally have access to young grass early in the lactation period so that the maximum level of supplementation indicated is not reached and, as soon as grass is adequate in quantity, supplementation is suspended unless a carrier for magnesium or other minerals is required. The lamb depends largely on the ewe's milk supply in the early weeks of life and if grazing conditions are reasonable for ewe lactation there is little to be gained by allowing the lamb access to a concentrated feed in a separate creep area, inaccessible to the ewe. However, supplementation depends very much on the stocking intensity and marketing policy. If pasture is very short separate supplementation may aid lamb growth, decrease parasite problems and allow earlier marketing of the lamb. The prime need of a weaned lamb in mid-season is clean pasture regrowth or a fodder crop such as rape.

INDOOR FEEDING

Housing of sheep during the winter months has long been practised in northern latitudes as in Finland and Iceland. It is rarer in the UK in recent years although it is thought that the practice was known in the eighteenth and nineteenth centuries. There has been a recent tendency for the practice to spread as labour becomes scarcer and as the potential losses due to pasture poaching, become more evident.

Feeding the housed sheep is rather different to supplementing the grazing sheep, since all the diet has to be supplied. Housed sheep have often been given diets traditional for outside feeding and based on similar feedingstuffs to those used for cattle feeding. This approach involves a basis of conserved grass, usually of hay, more rarely silage, or of roots, supplemented in the usual way with concentrates, comprised mainly of rolled cereals—oats or barley. The remarks about supplementing ewes outside apply in much the same way for this type of feeding and it is normal practice to limit the roughage allowance primarily to avoid undue physical waste.

The Use of Complete Diets

Another approach to the feeding of the housed ewe is to allow the self-feeding of a complete diet. A complete diet can have the same constituents as those used for traditional feeding methods provided that they can be uniformly mixed together to prevent selection. Complete diets that have been used in practice are based on mixtures of coarse dried roughage (hay or straw) with cereals, various by-products and protein-rich feeds. These diets are attractive from the point of view of labour economy in feeding, minimizing trough space and generally reducing the disturbance caused by normal feeding. Their use also affords a means of eliminating the waste of long roughage by sheep.

Table 6.7. *Percentage composition of ewe diets*

	A	B	C	D
Oat straw	70	60	50	40
Rolled barley	11	18	15	20
Rolled oats	8	10	15	20
Sugar beet pulp	5	6	7.5	7.5
Protein supplement*	4	4	10	10
Molasses	2	2	2.5	2.5
	100	100	100	100
CP (as percentage of DM)	6.8	8.1	9.7	11.2

* Composition of protein supplement (per cent)

CP	40	Fibre	5.0	PE	35	P	2.2
Oil	4.5	SE	60	Ca	4.3	NaCl	4.5

Diets suitable for housed ewes capable of high production can be formulated from coarsely ground cereal straw and concentrates (Table 6.7). The diet containing 40 per cent of straw ground through a 12mm screen is suitable for ewes at fairly high levels of production; less productive sheep can be wintered on 50 per cent or more of ground straw.

Changeover Diets

When ewes are changed from pasture or traditional feeding to self-feeding on complete diets the process has to be accomplished gradually to avoid death from acidosis. The transition can be made using the four diets shown (Table 6.7). The ewes can be allowed free access immediately to the diet containing 70 per cent straw. After a week on 70 per cent they can then be changed to the next diet in the series, i.e., 70, 60, 50 and eventually 40 per cent with a period of one week on each diet before progressing to the next. The incorporation of processed straw into such a diet is relatively expensive and the use of the diets may be confined to the period before and after lambing when they are most advantageous.

SELF-HELP FEED BLOCKS FOR SUPPLEMENTARY FEEDING

There has been some development during the last decade of self help feed blocks for cattle and sheep. These blocks can

Fig. 6.4. *Ewes feeding at self-feed trough. (By courtesy of Mr J. F. Reaper, School of Agriculture, Aberdeen).*

be seen as a development from the well-known mineral licks and recent estimates suggest that from the time of their introduction to the UK in the early sixties several tens of thousands of tons were consumed in the UK in 1972 (Stern, 1973). Most of the blocks are based on cereals and urea but others are based on sugars and molasses and some on minerals and glucose. The blocks weigh from 10–25 kg and the most common are formulated to contain 22 per cent crude protein (mostly in the form of urea) in conjunction with readily available carbohydrate from cereals, 16 per cent of sodium chloride (common salt) and other minerals.

The cost of the blocks as a source of energy is much higher than that of the constituents but they are aimed to solve a major practical difficulty—that of supplementing sheep under extensive conditions at low labour cost. The aim has not been fully realized in practice due to the difficulty of making the blocks sufficiently weather-resistant and that of adjusting the nutrient release from them so that they are used as a low level supplement available to all of the sheep in the flock.

The use of self-feed blocks for supplementing hill sheep has been investigated in Wales (MAFF, 1972). Observations in these trials indicated that a high energy self help block could be suitable as supplementary feed before and during lambing where it is difficult to practice hand-feeding of concentrates. Hand-feeding is not customary during lambing as it leads to an increase in mis-mothering especially where ewes are lambing on areas of 20 ha or more of an undulating terrain. On the basis of these results further investigation is required to evaluate the cost/benefit of using blocks in a more intensive system of hill land use.

The great merit of block feeding is that it is a new concept of easy feeding with enormous practical advantages and farmers have not been slow to see this. Unfortunately, the commercial exploitation of the system has been clouded by other aspects of block feeding whereby some dubious though plausible claims on their nutritional role have been made. The chief need of hill ewes for winter feeding in the UK is a cheap source of energy with possibly some specific minerals. The value of urea is not proven for European conditions except as an adjunct to all-straw feeding and molasses is an expensive form of energy. Block feeding, because of its convenience, has nevertheless found a place in farming practice in spite of high expense per unit of nutrients. It remains to be seen whether block feeding, based on cheap and necessary ingredients will fulfil its potential major role in sheep husbandry.

Grass 7

The use of pasture has always been the key feature of sheep production, and, of the major farm animals, the sheep is traditionally the most dependent on grazing for its food supply. Efficiency in pasture utilization will continue to be an important consideration in developing and improving sheep systems.

In the present chapter, some of the main factors influencing sheep production from grass and the efficiency of pasture utilization, are examined.

Grass Production

Production from any area of pasture depends, in the first place, on the amount of dry matter produced. In this respect, the potential raw material for sheep production is very high; under favourable conditions, in a temperate environment, the maximum animal production of grass can exceed 12 tonnes dry matter per hectare (Spedding & Diekmahns, 1972).

Several factors influence the annual yield of grass from a pasture within the inherent limitations of soil, climate and other physical factors. The main ones, as they affect sheep production, can be summarized as follows:

Plant Species and Variety

The main component species of pastures are grasses and legumes (mainly clovers) and the term 'grass' is often used even when referring to a mixture of grass and clover. These species are adapted to a varying extent, to withstand the continual defoliation involved in the act of grazing.

The annual dry matter yield of pure stands of clover, as measured by cutting, is usually less than that of the most productive grasses. This is particularly true for the white clovers, most commonly growing in sheep pastures; unlike grass, clover shows little response to fertilizer nitrogen (Spedding & Diekmahns, 1962). Table 7.1 gives data on the relative yields of various grass and clover species (NIAB, 1974).

A major difficulty in interpreting such results for the grazing situation is that comparative yields are obtained by cutting and not by grazing. There appears to be some inter-action between herbage variety and frequency of cutting (Table 7.1), and variety and species differences may be reduced, the more frequent the cutting. It is possible that under grazing management differences in herbage genotype in annual dry matter yield, derived from cutting, may be of little practical importance.

Level of Fertilizer Application

A large body of data exists showing the effect of the application of different plant nutrients on pasture growth.

Under acid soil conditions, it is necessary to apply lime to bring the soil acidity within the optimum range of pH for the pasture species concerned. Legumes have a more restricted optimum range than grasses, and there is a wide variation between grass species in their tolerance of soil acidity.

Potassium and phosphorus are important plant nutrients, and responses to their application are obtained under a wide variety of conditions. In the past, phosphates have been the main fertilizers applied to pastures containing a high proportion of legumes.

Nitrogen is an important nutrient for the growth of pasture species, and the response, in terms of the yield of grass dry matter, to the application of fertilizer nitrogen, is more or less

Table 7.1. *Yield of dry matter per annum from some grasses and herbage legumes in the UK (Based on NIAB 1973a & b)*

| Species | Variety | kg DM/hectare | | Number of cuts | Annual yield |
		Number of cuts	Annual yield		
Grasses					
Lolium perenne (perennial ryegrass)	S24	4	14 600	9	10 600
	Barlenna	4	14 160	9	10 390
Lolium italicum (Italian ryegrass)	S23	4	14 160	9	10 390
	RvP	4	16 900	9	12 900
	S22	4	14 870	9	10 710
Phleum pratense (Timothy)	S352	4	12 100	9	9 100
	S48	4	10 410	9	9 280
Dactylis glomerata (Cocksfoot)	S37	4	12 200	9	10 100
	S26	4	12 320	9	10 30
Legumes					
Trifolium pratense (Red clover)	Hungaropoly	3	11 700		
Medicago sativa (lucerne)	Europe	3	14 000		

linear up to a level of over 300 kg per ha, as shown in Fig. 7.1. Clovers do not respond to added fertilizer N (Spedding & Diekmahns, 1972). Therefore, as the proportion of clover in a sward increases, the yield of mixed herbage at low nitrogen application is high, but the less is the response to the application of nitrogen. Legumes possess root nodules, containing rhizobial organisms, which fix nitrogen from the air for use by the plant.

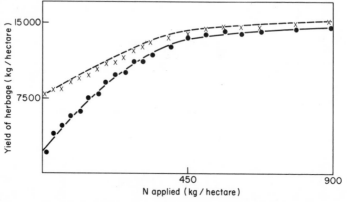

Fig. 7.1. *Yield of herbage dry matter (averaged over a 3 year period) from a pure grass sward and grass/clover sward as affected by rate of nitrogen fertilizer applied (based on Reid, 1970).*

An important feature of the grazing situation is the recycling of nutrients that occurs through the deposition of dung and urine. Whitehead (1970) has reviewed the effectiveness of this recycling and has pointed out some of the factors limiting the use of returned nitrogen. It is estimated that under normal circumstances 70–75 per cent of the nitrogen returned is voided in the urine, about 10 kg of N per sheep on an annual basis (Doak, 1952).

Although the nitrogen is in a form readily available to plants, the effectiveness of the return is diminished because of the uneven distribution of the urine and the losses that occur from various causes. The smaller proportion of N returned in the faeces of the sheep is less effectively utilized and contributes far less plant food than that returned in the urine. On grass/clover swards, intensively stocked with sheep, there appears to be little economic benefit from heavy applications of N fertilizer, apart from the use of early spring application to foster earlier growth.

Grazing and Cutting Frequency

Reference has already been made to the possible interaction of plant species with cutting frequency. Data shown in Table 7.1, illustrates the well-established finding that under a cutting regime the yield of grass dry matter falls as the frequency of cutting increases, although the effect is less on the yield of digestible dry matter (D × DM yield).

Once a pasture plant has been defoliated, its initial regrowth is at the expense of root reserves and a minimum period of recovery is needed to prevent depletion of these reserves, leading to a weakening and death of the plant (Voisin, 1959).

Continued grazing, or very frequent cutting, as in the management of a fine lawn, is not as harmful as it would appear from simple extrapolation of the relationship between cutting frequency and yield, derived at low cutting frequency. This is because of the radical change that occurs in the habit of growth of the herbage; the plants become dwarfed and prostrate and only a relatively small proportion of the green leaf is removed at a time. Fig. 7.2 shows how a very closely grazed sward retains an adequate green leaf cover under grazing or under a high frequency of defoliation. Little reliable information is available on the yield of grass from a continuously grazed sward, that can be easily compared with similar swards, subjected to grass cutting. However, comparisons of defoliation by sheep as compared with mower clipping at the same frequency have shown yields higher for grazed pasture than for cut swards (Cuykendall & Marten, 1968), except where moisture was limiting or at very high levels of N. This was mainly due to the return of nutrients in

Fig. 7.2. (a) *Hay stubble after a rotary mower with little leaf remaining*; (b) *A closely grazed sheep pasture with a high proportion of green leaf cover. (By courtesy of J. F. Reaper, School of Agriculture, Aberdeen).*

dung and urine, although the botanical composition of the sward deteriorated and weed infestation increased under the cutting regime as compared with the grazing.

A serious negative effect of grazing on pasture yield stems from the effects of treading. The extent of damage depends on climate and soil conditions (Edmond, 1966), and may justify changes in the system, e.g., winter housing, to minimize its effect.

Season

The seasonal nature of pasture growth presents an obstacle to the achievement of the high degree of utilization, which is discussed later. The extent of variation in Britain in aspects of grass quality is illustrated by the varietal comparisons given in Table 7.2 (Dent & Aldrich, 1968).

There is a marked difference between the grasses and the legumes in this respect—most varieties of grasses being considerably earlier in commencing growth in the spring.

Seasonality of growth varies according to geographical location and particularly according to latitude, altitude and rainfall pattern. The pattern of food availability in Australia, described earlier, is distinctly different in the predominantly winter rainfall to that in the summer rainfall areas.

At higher latitudes, the winter cold becomes more intense and, whatever the pattern of precipitation, growth virtually ceases for several winter months.

Pasture Utilization

In the foregoing section, the possibilities of grass production have been discussed and, as previously indicated, when the various factors are at their optimum, under good inherent conditions of climate and soil fertility, yields of 12 000 kg DM per ha are obtainable from grass. If completely harvested and used to meet the requirements of a ewe over the year this provides enough feed dry matter for about 14 productive ewes

Table 7.2. *Seasonal pattern of digestibility and composition in a grazing management system*

Cut no. Date	1 10 April	2 1 May	3 21 May	4 10 June	5 1 July	6 1 Aug.	7 1 Sept.	8 1 Oct.	9 1 Nov.
					Mean of two seasons (1964–65) at two centres				
Digestible dry matter (per cent)									
Perennial ryegrass	81.3	79.8	79.4	78.3	76.7	75.0	76.2	77.6	78.9
Cocksfoot	77.2	75.7	76.1	74.4	72.7	68.6	71.2	73.1	73.1
Crude protein (per cent)									
Perennial ryegrass	25.0	21.8	18.6	19.7	16.7	15.1	17.0	19.8	26.8
Cocksfoot	28.1	24.6	21.3	21.5	18.0	15.8	18.6	24.6	30.0
Crude fibre (per cent)									
Perennial ryegrass	16.9	20.2	22.6	23.7	22.1	24.6	22.4	21.0	18.2
Cocksfoot	16.7	21.1	23.2	24.3	24.9	28.7	27.0	23.2	18.2
Soluble carbohydrates (per cent)									
Perennial ryegrass	17.7	16.1	17.2	13.5	19.2	16.1	17.9	17.1	15.3
Cocksfoot	11.3	8.5	10.3	9.4	12.0	8.8	8.3	7.8	10.4

and their lambs for a year. In the UK only about 8 ewes are sustained per hectare of forage grown on recorded farms (MLC, 1974). It is the aim of this section to examine factors responsible for this shortfall between the theoretical target and actual achievement.

Utilization in the broader sense covers the whole process from the pasture plant to the animal product. Pasture utilization has, however, been used in a narrower sense as the proportion of the pasture available that is actually consumed by the animal. Pasture that is not consumed by the grazing animal, due to soiling, trampling or due to oversupply, simply remains on the sward surface either to be consumed at a later period of scarcity or to form the mat of decomposing, dead, material on the surface of the sward.

Pasture utilization varies enormously according to conditions. Under Scottish hill conditions where summer stocking rate is very low, due to shortage of winter keep, less than 30 per cent of the dry matter grown in a season is utilized (Eadie, 1968) whereas under intensive stocking conditions on lowland pasture one could expect a level of utilization of 90 per cent or more, although no reliable figures are available to quantify this surmise for set-stocked sheep.

The main reasons for the variation in the degree of utilization of herbage growth is the seasonal discrepancy between herbage availability and flock demand (Fig. 7.3).

Compared with other livestock systems the sheep flock's demand is well synchronized with grass growth; the autumn calving dairy herd is probably the least related to seasonal food supply. Sheep differ from cattle in that they can overwinter in the temperate zone with no regular need for supplementary feed.

The extent of seasonal imbalance in feed supply is influenced by the date of mating or tupping and by the choice of slaughter weight for the lamb. The aim to sell lambs at a high price level, usually militates against the aim of synchronizing flock needs with feed supply. Fig. 7.3, shows how advancing the date

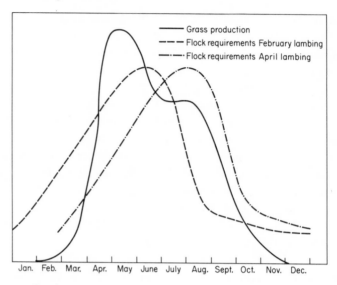

Fig. 7.3. *Requirements of flocks lambing at different times of the year in relation to seasonal grass supply.*

of lambing from an optimum in early April to late February, gives a different feed consumption pattern, which corresponds less well with the feed availability pattern. This effect is exacerbated when it is considered that the quality, as well as the quantity of herbage, changes seasonally and that lactation and early growth should coincide as far as possible with the spring period of high grass quality. Full utilization of growing grass can, however, do much to reduce fluctuation in grass quality during the grazing season. The choice of optimum slaughter weight of the lamb has been considered earlier and, in addition to the other factors, it is necessary to take account of the seasonal change in price level. Slaughter at lighter weights can usually be justified only in a situation of tumbling prices in early summer. A lamb of about 36 kg liveweight, growing at 2 kg/week at very low marginal cost, can sustain a fall of up to £0.02 per kg per week before exceeding optimum slaugher weight.

THE EFFECTS OF UNDER-UTILIZATION

To a limited extent a degree of under-utilization at one period can help to even out the feed supply. Inevitably, in such 'in situ' storage, there is deterioration of the forage, partly by the physiological processes of maturity in the plant, and partly by the weathering and decay of dead material. In some circumstances, surplus herbage from moderate under-utilization, contributes to the active organic layer at the soil surface and forms part of a generally beneficial recycling process.

Where under-utilization is more severe and where climatic conditions and the nature of the soil inhibit vegetation breakdown, a surface mat of lignified material is formed which restricts water movement and the establishment of new growth. The conditions described lead to a cycle of deterioration and to a consequent change in the flora to species favoured by acid peat conditions.

SELECTIVE GRAZING

Another consequence of under-utilization, which has far reaching effects on both sheep and pasture, is that it provides an opportunity for selective grazing. On a sward containing the common cultivated varieties of grasses and legumes, sheep show little selective grazing when the rate of stocking is high. Certain weed species such as *Urtica dioica* (common perennial nettle), the various *Cirsium* (thistle) species, particularly *Cirsium arvense* (Creeping thistle), and the flowering stem of *Cynosurus cristatus* (crested dogstail) usually escape grazing to some extent under most circumstances.

Within the cultivated species and varieties there are differences in palatability for the grazing animal (Ivins, 1955; Garner, 1963) which may become apparent in mixed swards as the intensity of stocking is relaxed. Some varieties of *Dactylis glomerata* (cocksfoot) for example, are amongst the first components to be rejected by sheep when grazing pressure is lax, whilst clovers appear to be favoured. Stage of growth has an important effect on palatability. Under conditions of close

I

grazing, sheep are less influenced by fouling than cattle and will graze a pasture evenly.

Another consequence of underutilization, brought about by the opportunity for selective grazing, is a change in the botanical composition of the sward towards the coarser, less palatable and more vigorous species. This effect was well demonstrated in the classic experiments of Jones (1933a & b). He showed that under lowland conditions, by varying the degree and timing of grazing, the composition of an initially uniform sward could be modified towards clover dominance, *Lolium perenne* (ryegrass) dominance, *Dactylis glomerata* (cocksfoot) dominance within the space of one or two seasons.

The effect of grazing pressure is also marked under poorer range conditions. The effect of grazing pressure depends not only on the rate of stocking and the frequency of grazing, but on soil type and climatic conditions. Overgrazing of ranges in semi-arid areas can lead to complete denudation of vegetation cover, resulting in desert. This is a serious problem in regions such as the Middle East. Ancient practices such as the 'Hema' system, of the Muslim people were designed to prevent the serious consequences of uncontrolled grazing (Draz, 1974). Increased grazing pressure can cause radical changes in the botanical composition of hill pasture, notably the replacement of *Calluna* (heather), *Molinia* and *Nardus* by other species (Jones, 1967). On *Calluna* dominated peat soil the result of heavy grazing leads to the disappearance of heather leaving little herbage of any value in its place. Although selective grazing usually has a deleterious effect on botanical composition of the sward, it is a useful mechanism for the sheep because it enables it to obtain a diet superior to the average herbage on offer, and helps to buffer the sheep against fluctuation in the nutritional value of the herbage.

Efficiency of Conversion of Grass into Sheep Products

The third and final step in the process of converting grass into sheep products relates to the use made of the consumed grass. Efficiency of feed conversion for any genotype within any pasture situation, depends primarily on the achievement and maintenance of a high level of herbage intake and on the nutrient content of the herbage consumed.

GRAZING INTAKE

Reference has been made to the factors influencing the voluntary intake of food by sheep under controlled conditions. Relatively little work has been done on the intake of grazed pasture, in spite of its importance as sheep feed, because of the formidable difficulty involved in estimating grazing intake. Several methods have been attempted with varying degree of success.

Sheep Weighing

A simple but limited method, is to weigh a sheep before and after a period of grazing, to estimate the intake of grass by difference. This method has some application when applied for a short period, if precautions are taken to avoid loss of faeces and urine. Allden (1962) has used the method to study factors affecting the rate of intake in sheep, described later.

Cutting Methods

This involves cutting the grass to a standard length before and after grazing, and assuming that the difference is the herbage consumed by the sheep. This method could be applied to conditions where grass is rotationally grazed and subjected to rapid defoliation. Ideal conditions for its use are not often found for sheep although it has had some application in cattle studies.

Estimation from Faecal Output

Most studies of pasture intake in sheep have relied on estimations based on the output of faeces.

Faecal output can be determined directly by harnessing the sheep and collecting the faeces in a bag. The method is more difficult to apply to ewes than to male sheep because of the necessity to separate faeces and urine (Owen & Ingleton, 1961). When sheep are consuming a considerable amount of grass, the collection bags have to be emptied frequently, thus increasing the labour requirement and causing disturbance of grazing activity.

Indirect methods of estimating faecal output have been developed, where the concentration of an 'indicator' substance is determined in a sample of the faeces. For this purpose, chromic oxide (Cr_2O_3), which is virtually indigestible by the sheep, has been commonly used. Small quantities (1–2 g daily) are administered by mouth to the sheep, once or twice per day, and the daily output of faeces estimated from the concentration (i.e., the degree of dilution) of the chromic oxide in the faeces produced.

Sources of error in the estimation include the incomplete recovery of chromic oxide. This may be due to the sheep being able to get rid of some of the chromic oxide, or even the whole capsule, after an apparently successful administration.

Another problem is that the concentration of chromic oxide in faeces shows a diurnal pattern according to the frequency and timing of dosing and according to the pattern of grazing and other activity by the sheep (Corbett, 1960). This variability can be reduced by adopting a standardized and well calibrated procedure for sampling the faeces over the twenty-four hours. It can also be reduced by administering chromic oxide impregnated on paper (Corbett, 1960). In many investigations, e.g., in comparisons of breeds and crosses, it is desirable to allow groups of ewes, containing replicates of all the types to be compared, to graze together. For this purpose, individual identification of faeces is necessary. Up to 6–8 different classes of faeces can be separately identified by including, in addition to the chromic oxide, a quantity of coloured polystyrene particles as described by Owen and Ridgman (1967). Faeces voided on the pasture can then be identified by colour.

For many studies concerned with differences between sheep,

the estimation of faecal output by itself can provide some useful information. Individual sheep within a group kept together on well grazed pasture can usually be assumed to be consuming herbage of similar digestibility. Although this assumption is not strictly true, small variations in the quality of herbage ingested are unlikely to be associated with many factors under study. On this basis, faecal output is a direct reflection of herbage intake, provided that allowance is made for the fall in digestibility associated with the level of intake itself.

For many studies of grazing intake, particularly those concerned with factors other than characteristics of the sheep itself which influence intake, it is necessary to ascertain the digestibility of the ingested herbage in order to estimate the intake of herbage dry matter. Such studies include the assessment of intake differences between herbage species and varieties, between fertilizer treatments and of differences over the course of a season.

Several methods have been used to estimate the digestibility of ingested herbage dry matter. These include:

The estimation of digestibility of a sample of herbage cut or plucked from the pasture. This method suffers from the difficulty of obtaining a representative sample of the herbage consumed by the sheep, and it usually necessitates the estimation of digestibility 'in vitro', using laboratory methods suitable for small samples.

The use of a sample of herbage derived from the sheep itself. The development of the oesophageal fistula technique where a sample of feed ingested is obtained directly into a polythene bag attached at the neck (Cook et al., 1963), has provided a direct approach to this problem. The mastication of the grass, however, and the admixture with saliva, presents problems in the analysis of the samples, and there are reservations about the 'normality' of the behaviour of sheep subjected to this procedure.

The use of internal faecal markers. The concentration in the faeces of several constituents have been found to be related to the dry matter digestibility, although the precise mode of action for the association may differ from constituent to constituent. The most widely used of these faecal markers has been the nitrogen content of the faeces (Streeter, 1969). The method can only be used with any precision when the regression of faecal nitrogen content on digestibility or on intake can

Fig. 7.4. *Sheep fitted with equipment that enables automatic sampling from the rumen. This is used by CSIRO scientists in Armidale, Australia to carry out metabolism studies in grazing sheep (By courtesy of the Australian News & Information Bureau).*

be determined from a range of material cut from saved pastures spanning the same range of botanical composition under the same conditions.

Finally, estimates of the grazing intake of sheep have been derived indirectly from the results of energy transactions carried out, using portable equipment suitable for metabolism studies on the grazing sheep (Corbett & Farrell, 1970).

Some studies of the grazing intake of sheep have indicated

that maintenance energy requirements at grazing are in-explicably higher than for pen-fed sheep (Coop & Hill, 1962). It is possible that some of the estimates of grazing intake are inflated, due to errors involved in measurement, although, where pasture is scarce, it is to be expected that extra main-tenance energy is expended in walking and food gathering.

Table 7.3. *The pattern of dry-matter intake changes (kg) during pregnancy and lactation in grazing ewes.*

| Approximate average days before lambing | Dry-matter intake changes (kg) | | | |
| | Supplemented ewes | | Unsupplemented ewes | |
	with twins (no. in average 4)	with singles (no. in average 6)	with twins (no. in average 4)	with singles (no. in average 6)
63	1.0	1.0	1.1	1.1
49	1.0	1.1	1.2	1.1
35	1.3	1.3	1.1	1.0
21	1.5	1.3	1.0	0.9
7	1.3	1.3	1.1	1.1
Approximate average days after lambing				
10	1.5	1.6	1.5	1.2
30	1.7	1.6	1.4	1.2
45	1.9	1.6	1.3	1.3

The work of Corbett and Farrell (1970) referred to earlier, confirms that the energy requirements of grazing sheep are within the range of normal expectation from controlled studies. In their studies there was good agreement on this finding from calorimetric studies and from estimates based on the concen-tration of volatile fatty acids in the rumen.

A detailed study of the grazing intake of Clun Forest ewes (Owen & Ingleton, 1963) during pregnancy and lactation, in winter and early spring, showed the levels of estimated dry matter intake given in Table 7.3.

These data do not indicate that grazing ewes consume much more food than similar sheep on indoor feeding.

The study confirmed a similar pattern of intake during pregnancy and lactation to that established for ewes under controlled conditions indoors.

An interesting finding was the repeatability of grazing intake in the various periods of study, in spite of the differences in availability of grass. Ewes with a high intake when grass was relatively plentiful tended to have above average intakes when grass was scarcer. The grazing intake of ewes also varies with the liveweight of the ewe and with the level of milk production; in particular, ewes suckling twins consume more than those suckling singles.

Australian studies (Arnold & Dudzinski, 1967) have also illustrated the substantial increase in intake associated with lactation in the ewe. They found that Border Leicester × Merino ewes had a higher peak intake than Corriedale ewes, although the body weight of the two types were similar.

Factors, other than lactation, shown to increase grazing intake, are previous under-nutrition and the process of shearing. With regard to shearing, Wheeler et al., (1963) have suggested that the substantial increase in grazing intake, 40–60 per cent, in their experiments, that occurs shortly after shearing, is a response to cold-stress and is minimized if environmental temperature is high.

There are few adequate contemporary comparisons of ewes of various breeds and crosses, in relation to production traits and feed intake, and it is possible that many differences that do exist are a reflection of differences in body size.

Selective Grazing in Relation to the Quality of Herbage Intake

Reference has already been made to the phenomenon of selective grazing. The results of selection are beneficial to the sheep, particularly when it is grazing on poorer quality pasture. The use of the oesophageal fistula has greatly aided the study of the effects of selection. Previously, such studies were largely qualitative in nature and relied on visual observation, examination of the rumen contents of slaughtered sheep, or on the examination of the plant cuticles identifiable in the faeces (Martin, 1964).

Fig. 7.5. *Sheep fitted with oesophagul fistula for grazing intake studies in South Africa. (By courtesy of the Republic of South Africa Embassy, London).*

Table 7.4 shows the results obtained using animals fitted with oesophageal fistulae.

The results confirm that both sheep and cattle can select a diet which is more nutritious than the average of the herbage available, and that sheep appear to be capable of more discriminating selection than cattle.

In order to find the mechanism for selective grazing, Arnold (1966), in some Australian studies, used sheep, deprived of various senses in turn, by surgical interference or other means. He concluded that sight was relatively unimportant in this respect. The senses of smell, taste and touch all played their

Table 7.4. *Average composition of herbage selected by cattle and sheep, as estimated from oesophageal fistulae, for stock grazing in common on summer range in Utah (USA) (Based on Cook et al., 1967)*

Species	Plant components as percentage of herbage consumed			Total protein (per cent)	Ash (per cent)	Lignin (per cent)	Cellulose (per cent)
	Grass	Forbs	Browse				
Cattle	61.3	23.5	15.2	10.3	11.2	8.2	32.1
Sheep	56.6	38.5	4.9	13.2	11.7	9.8	22.9

part to a certain degree although, over a long term, he found it difficult to discern any major difference in sheep that had been deprived of any one of these senses. Selectivity is obviously a luxury indulged in when there is plenty to choose from and under restricted grazing conditions a great deal of the selectivity disappears. Another feature of pasture selectivity, common to food preference generally, is that preferences established when there is a choice of various alternative foods, are not necessarily reflected in the voluntary feed intake, when given no choice of the separate ingredients.

Grazing Patterns in the Sheep

Several aspects of grazing behaviour, other than the quantity and quality of herbage consumed, are important in dealing with the utilization of pasture. The three main aspects to be considered in this section include (a) Individual and flock movements on pasture, (b) Duration and pattern of daily grazing and (c) The rate of grass consumption during grazing.

Movements on Pasture

There are numerous recorded observations of differing patterns of grazing behaviour in the sheep (Hunter, 1960). Some breeds of sheep, for example, many of the Mediterranean breeds, exhibit a close herding behaviour. Other breeds, notably the mountain and hill breeds, tend to show wide dispersion over a given area of pasture, although there may still be a tendency to remain in small family subgroups. To what extent such behaviour is hereditary, or simply learned, is not clear, although there is likely to be some element of learned behaviour involved.

Reference has already been made to the territorial behaviour of sheep, whereby individuals and related groups stick closely to a prescribed territory within a large unfenced expanse of

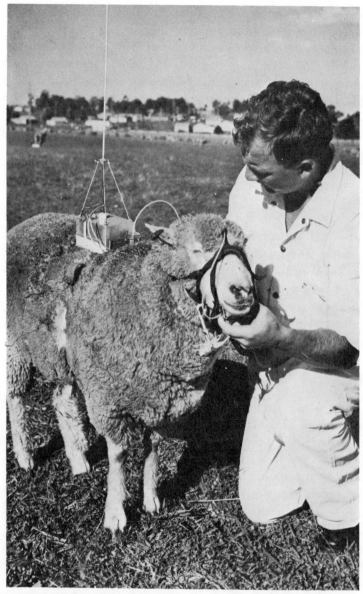

Fig. 7.6. *Sheep fitted with a portable radio transmitter for grazing behaviour studies in Australia. (By courtesy of the Australian News & Information Bureau).*

mountain. There are also the diurnal movements within a territory; congregation into night camps (Jones, 1967; Hilder, 1966) and dispersal during the day over the grazing areas. Hunter (1962) has made interesting observations of grazing behaviour in hill sheep as related to the grazing of distinct plant communities, within a prescribed area of a hill. Hunter's work, and that of those reviewed by Jones (1967), confirm that hill sheep form small family groups which live in a restricted local area of a mountain. The establishment of a territorial group does not appear to be disrupted by the practice of sending ewe lambs away to other farms during their first winter (Hunter & Davies, 1963). Because of the differing food potential of mountain grazings it is natural that sheep density varies in different parts of an undivided area, particularly according to the distinct classes of herbage communities found in such areas.

The territorial behaviour of hill and mountain sheep has repurcussions on the appropriate management for hill flocks. It is obvious that changes of stock cannot be made at will if, for instance, the farm is sold. The placement of fences will also require some care, since it may interfere with stock movements during stormy weather. The territorial behaviour may also limit the possibility for genetic improvement by orthodox selection since the sheep are essentially subject to their own distinct environment. In general, however, there tends to be an interaction between population density and herbage productivity, such that differences in sheep performance are reduced (Hughes et al., 1964).

Duration and rate of Grass Consumption

A sheep can increase its grazing intake either by spending more time in grazing activity or by increasing the rate of intake during a period of grazing activity. Arnold and Dudzinski (1966) carried out experiments to discover how sheep with a large appetite drive, such as lactating ewes or sheep that had suffered a period of feed restriction, were able to eat more grass when grazing in the company of sheep with a low appetite drive. Table 7.5 summarizes the findings of one such experiment where short term estimates of the pasture intake of sheep were examined.

Table 7.5. *Relative differences in responses of sheep with high appetite drive on scant pasture (Arnold & Dudzinski, 1966)*

	Organic matter intake	Grazing time	Intake per hour
Fat sheep (135 kg)	100	100	100
Thin sheep (84 kg)	131	99	132
Dry ewes	100	100	100
Lactating ewes (third week of lactation)	151	114	132

Although the methods used for measuring the three parameters were limited, the results indicate that both rate of consumption and duration of grazing can contribute to higher pasture intake. They also confirm that animals with high voluntary intake under conditions of high pasture availability (high appetite drive), are able to express some of this characteristic under conditions of scanty pasture supply.

Allden (1962) used a device called the vibra-recorder for measuring the time spent grazing by wether sheep and used it to determine the rate of pasture intake and length of grazing time, in sheep given access to plots with varying amounts of herbage on offer. Intake was measured by weighing the sheep, fitted with faeces and urine collectors, just before and an hour after they were released on to the plot. The results are summaraized in Fig. 7.7 a diagram based on Allden's data.

Within the limitations of the techniques employed, it can be concluded that when plenty of pasture is available (a minimum of 300 kg/dry matter per ha on offer) dry sheep graze for about 7 hours per day, and consume grass at the rate of 7–800 g green material per hour. As grass becomes scarcer, grazing time increases in an attempt to compensate for a lower rate of intake.

Arnold (1963) has obtained similar findings and has further shown that mean grazing time by groups of wethers does not exceed $10\frac{1}{2}$ hours per day, however short the feed supply;

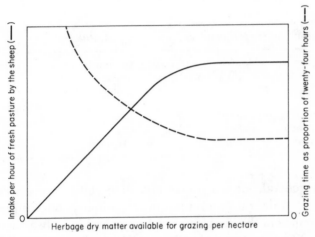

Fig. 7.7. *The relation of herbage on offer to rate of intake and time spent grazing (based on Allden, 1962).*

ewes however, particularly if they are lactating, can graze for longer than wethers, up to about $11\frac{1}{2}$ hours per day. As is the case with pasture intake, Arnold has shown that individual differences in lengths of grazing time persist over long periods and under varying pasture conditions.

NUTRIENT CONTENT OF PASTURE INTAKE

The performance of the grazing sheep depends not only on the intake of dry matter but on the nutrient content of the herbage.

Digestible Energy Content

The digestibility of the herbage is usually an important criterion of its value, although at the higher levels (65 per cent digestible organic matter (D) or greater) commonly found with closely grazed pastures, digestibility per se may be of lesser importance, if the pasture is high yielding and is conducive to high animal intake.

Table 7.6. *Dry matter intake and animal performance from dried grass of comparable digestibility cut from pure swards and given to sheep.* (*WPBS, 1967*)

Species	Variety	percentage in vitro digestibility	percentage crude protein	Intake kg DM/day	Gain g/day
Perennial ryegrass	S24	62.0	9.8	0.95	113
Cocksfoot	S37	63.0	11.3	1.00	113
Timothy	S51	61.0	10.6	0.68	32

In general, animal intake and digestibility are associated over a wide range of pasture digestibility but important differences in the intake of pasture material have been demonstrated at similar levels of digestibility (Table 7.6; WPBS, 1967). In particular, the intake of legumes appears to be 20–40 per cent higher than grasses of the same digestibility (Spedding & Diekmahns, 1971).

Table 7.7 shows the values for D (estimated by 'in vitro' methods) obtained for several varieties of grass and clover species (NIAB, private communication). It appears that where 9 cuts per season are taken, most varieties of grass have a D value of 68–70 with the exception of the cocksfoot varieties, with a mean of 64. Values for the clover species are not directly comparable with the grasses although, with the exception of white clover, digestibility is lower in the clovers.

Digestibility of herbage is chiefly affected by its maturity and under close grazing the digestibility is higher and less variable throughout the season. This is chiefly a reflection of leafiness,

Table 7.7. *Mean digestibility (D) values for several species and varieties of herbage. (Digestible organic matter as percentage of dry matter).*

Species	Variety	9 cuts/annum (mean value)	4 cuts/annum Cut 1	Cut 2
Perennial ryegrass	S24	69	63	66
	Reveille	70	64	67
	Barlenna	69	64	66
	S23	69	64	66
Italian ryegrass	Prima Roskilde	69	64	63
	RvP	69	65	60
	S22	69	64	62
Timothy	S352	68	64	66
	Scots	68	64	65
	S48	68	64	65
Cocksfoot	S37	64	64	60
	Roskilde late	64	64	62
	S26	64	63	60
Meadow fescue	S215	68	63	66
	Rossa	68	63	67
	Bundy	68	62	67
		3 cuts/annum (mean)		
Red clover	Hungaropoly	61		
	Essex BR	61		
	S123	61		
Lucerne	Europe	59		
	Vertus	59		
White clover	Kent	70		
	S100	70		
	Kersey	70		
Heather*	10 year old	46 ⎫ 1 cut from		
Calluna vulgaria	4 year old	50 ⎭ existing stand		

* Based on data of Thomas and Smith (1954).

since the stem of mature plants is usually much less digestible than the leaf in both grasses and legumes (Terry & Tilley, 1964).

Apart from the effect of management on the proportion of pasture plants allowed to mature, and the choice of plant varieties, few factors seem to influence pasture digestibility.

Dent and Aldrich (1968) have shown that the application of nitrogen fertilizer appears not to affect D significantly, although there is a tendency for crude protein content to increase and for soluble carbohydrate content to decrease. Experiments such as those of L'Estrange et al. (1967) have been designed to study possible effects of heavy nitrogen fertilizer application on sheep performance, but there is no conclusive evidence that such effects exist other than those mediated through increased pasture output. Clover rich swards, because they are conducive to high feed intake and thus improved performance, are usually preferred for sheep production and in such circumstances heavy nitrogen applications, appropriate in other circumstances, are not desirable.

Under hill conditions, because of the degree of pasture under-utilization and of the herbage species present, the digestibility of available herbage is usually much lower than under lowland conditions. For short periods of the year, most hill pasture species have a high level of digestibility (Black, 1968) but the pasture consumed by sheep quickly declines with advancing season to a D level of about 50 (Eadie, 1968). Much of the available material from *Calluna* species (heather) is of low digestibility in well established heather stands, but for short periods in the spring new growth has been shown to have a moderate level of digestibility (Table 7.7).

Protein content

Grass, from a number of species, cut monthly, has been shown to have a mean crude protein in the dry matter of about 20 per cent (Spedding & Diekmahns, 1971). It can, therefore, be concluded that where grass is closely grazed, protein is not usually limiting for sheep whatever their level of production. Poor quality, mature herbage is usually indigestible, in addition to being deficient in protein, and it is only rarely that the addition of protein or non protein nitrogen, without some other nutrient or additional source of energy, can give economic returns. The protein supplementation of more mature forage has already been discussed in Chapter 6.

ENERGY DEFICENCY

Pregnancy toxemia

One consequence of reduced energy intake in the ewe is pregnancy toxemia although it is not necessarily a consequence of low digestible energy content of herbage.

Pregnancy toxaemia is a common and severe condition in ewes called 'twin lamb disease', snow fever and other localized descriptions. It is a metabolic disorder of some complexity and was reviewed in some detail by Reid (1968). Although the disorder can occur in different forms they all basically stem from a breakdown in the carbohydrate metabolism as a result of severe imbalance between the demands of the unborn lamb or lambs and the energy intake of the ewe.

Symptoms: The main symptoms of the disease arise from the damage to the central nervous function, manifested in a progressive depression of consciousness. At first, it may be only a tendency to stand apart from the flock but as the condition progresses the ewe becomes less aware of her surroundings, wandering aimlessly, often blundering into obstacles and unaware of the presence of other animals or man. Eventually, the ewe stops moving and may stand transfixed before finally going down and losing the ability to stand.

Within this general pattern of disturbed movement may be disturbances of posture, balance, and muscular movements resulting in twitching movements, grinding of teeth and other manifestations.

Cause: Where ewes carrying twin lambs are exposed to a constant level of underfeeding in a stable environment the ewe can maintain normal functions in spite of progressive undernourishment as pregnancy proceeds. Hypoglycemia (low blood glucose) and hyperketonemia (high blood ketones) may be severe but the normal homeostatic mechanism for mobilizing body reserves, to provide energy for survival of ewe and lambs, is still functioning. The mechanism involves an endocrine response with an increase in adrenal cortex activity leading to increased blood cortisol levels accompanied by glucose conservation in the body and increased production of glucose from increased mobilization and catabolism of body tissues. This results in a loss of condition in the ewe and a restriction of growth of the fetuses.

It is when extra and sudden demands are added that the mechanism fails and pregnancy toxaemia ensues. This can be a sudden rapid fall in the food supply as in snow conditions or even the direct physical stress resulting from bad weather or sudden movement to a new environment. Sometimes the progressive undernourishment just goes too far or the number and genotype of lambs is such that sufficient reduction in their demands is impossible. It may be that at a certain stage of under-nourishment and stress that the ewe's appetite mechanism fails, thus precipitating the breakdown even though some feed may be available. The occurrence of pregnancy toxaemia in fat ewes may well be a reflection of an initial breakdown in appetite, accentuating any sudden change that may have triggered off this appetite failure.

Treatment: Ewes in advanced stages of pregnancy toxaemia will not usually respond to treatment. Depending on the stage of toxaemia the ewe that lambs normally or aborts may recover spontaneously and death of the fetuses may also have the same result. The main treatment of value, when applied at an early stage of the condition, appears to be the administration of glycerol to provide a readily available source of glucose to the ewe's tissues. It has also been suggested that fat ewes with an appetite breakdown might respond to cortisone administration.

Prevention: Pregnancy toxaemia does not occur in ewes which maintain an adequate food intake, although as noted earlier, it can, and often does, happen in the case of ewes that are in good condition, even in the presence of an apparently satisfactory food supply. Prevention is mainly a matter of maintaining a good feed level and attempting as far as possible to reduce the sudden changes of diet or of conditions that are often associated with outbreaks. The provision of shelter from severe climatic conditions is also a useful measure.

OTHER NUTRIENT DEFICIENCIES

Because of the activity of the rumen micro-organisms, the grazing sheep should seldom lack vitamins, since normally limiting amino acids are synthesised in the rumen and passed on to the host along with the food. Grass and legumes are rich sources of carotene, the precursor of vitamin A, and the requirement for vitamin D is much bound up with the availa-ability of calcium and phosphorus as shown later. Vitamin E and selenium are also interrelated and discussed later. Vitamin B_{12} is synthesised in the rumen.

Cerebrocortical necrosis

Cerebrocortical necrosis is a source of wastage in sheep that is associated with vitamin B_1 deficiency. The aetiology of this disease has been described by Markson and Terlecki (1968) and it has been increasingly reported in Britain from about 1960. The lesions of the brain result in characteristic nervous symptoms, loss of appetite, and eventually, in death. Prompt administration of thiamine (vitamin B_1) appears to effect a cure, and it is postulated that some agent causing inactivation of thiamine in the rumen is responsible.

MINERAL DEFICIENCIES ON PASTURE

The usual range of nutrient minerals in pasture has been reviewed by Whitehead (1966) and summarized in Table 7.8, and compared with the nutrient requirements for sheep as set out in ARC (1965) and Underwood (1966).

Variation in pasture mineral content can have several causes. Species and variety of herbage are an important cause of variation; in particular, clovers have a higher content of calcium and magnesium than do the grasses. Herb species, like *Cichorium intybus* (chicory) and *Plantago lanceolata* (plantain), have higher

Table 7.8. *Mineral content of mixed pastures in relation to sheep requirements*

Element	Range reported in herbage plants (per cent)	Range in most mixed pasture (per cent)	Sheep requirements growing lamb	lactating ewe (per cent)
Calcium	0.04–6.0	0.4–1.0	0.6	0.61
Phosphorus	0.03–0.68	0.2–0.5	0.28	0.43
Magnesium	0.03–0.75	0.08–0.3	0.07	0.10
Sodium	0.002–2.12	0.05–1.0	0.11	0.08
Chlorine	0.015–2.05	0.02–1.7	0.14	0.18
	parts/10^6	parts/10^6	parts/10^6	
Iodine	0.069–5.0	0.2–0.5	0.12	0.80
Copper*	1.1–29.0	2.0–15.0	5.0	
Molybdenum*	0.01–156	0.1–4.0		
Cobalt	0.016–4.7	0.05–0.3	0.1	
Selenium†	0.01–4000	0.3–1.0	0.06	

* Maximum safe levels: 20.0 (if Cu. adequate) † Maximum safe levels: 4.0

levels of nutrient minerals than most cultivated species. Under hill conditions, there is substantial species variation and certain plants such as *Calluna vulgaris* (heather), *Vaccinium myrtillus* (bilberry) and *Eriophorum vaginatum* (draw moss) may be important because of their relatively high mineral content.

Mineral content varies with the degree of maturity of the pasture and with season, but there is no consistent pattern for all minerals. Important causes of variation in herbage mineral content are the underlying soil type and the modifications brought about by fertilizer application and by the return of nutrients by the grazing animal. A particular problem in sheep nutrition results from overliming the soil, which reduces the availability of the metallic trace elements and increases the availability of molybdenum. It is also known that the trace element content of herbage is lower on well drained soils than on wetter land.

From Table 7.8, it can be seen that the content of several elements in pasture can deviate substantially from the recommended requirements and may, therefore, pose a nutritional problem with sheep in certain circumstances. In the sheep many of these mineral elements are required by the rumen organisms in the first place. Underwood (1966) has extensively reviewed the mineral nutrition of livestock and the following summarizes the main findings as far as sheep are concerned.

Calcium and Phosphorus

Straight dietary calcium deficiency in grazing sheep is rare but in areas of high altitude, where synthesis of vitamin D in the skin is below optimum, symptoms of inadequacy in the calcium, phosphorus, vitamin D complex can occur at herbage levels of calcium and phosphorus which would otherwise be adequate. Phosphorus deficiency in grazing animals, particularly in cattle, is well known. Sheep are only affected in severely deficient areas, notably some of the South African veldt grazings and some of the northern Australian pastures. Deficiency symptoms in the sheep include bone and teeth abnormality, lowered food intake, growth performance, and lowered fertility. Depraved appetite (pica) is a well known feature of phosphorus deficiency. The 'Double scalp' condition of young sheep on the poorer hills of Northern England and Scotland is one manifestation of the deficiency. Rickets is another common form of bone deformity called by a variety of names (e.g., 'bent leg' in Britain). Phosphorus deficiencies can be prevented by application of fertilizers, although in areas where phosphorus deficiency occurs, supplementation, commonly in the form of phosphatic licks in troughs, is more economic, because of the huge areas involved per head of sheep. Licks that have been used successfully include mixtures of 50–60 per cent dicalcium phosphate and 40–50 per cent common salt.

Magnesium and Calcium

These are both involved in important metabolic disorders of sheep hypomagnesaemia (staggers) and hypocalcaemia (lambing sickness). Hypomagnesaemia may be influenced by the supply of magnesium in the herbage but neither of these conditions are simple deficiencies. Hypomagnesaemic tetany is a major source of loss in sheep and occurs most commonly during the peak of lactation, in the first month after lambing, particularly in ewes suckling twin lambs. Usually, the condition appears suddenly and is characterized by incoordination of movement (staggering), muscle twitching and later by intense convulsions and death within a few hours. A chronic form, not easily identified in sheep, resulting in loss of appetite and loss of condition, may precede the final classical attack (Owen & Sinclair, 1961). Hypomagnesaemia is characterized by a low level of magnesium in the blood serum which is normally within the range 1.8–3.2 mg per 100 ml. Clinical signs are most often seen when the level falls below 1·0 mg.

The basic cause of hypomagnesaemia is the imbalance between the high output of magnesium from the lactating animal and the supply available to its tissues, either from the diet or from mobilization of the limited body reserves. Levels of magnesium in herbage has shown association with hypomagnesaemia in dairy cows and dietary supply from herbage may be affected by heavy dressings of nitrogen fertilizer, particularly if potassium is also added, although there is no conclusive evidence of this for sheep. There is some evidence that underfeeding of energy by itself affects the utilization of magnesium and increases the dietary requirement for magnesium. Several factors, causing stress, such as sudden cold weather or undue disturbance, can precipitate hypomagnesaemia, normally in lactating ewes in late winter or on early spring grass. Affected animals can be treated by subcutaneous injection of 100 ml of a 25 per cent solution of magnesium sulphate at various points in the body, although success depends on early treatment. One preventative measure is by applying magnesium in the form of magnesian limestone at the rate of 5 tonnes/ha or 600 kg calcined magnesite, if the lime status is already adequate. The most effective method of preservation is to ensure adequate levels of magnesium in supplementary feed, if necessary adding calcined Magnesite (87–90 per MgO) during the period of early lactation.

Lambing sickness (hypocalcaemia) is similar to milk fever in cows and occurs just before, during or after lambing, mainly in older ewes. The condition is characterized by muscular tremor followed by difficulty of movement so that the ewe goes down. Levels of calcium and phosphorus in the blood serum fall rapidly and the condition can be corrected by prompt sub-cutaneous administration of 100 ml of a 20 per cent solution of calcium borogluconate at several sites in the body. Since the intake of calcium from pasture is not associated with the condition, there is no known management method by which the disorder may be prevented in normal flock practice.

Sodium and Chlorine

It has long been observed that animals usually find salt attractive and the sheep is no exception. There is no evidence of a dietary chlorine deficiency, as distinct from sodium. Very low sodium levels in pasture have been reported in different parts of the world particularly in tropical Africa and the semi-arid regions of Australia. Under these conditions, lactating and young growing sheep may suffer from sodium deficiency, which is corrected by giving salt. In spite of many experiments there is no evidence that salt is beneficial to sheep on temperate pastures, even though they consume it avidly. The most likely conditions for sodium deficiency in temperate regions, could be a sandy soil heavily fertilized with potassium. Sodium deficiency, where it occurs, is mainly characterized by abnormal craving for salt and eventually a loss of appetite and condition.

Excess salt in water is a problem of many of the arid and semi-arid areas of the world since sheep have to exist for many months of the year on water from deep wells which is often intensely saline. Sheep are more tolerant than many other animals and can tolerate a salt concentration of 1 per cent or more provided there is only a small proportion of other soluble salts.

Iron

Iron deficiency is not known in grazing sheep apart from an iron deficiency type of anaemia observed in lambs with a heavy worm burden.

Iodine

Low levels of iodine in soil, pasture and in drinking water in certain areas is widespread and, as in other animals, iodine deficiency leads to an enlarged thyroid gland and symptoms of thyroxine deficiency in the sheep. Where iodine is low in the pasture and water, the incidence of overt iodine deficiency varies according to the types of plants consumed. Some plant species such as the Cruciferae (e.g., kale) and also some of the pasture plants contain goitrogenic substances which can cause high incidence of goitre. In addition to the swelling of the thyroid gland goitre leads to reduced growth and lowered reproductive performance. It can cause death of the fetus at any stage as well as to the birth of weak or hairless lambs, or to permanent changes in the fleece quality. It has been widely reported to result in a reduction in the quantity and quality of wool in the adult sheep. Iodine deficiency, not obvious to the eye, can be diagnosed in a flock by examining the thyroid glands of newborn lambs, since the normal fresh gland weighs less than 1.3 g. Glands exceeding 2.8 g are definite indicators of goitre. The level of protein bound iodine in the blood serum is normally 3–4 µg per 100 ml in the normal adult sheep and frequent occurrence of values much lower than this are indicative of iodine deficiency. The usual method of preventing iodine deficiency in areas where it occurs, is to provide iodized salt licks.

Copper and Molybdenum

Simple dietary deficiency of molybdenum in grazing animals is not known but molybdenum is closely related with copper metabolism; excess molybdenum lowers copper retention in the sheep, the effect being more pronounced if the level of inorganic sulphate is high.

Copper is associated with many important body processes and copper deficiency in sheep, in various forms, is widespread. Sometimes as in the 'coast disease' of sheep in southern Australia, copper and cobalt are deficient together. Simple copper deficiency is usually associated with pasture copper levels below 6 parts/10^6 in the dry matter. However, in areas where molybdenum and inorganic sulphate levels are high, copper deficiency occurs at otherwise normal levels of pasture copper. Swayback, one of the copper deficiency conditions in sheep, is not always associated with low pasture copper levels and there may be some other factor present that reduces copper utilization.

Copper deficiency manifests itself in many forms. Neonatal ataxia—a disorder of the nervous system in lambs, that is called by a variety of names, e.g., swayback (England), Lamkruis (S. Africa), renguera (Peru), gingin rickets (Australia). The disorder is associated with copper deficiency during the ewe's pregnancy and is either evident at the birth of the lamb or is delayed for some weeks. In mild cases, the lamb shows the typical incoordination only when disturbed when the sheep are gathered. Copper deficiency may also show up as anaemia and in bone deformities which cause fractures. An early symptom of copper deficiency in sheep with some black wool is a greying of the wool through lack of pigment. Wool growth and quality are sometimes lowered and changes in the wool causing 'stringy' or 'steely' wool are often seen, particularly in copper deficient areas of Australia. Copper deficiency can best be diagnosed by assessing the copper levels in the blood serum and in the liver. Liver copper levels in sheep are mainly in the region of 200–300 parts/10^6 whilst in blood serum a high proportion of values fall in the range 0.8 to 1.2 mg copper per litre. Usually, liver copper levels less than 20–25 parts/10^6 and blood serum levels below 0.5 mg per litre are taken as indicative of deficiency.

Copper deficiency has been prevented for periods of 3–4 years by applying fertilizer containing copper, to supply about 5–7 kg/ha, except on calcareous soils. Because the sheep is very efficient in retaining copper in the liver, dosing with copper sulphate at intervals of one month or longer, or injections of organic copper complexes (e.g., copper glycine cerate) at intervals of up to three months, are effective. Where swayback is the only manifestation, one or two doses of copper sulphate during pregnancy may suffice. Such infrequent drenching has not been effective for cattle treatment where molybdenum levels in pasture are very high (as in the 'teart' pastures of England).

Because copper is so easily retained by the sheep great care is needed to avoid copper poisoning although the risk is small in grazing sheep if care is taken to avoid free access to copper in licks, etc. Copper poisoning on grazing is known in parts of Australia.

Cobalt

Cobalt deficiency in sheep grazing on particular cobalt deficient areas of pasture, is well known throughout the world and has been given a wide variety of local descriptive names 'pining' (UK) 'wasting disease' (Australia).

The symptoms manifest themselves most clearly in growing lambs and the severity of the condition is variable. Often the symptoms are difficult to distinguish from the effect of worms and the existence of cobalt deficiency can only be established by examining the results of administering cobalt or injecting vitamin B_{12}. However, some indication of the need for cobalt supplementation may be given by the cobalt content of the pasture, which should not be below 0.1 parts/10^6 on a dry matter basis. Also, liver cobalt levels may be an indication – normal levels in sheep being 0.2–0.3 parts/10^6 cobalt in the dry matter. Cobalt deficiency symptoms are usually associated with liver levels less the 0.06 parts/10^6. A rather better indicator of cobalt deficiency is the level of vitamin B_{12} in the liver, usually above

0.19 μg per g of fresh liver in normal sheep. The level can fall to less than 0.07 parts/10^6 in severe cases of cobalt deficiency. Serum vitamin B_{12} levels are easier to obtain but do not afford such good indication as the liver values. However, it has been shown that in grazing ewes and lambs a level of 0.3 μg Vitamin B_{12} per ml of serum is indicative of cobalt deficiency.

Cobalt is required by the sheep for the synthesis of vitamin B_{12} in the rumen and the administration of cobalt by mouth, or the injection of vitamin B_{12}, can be used to rectify cobalt deficiency. The deficiency can be prevented on some soils by including Cobalt in fertilizer at the rate of 0.25–1.5 kg per ha at intervals of up to 4 years, except on lime rich soils where cobalt deficiency is often found. Dosing with cobalt is difficult in practice since it is not stored in the body like copper. Cobalt can be administered in salt.licks containing 0·1 per cent cobalt, in supplementary feed, or by giving cobalt bullets which lodge in the rumen or reticulum and release minute quantities of cobalt over many years. The bullets contain cobalt oxide in a dense mass of ferruginous clay with a specific gravity of 4.5–5. This form of administration may be difficult with young lambs where the rumen is not well developed, since the bullets may be disgorged and it is difficult then to detect the unprotected lambs. A reduction in the effectiveness of cobalt bullets can occur from the formation of an impervious coating of calcium phosphate on the surface of the bullet. This can be prevented by the administration of two bullets per sheep so that there is sufficient abrasion between the two to prevent the formation of the coat.

Fluorine

Deficiency of fluorine in grazing sheep is not known to be a problem but excess fluorine, usually from drinking water tapped from deep wells, can cause chronic fluorosis in sheep in many areas of the world. Excess fluorine is deposited in the bones and causes malformation of the bones and teeth, particularly in growing lambs. Little can be done about the condition where sheep have to depend on water of high fluoride content, but the effects can be mitigated by preventing excessive evaporation of water before drinking and by the intermittent use of low fluoride water for growing lambs.

Selenium

Selenium, like copper, can be important both in excess and when in deficit. Excess selenium occurs on alkaline, mainly heavy clay soils and certain plants have a high capacity to absorb and retain selenium. Herbage containing 4 parts/10^6 or more is potentially dangerous although mean values may hide a small proportion of plants with very high levels.

Selenium deficiency has been reported from many areas of the world and can give rise to many of the disorders normally associated with the deficiency of vitamin E (tocopherol). These include muscular dystrophy (white muscle or stiff lamb disease) in lambs and unthriftiness known as 'ill thrift' in 6–12 month old sheep, and infertility of ewes. Subclinical deficiency is known to decrease lambing rates and wool yield. Conditions that are alleviated by the administration of selenium do not necessarily arise from simple selenium deficiency in the herbage and certain stresses may precipitate overt symptoms in conditions where deficiency is marginal. The effects of selenium deficiency on growth and reproduction in sheep are variable, but there have been serious economic losses in New Zealand from 'hogget ill thrift' and from barrenness and loss of lambs in ewes. Lambs may be affected by muscular dystrophy at birth and unable to get up to suckle. In older lambs early symptoms include stiffened gait and an arched back which may only be apparent intermittently. Selenium deficiency often occurs on leguminous pastures in high rainfall areas and in areas deficient also in cobalt and copper. Levels of selenium in pasture below 0.04 parts/10^6 are sometimes associated with muscular dystrophy, although there is much variation in the association. The concentration of selenium in whole blood in normal sheep is usually within the range of 0.1–0.2 µg per ml, but selenium deficient sheep frequently show levels less than 0.02 µg per ml.

Selenium deficiency in sheep can be prevented by dosing with sodium selenite and in the selenium deficient areas of New Zealand ewes are dosed with the equivalent of 5 mg selenium a month before lambing, and lambs at two to three weeks of age are given 1 mg. Another possible method is the incorporation of selenium in fertilizer, although selenium levels in herbage can rise to toxic levels shortly after application.

Pasture Management

Pasture management describes the process by which the farmer manipulates his resources—chiefly pasture, grazing stock and labour—within the constraints of a whole farm, usually including a variety of complementary enterprises. The objectives of good pasture management include a variety of facets and success depends on the integration of several, sometimes conflicting aims.

Several important components can be isolated from the armoury at the disposal of the grazier and these can be examined in turn:

GRAZING SYSTEMS

Several distinct grazing systems can be operated for sheep. These include:

Continuous Grazing or Set Stocking

In this system the flock of sheep is allotted to the available area of pasture and allowed to graze all or part of the area continuously. The more extreme form of this system is where sheep only are stocked continuously, on a year-round basis, on the whole of one area and have access to no other grazing. This extreme is virtually the wild state of the sheep and is only approached, in modern sheep systems, by some of the larger extensive range or plain farms. Even in these situations it has already been shown how the sheep themselves can become divided into distinct groups with their own sub-flock movements; on a larger scale the men and their flocks tend to move between summer and winter from one part of the grazing to another. Set stocking is normally practised in a less extreme form, where only part of the area available is continuously grazed; during the growing season part of the area is protected for conservation of winter feed. In a more local form set stocking may simply imply that a group of sheep occupy one area for several weeks in the one growing season.

Whatever form of set stocking is practised it usually involves a group of sheep remaining together on a specific area of pasture for an extended period. This means that the stocking density (the number of sheep per hectare with access to a given area at any one time) is relatively low and that time is allowed for some equilibrium to be established between grazing stock, pasture and all the other components involved. The system does not necessitate much interference with the sheep's normal behaviour within the perimeter of the allotted area.

Rotational Grazing

All other grazing systems can loosely be described as rotational, even if this only means, in its simplest form, the division of the area available into two parts and moving the sheep from one to the other at intervals. Several forms of rotational grazing are employed in practice.

Folding

The close folding of sheep on arable forage crops is the most intensive form of rotational grazing for sheep and was widely practised in the lighter arable areas of Western Europe notably in Eastern England in the nineteenth and early twentieth centuries. In this system sheep were moved on to a fresh 'break' once or twice a day. The system is seldom practised in the traditional form today, because of the rise in labour costs. Where roots or sugar beet tops are grazed by sheep, areas are fenced off so that each subdivision provides food for several days.

The close herding of suitable sheep in unfenced arable areas, in many parts of the world, is somewhat akin to close folding, although the control is exercised without the fences or hurdles of the true folding system.

Field by Field Rotation

Most lowland farms in developed temperate countries are enclosed and subdivided into fields so that the sheep can be moved from one field to another. The old saying, that 'sheep should not hear the church bells ring twice in the same field', is an indication that, in England at least, the practice of rotating the sheep flock at frequent intervals was common practice. The system is difficult to operate on mixed farms, where the sheep flock is only one of several enterprises and it is more common to find a modified set stocking system where sheep are confined to a certain area in the early growing season until new 'aftermath' growth, following grass conservation, is available in mid season.

A more sophisticated version of the field by field rotational system is one based on specially divided paddock areas, often 6–8 in number where the flock is rotated at intervals of three to six days. It is more commonly modified by the inclusion of a 'creep' arrangement for the lambs.

Rotational Creep Grazing

The traditional folding system was often modified in operation by enabling lambs to 'creep' through gaps in the hurdles so that they had prior access to a fresh break. This system was adapted to pasture utilization and developed as the 'forward creep' grazing system largely at Newcastle University in the UK in the early 1950s. (Cooper & Morris, 1973). The system commonly involved the division of the grazing area into six paddocks as shown in Fig. 7.8 with each

K

paddock occupied by the ewe flock for three to four days. Access by the lambs to the next paddock is allowed through gaps in the dividing fence. The system normally operates after active grass growth commences in the spring until mid-summer, when the ewes are sheared and differential creeping by the lambs is no longer possible.

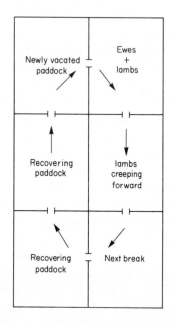

Fig. 7.8. *Outline of a creep grazing system.*

In spite of active development work in the UK during the 1950s and 1960s, rotational grazing systems have not ousted the traditional versions of set stocking as the normal means of lowland lamb production, and it is useful to consider the reasons for the lack of success of the system.

Objective information, upon which to compare rotational grazing with set stocking, is not plentiful. Wheeler (1962) reviewed the merits of different grazing systems for cattle and sheep and concluded that, at equal stocking rates, there were negligible differences in annual production of meat or milk between set stocking and rotational grazing. Since then, a number of experiments at the British Experimental Husbandry Farms have compared, at a number of stocking rates, set stocking, forward creep grazing and a modified (sideways) form of creep grazing. A summary of the results at the various centres by Hastings and Thompson (1965) contains few estimates of the individual variation involved but reveals no clear difference in production between the various systems; furthermore, there was no appreciable difference in the faecal worm egg counts.

In the USA a three year trial by Jordan and Marten (1970) failed to reveal any advantages for including a 'forward creep' in a rotational system; there was a tendency for forage production to be reduced and for weight loss in suckling ewes to be increased with the inclusion of the creep.

One advantage of rotational grazing that emerges from many studies (Wheeler, 1962), is the increase in grass growth during the peak growing season, leading to the availability of more herbage for conservation from the area than under a set stocking system. Work at the West of Scotland College (Anon., 1970) suggests that this could be important in late summer in a lamb production system if a large stock of lambs remain to be finished off at that time.

Owen (1961) has pointed out that some of the initial tenets underlying the rotational system were not applicable in practice. The rotation of grazing involved in the system does not afford a means of controlling parasite infestation because of the unpredictability of the period that elapses before the translation of faecal worm eggs into infective larvae and the persistence of potential infestation. The preferential treatment given to the lamb by the possibility of creeping is not of major significance in the short period for which creeping can operate. Perhaps the main cause for the shortcomings of rotational grazing stem from the disturbance involved to ewes and lambs by the change from one paddock to the next, particularly severe in flocks of several hundred sheep.

A practical objection levelled against set stocking is that it is not possible to apply fertilizer to pasture whilst sheep have access to it. Work with dairy cows (Hood, 1974) and with grazing ewes and lambs (Anon., 1970) has demonstrated the feasibility of applying nitrogen fertilizer at least to a proportion of the pasture, without any discernible ill-effects.

Many of the apparent benefits of rotational creep grazing in the 'intensive use of grass' have been due to the confounding of the system's intrinsic worth with the greater degree of fertiliser and management input associated with it, and with the ensuing practice of setting high target stocking rates for the system. On the other hand the real benefits of the development of an equilibrium state under a set stocking system, both in terms of animal well-being and in terms of creating a different sward structure (Morris, 1969), have been largely overlooked. It is concluded that, for most farming situations, the simplicity and cheapness of a set stocking system together with its salient advantages, outweighs the rival merits of rotational systems.

MIXED GRAZING

There has been some controversy about the value of the mixed grazing of sheep and cattle—a widespread practice in traditional grazing management. The design of adequate experiments to test the value of mixed grazing is difficult, since the answer may depend on the relative proportions of sheep and cattle and it is difficult to make valid assumptions about the relative replacement rates of sheep for cattle. Conway (1972) reporting a long term comparison of all cattle, all sheep, or mixed systems, evaluated on a farmlet basis, from 1964–1970, concluded that the mixed stocking did not affect individual cattle gains but resulted in improved performance of lambs. A similar study was carried out under rather different conditions at the Rutherglen research station, Australia (Hamilton & Bath, 1970). Over four years they studied the effect of grazing together autumn lambing ewes with young steers, in the proportion four ewes for each steer, at three rates of stocking. Similar ewes and steers were also grazed separately at each of five stocking rates. The experiment has to be interpreted in the context of a predominantly winter rainfall area and of the chosen ratio of sheep to steers. Mixed stocking of cattle and sheep increased overall production per ha in most years and it was evident that the main benefit was to the sheep which resulted in higher growth rate of lambs and higher wool production than in the sheep only treatments. The effect on cattle was less clearly beneficial. The results are summarized in Table 7.9.

Earlier, investigations on the British EHF's (Culpin et al., 1964) showed that the addition of sheep to existing cattle stock on summer pasture could reduce cattle gains. However, at one of the centres (Trawscoed), where the sheep were removed in July, overall gains by the cattle were as good on the mixed systems. The performance of twin lambs in the mixed treatments was good. Unfortunately, there were no 'all sheep' treatments in these trials.

Taken together, these results from different centres, suggest that mixed grazing is beneficial, mainly because of improved lamb performance. The reason for the good effects of mixed grazing on lamb gain is not certain but it can be partly due to the dilution of lamb stocking as compared to an all sheep system, which reduces risks of parasite infestation. Another possible reason is that there is a complementarity of grazing such that the sheep can exercise greater selection of herbage over the larger area allowed per sheep, without any deleterious effect on cattle performance.

An interesting aspect of mixed grazing is the social cohesion that develops between sheep and steers as reported by Bond et al., (1967). Too little attention has been paid to social behaviour in developing new grazing systems.

Table 7.9. *Mean values per head for steer gain (G), lamb liveweight (L), and clean wool production (W), when steers and sheep grazed separately and together*

| Stocking rate | | 1964 | | | 1966 | | | 1965 | | | 1967 | | |
Steers	Ewes	G	L (lb)	W	G	L (lb)	W	G	L (lb)	W	G	L (lb)	W
number/acre													
1.14		316			178*			191			171		
0.86		404*			240			288			230		
0.57		378			246			361			313		
0.43		466			274			514			372		
0.29		427			354			544			363		
0.57	2.28	256	76.5	5.50	160*	73.0*	4.08*	241	90.0	6.50	172*	85.0	4.80
0.43	1.71	340	84.5*	6.04	172	78.1	4.28	306	95.5	6.60*	260	92.5	5.95
0.29	1.14	412	108.0	6.68	258	90.0	4.87	465	108.5	7.30	286	96.0	5.80
	4.57		69.5*	4.82		n.e.†	n.e.†		73.0*	5.30*		76.0	4.60
	3.43		77.5	5.56		74.2	4.38		83.5	5.35		80.0	5.00
	2.28		89.0	6.47		74.4	4.80		96.0	6.25		90.0	5.70
	1.71		102.0	5.92		86.6	4.92		102.5	7.45		96.0	5.55
	1.14		110.5	6.70		90.2	5.37		112.5	7.90		101.5	6.25

* Mean calculated using a computed missing value.
† n.e. = no estimate of the mean available.

Fig. 7.9. *Mixture grazing by sheep and cattle in Western Victoria, Australia.* (*By courtesy of the Australian News & Information Bureau*).

STOCKING RATE IN RELATION TO CONSERVATION AND
SUPPLEMENTATION

The rate of stocking on a pasture—normally measured as
the number of animals per unit area over a specified period,
usually the grazing season—is a most important factor in determining animal production from pasture. Wheeler (1962) and
McMeekan (1960) are amongst those who have concluded, on
the basis of extensive experimentation, that stocking rate is
far more important than grazing system in this respect.
Broadbent (1964) confirmed that stocking rate was the important factor in fat lamb production from grass.

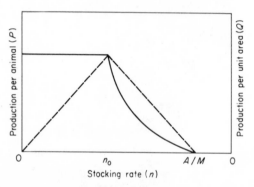

Fig. 7.10. *The relation of production to stocking rate* – – –, *production per unit area*
(Q); ———, *Production per animal* (P).

The theoretical underlying relationship between stocking
rate and animal production per ha has been described in its
simplest form by Owen and Ridgman (1968) (Fig. 7.10).

This analysis shows that for any pasture, at any point in
time, stocking rate can be raised from low levels, with little
effect on individual animal performance, so that animal production per ha increases virtually linearly. In practice, some
decrease in sheep performance is entailed at this stage, partly
because the opportunity for herbage selection decreases, and

partly because of the extension from any instant to a grazing season. When the stock are consuming the herbage as fast as it grows there is a break-point where further increases in stocking rate quickly lead to rapid deterioration in individual performance and progressive decrease in production per hectare. Over a whole season when other effects are considered, including parasites, treading, unevenness of feed supply, the simple relationship becomes obscured, although, as far as dry sheep, the main outcome is essentially inchanged (Owen & Ridgman, 1968).

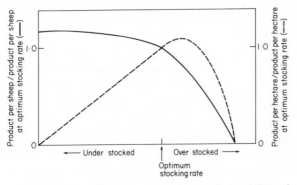

Fig. 7.11. *The relation of stocking rate to the product per sheep and the product per ha (based on Mott, 1960).*

Mott (1960) plotted data from several experiments on grazing cattle and showed the relationship illustrated diagrammatically in Fig. 7.11. This gives an indication of the form of the relationship between animal production per ha and the performance of the individual animal with change in stocking rate that is normally observed in practical situations. Hart (1972), reviewing the relationship of forage yield, stocking rate and gain of beef cattle on pasture, showed that the maximum animal production per ha is not the point which maximizes profit. This may be particularly true in a lamb production system where the price per kg is falling and a minimum weight and finish of carcass is specified.

Whatever the precise form of the relationship in any given situation, the principles involved are far-reaching in their implications for pasture management, particularly as a rational basis for the use of supplementary feeding and the integration of conservation with grazing. Over much of the active grazing season, sheep systems operate below the break-point in production per ha illustrated in Fig. 7.10, particularly in the peak growth period. Thus, whilst some improvement in individual performance might be achieved, supplementation with cereal based concentrates largely replaces grass consumption and is unprofitable.

Thorpe (1963) studied the effect of supplementation at two rates of stocking on the performance of ewes and lambs. His results showed that there was little effect on lamb performance except at the high stocking rate in one of the two years of study. The consumption of supplement by the lambs, however, led to lower grass consumption, which resulted in higher weight gains by the dams.

The aim in practice is to achieve as high a stocking rate as possible, without running the risk of overstepping the break-point for any appreciable period. Because normal conservation methods demands that pasture be withdrawn from grazing, for a minimum of several weeks, the proportion of the area conserved to that grazed, must be a compromise, which involves some under-utilization with a reserve of pasture growth to even out temporary fluctuations in grass growth. If supplementary feed is not available the compromise has to be set at a lower stocking rate than otherwise since the farmer has to cover the expectation of a poor growing season. The availability of supplementary feed and its judicious use to cover the eventuality of infrequent droughts or other natural phenomena, can allow the adoption of much higher stocking rates and improved production per ha. Hutchinson (1971) has shown that in the long term the proportion of grazing to conservation and the use of supplementation needs to be examined in the context of the whole system where the storage of nutrients as un-utilized pasture and in the sheep's body energy store is taken into account.

In general, supplementation during the grazing season is seldom justifiable unless it enables a significantly higher stocking rate to be safely sustained and that the extra stock can be carried through the winter.

The same principles apply to the supplementation of hill sheep. Here the situation is often different in that the system stocking rate often exceeds the 'break-point' in late winter, when the demands of pregnancy in the ewe are increasing. In such a situation supplementary feeding and even reduced stocking (MAFF, 1972) can be justifiable and profitable. However, on better hills where average lambing performance is limited more to lower ovulation rates than by lamb mortality, supplementary feeding just before lambing will give little response, except in hard winters (Robinson et al., 1961). In such circumstances, efforts to improve body condition of ewes at mating by better autumn nutrition, are likely to be more fruitful. In situations where hill pasture is more intensively stocked, the use of judicious supplementary feeding in late winter, a period where nitrition is often most limiting, may be profitable simply as a direct means of increasing stock at that period, without any improvement in individual performance. The extra stock, carried for the whole year, boost total production from the system and may confer further benefit by reducing under-utilization of pasture during the peak growth season, in a situation where conservation is not possible. Even though it may be practised for only a few weeks in the year, the economic evaluation of supplementation needs to be carried out in the context of the whole sheep system, as it operates over a period of several seasons.

Health 8

Many aspects of sheep health have been dealt with in relation to nutritional aspects and to breeding problems; In the previous chapter, a number of disorders of grazing sheep were shown to be associated with nutrient deficiencies in the pasture. The following section deals with additional health problems, mainly, those associated with the presence of other organisms, although there is a large degree of interrelationship between the various biological and physical agents involved in sheep health.

Parasitism

Parasites are a major source of loss to the sheep industry of the world. Because of its ubiquity and the variability of its effect on performance, it is difficult to assess the true extent of the cost of parasitism. However, there are few sheep that are not affected to a degree or where resources are not used for prevention.

INTERNAL PARASITES

The chief groups of internal parasites of general economic importance in sheep production are the roundworms or nematodes, the flukes, tapeworms and coccidia. These parasites have been described in detail elsewhere (Spedding, 1970) and only a brief summary of aspects that are pertinent to sheep management practice are dealt with in the present section.

Roundworms

Several nematode species are found in the digestive and respiratory tracts of the sheep. Those living in the digestive tract are the most important economically and include several genera, the most important of which are *Ostertagia, Haemonchus, Trichostrongylus, Cooperia, Strongyloides, Nematodirus, Bunostomum, Oesophagostomum, Chabertia* and *Trichuris*. These parasites normally co-exist with the host sheep in a state of equilibrium, where the numbers of parasites remain limited and the effect on performance, although possibly significant, is relatively small and unimportant. A breakdown in the equilibrium, leading to rapid increase in infestation has marked effects on sheep performance and may result in severe illness and death. The effect of the parasites is not completely understood but it includes the competition for food (mainly the sheep's blood) and the damage and inflammation of the gut wall. There may also be physiological effects such as those manifested in the reduction of voluntary feed intake and in scouring (diarrhoea) which multiply the deleterious consequences of heavy infestation. Some features of the biology of parasites and the host parasite relationship are an essential basis to the understanding and development of control methods.

1. *Life cycle of the Nematodes.* With the exception of *Nematodirus,* the important features of the life cycle of the nematode parasites of sheep can be uniformly summarized. Part of the life cycle involves a period outside the sheep on the pasture. The mature worms lay eggs which are deposited on the pasture in the dung. The rate of egg deposition by the ewe varies seasonally and is characterized by a 'post parturient rise' where the output of eggs shows a pronounced rise some 3–4 weeks after lambing. The level then declines to normal, which usually does not exceed a few hundred eggs per g of fresh faeces. The eggs hatch on pasture and develop through several stages. At a particular stage, the larva becomes 'infective' and if consumed by a susceptible sheep the larva develops within the digestive tract and becomes a mature egg laying worm in a period of 2–4

weeks from ingestion in most cases, depending on the conditions and on the species concerned. Of major importance in grazing control methods, is the time that elapses between deposition of the eggs on the pasture and the presence of the infective larvae on the herbage grazed by the sheep and the persistence of such infestation. Depending on species, in exceptionally favourable conditions (high temperature and humidity), the period between deposition on pasture and reaching the infective stage may be a matter of several days in a few individual cases. In practice, however, it is usually much delayed and highly variable, depending on species and individuals and on the general environment, particularly the temperature.

The result is that larvae reach the infective stage at progressively shorter intervals, after deposition as the season progresses, varying from as long as 3 months when deposited in early spring to 2–4 weeks in mid-summer. These larvae subsequently remain infective for varying lengths of time. The net result is the build up of infection on a pasture, initially clean in early spring, from the early summer, to reach a peak later in the summer and autumn, when a lengthening of development period again causes the pasture infestation to drop. The eggs of most parasitic worms do not survive the winter but the infective stage, which does not persist long in warm, dry conditions, is more resistant to cold conditions and may overwinter in significant numbers, particularly the larvae of *Ostertagia*. If no more parasites are dropped on the pasture, the residual infestation soon disappears when warm conditions return; in the UK the pasture is usually free by early June if not further contaminated. The potential rates of reproduction by parasites are astronomic and it is fortunate that only a minute fraction of the potential parasites survive the various stages of the life cycle. Care must be taken, therefore, in departing from traditional practices of sheep husbandry, to avoid circumstances favourable to catastrophic infestation with resultant heavy losses.

The *Nematodirus* group differs from the other Nematodes in

that the eggs can remain unhatched for a long period and a high proportion overwinter to provide infestation for the following season. This is potentially the most dangerous of the roundworms since it infects lambs early in the season and is associated with severe outbreaks and high mortality.

2. *Host resistance.* Another important facet of host/parasite biology is the phenomenon of host resistance, whereby the sheep, within limits, can reduce the danger from ingesting parasitic larvae. The physiological mechanism of the resistant sheep prevent the development of any but a few of the larvae contained in the herbage, so that an equilibrium is established, where both sheep and parasite can exist. This resistance is limited in its capability in the face of adverse conditions and gradually disappears when exposure to infection is removed. Resistance develops with age in lambs exposed to infection, provided that they are well nourished and not challenged by excessive levels of pasture infestation.

3. *Species specificity.* Some of the species of nematode worms in sheep, such as the lung worm (*Dictyocaulus filaria*), do not affect

Table 8.1. *Efficiency of anthelmintic compounds against gastrointestinal nematodes in sheep*

Anthelmintic*	Dose rate mg/kg body wt	efficiency (percentage) against							
		Haemonchus contortus				*Trichostrongylus axei*			
		2	7	14	28	2	7	14	
Phenothiazine (Micronized)	600	57	30	98	98	72	30	42	
Haloxon	50	91	94	100	100	20	57	87	
Methyridine	200	34	54	87	52	36	94	77	1
Thiabendazole	50	96	100	100	100	97	100	100	1
Tetranisole†	15	100	100	100	100	13	95	100	1
Pyrantil tartrate	25	93	83	99	100	80	100	100	1
Parbendazole	15	100	100	100	100	100	100	100	1
Morantel		99	63	100	99	92	100	100	1

* Newer compounds Cambendazole, Thiophanate, Fenbendazole, Mebendazole are also
† Effective also for lungworm treatment.

cattle whilst others are common to both species, although they may not be of equal importance in both species.

4. *Antiparasitic drugs.* Several effective chemicals are available which destroy nematodes within the sheep. One of the earliest used was copper sulphate which gave good control of the Haemonchus group but did not adequately control several other important species. More recently, efficient drugs have been developed which are remarkably effective against a wide range of parasite species in mature and immature stages. The first of these to be widely used—phenothiazine—has been superceded by others such as thiabenzole which combine effectiveness of parasite destruction with the least toxic effect on the sheep. (Table 8.1)

The features described in paragraphs 1–4 above, taken together, can form the basis for successful control of sheep parasites. In practice, there is usually no one simple answer if the aim is to intensify the use of grass for sheep production. Steps likely to aid parasite control can be summarized as follows:

(a) Grazing systems, involving short term rotation of grazing,

formation supplied by Mr. T. E. Gibson, Central Veterinary Laboratory, Weybridge, UK).

vae of four ages (days) (Gibson, 1963)

	Ostertagia circumcinta				Trichostrongylus				Nematodirus battus		
2	7	14	28	2	7	14	28	2	7	14	28
	81	62	65	56	73	52	52	45	13	71	89
	11	68	100	53	89	90	92	0	0	0	35
	39	98	74	43	92	93	25	97	99	100	100
	99	99	94	100	100	100	100	85	83	23	69
	60	99	99	100	100	100	100	100	100	100	97
	42	99	100	97	92	88	80	100	100	100	100
	100	100	100	100	100	100	100	85	76	43	65
	87	99	100	100	94	88	98	100	100	100	100

reported to be highly efficient.

are not likely to reduce parasitic infestation. However, pasture rested from sheep for the whole of the previous season, or (apart from Nematodirus) even just free of sheep over the previous autumn and winter, should have only a low level of initial infestation.

Pasture that has been rested for conservation early in the season should provide regrowth in summer that has low infestation and provides a useful break from pastures that have been grazed in early season and where infestation is becoming heavy.

(b) Mixed grazing of cattle and sheep is beneficial, particularly if the cattle are relatively mature animals. The concentration of susceptible lambs per hectare is thereby much reduced and it is the lambs which are the media for rapid build-up in pasture infestation. Herbage is consumed by cattle, with any parasitic larvae it contains, and only a few eggs from the worms common to both species returned.

(c) All the factors that favour a good level of nutrition in the ewe and the lamb are likely to foster parasite resistance. Single lambs receiving a high milk intake and growing at a fast rate, are less prone to parasitism than twin lambs.

(d) Judicious use of anti-parasitic drugs can be an added help. Ewes that are turned on to clean spring pasture with their lambs can be dosed at that stage, so that the post parturient rise in worm egg output and consequent pasture infestation is minimized. Lambs that are weaned in summer at 3–5 months of age can again be dosed before moving on to clean regrowth following conservation.

On many farms it is not practicable to turn ewes and lambs on the clean pasture in the spring, so that dosing the ewes is not a major safeguard. In such cases it is important to dose the ewes and lambs and move the sheep from the pasture, before contamination reaches serious levels in early summer. In the UK this involves moving the sheep in early June on to silage aftermath or pastures grazed by cattle (Thomas, 1974). Dosing lambs without moving to clean pasture is much less effective and usually uneconomic (Reid, 1973).

Lungworms

The lungworms of sheep, some of which require a secondary host to complete their life cycle, are not of such economic importance as those of cattle. Mild bronchitis, which causes coughing in sheep, particularly when driven, is common; more severe infestation, causing loss of performance and death, is rarer. Sometimes lungworm damage can lead to infection from an organism such as the Pasteurella species which can cause heavy losses in lambs.

Liver Fluke

The fluke parasites of sheep and cattle are of high economic importance in the wetter lowlands where sheep are kept. At the end of the nineteenth century there are records of heavy losses in British sheep from fluke infestation during a series of wet years. The most common fluke infesting sheep is the common liver fluke (*Fasciola hepatica*) which infects both sheep and cattle and is characterized by a life history which involves a seondary host. In Britain this is the small water snail, *Limnea trunculata*, which accounts for the association of infestation with wet land. The flukes differ from the nematodes in that 10–14 weeks elapse from ingestion of the parasitic larva or cercariae to maturity, so that fluke is a problem of older sheep rather than the young lamb. The liver flukes after ingestion make their way to the liver and even the immature forms can cause extensive damage to the liver. Commonly, the disease develops for some time with anaemia as a prominent symptom. A secondary infection by Clostridial organisms is sometimes associated with damage from the immature flukes–called Black disease–it can cause heavy losses when it occurs.

The infestation of fluke larvae on pasture may be high in the autumn where the snails have become infected in spring and early summer. The level may also be high in the summer where the snails were infected the previous autumn and early winter. In the UK the highest peak of pasture infestation is usually in the autumn from August onwards.

The fluke problem can be controlled by tackling the inter-mediate host snail by drainage of the land or by dressing the land with a compound like copper sulphate. A more immediate remedy is to dose the sheep with an anti-fluke compound in the autumn, followed by a second dose in winter.

Table 8.2. *Efficiency of anthelmintic compounds against* Fasciola hepatica *(fluke worm) in sheep. (Based on data from J. C. Boray, quoted by T. E. Gibson, private communication).*

Anthelmintic*	Maximum dosage rate mg/kg live wt.	Minimum dose required to destroy >90 per cent of parasites of three ages mg/kg live wt.		
		4 weeks	6 weeks	12 weeks
Carbon tetrachloride	800	640	480.0	80.0
1, 4-bis-trichlor-methyl benzol	600	–	1200.0	150.0
Hexachlorophene	30	30	20.0	15.0
Hexachlorophene monophosphate	40	40	25.0	20.0
Hilomid	60	120	60.0	20.0
Disophenol	40	50	34.0	15.0
Oxyclozaride	60	60	40.0	15.0
Niclofolan	12	8	6.0	2.7
Clioxanide	100	135	40.0	15.0
Nitroxynil	40	30	13.5	6.7
Brotianide	27	–	4.7	2.3
Rafoxanide	45	15	7.0	2.5

* Diamphenethide, not included in this table, is also highly efficient against im-mature flukes.

Dosing in spring can also help by reducing the snail infection. Carbon tetrachloride was the first effective drug to be widely used against fluke but newer compounds (Table 8.2) are effec-tive against both mature and immature worms. Fluke infesta-tions are very variable, depending on the suitability of condi-tions for the snail host, and some degree of confidence has been attained in forecasting conditions during the summer that are likely to encourage heavy fluke infestations in the sheep in the following autumn and winter. Such forecasts given for local areas guide farmers as to the necessity for an intensive dosing programme for their sheep.

Tapeworms

Sheep suffer from infestation by several tapeworms, some of which like the broad tapeworm (*Moniezia* species), lodge in the small intestine and can cause blockage as well as the usual competition with the host.

An important feature of some tapeworm species is that their larval forms, commonly called bladderworms, infest the sheep and can cause severe damage. An important example is *Taenia multiceps* which exists as a tapeworm in the dog and related species like the fox. The larval form lodges in the brain and spinal cord of the sheep and causes 'gid'. The symptoms of this condition are the marked abnormal behaviour of the sheep, usually moving around blindly in circles. Much of the problem may be alleviated by regular dosing of sheep dogs against the causative tapeworm.

Coccidiosis

Coccidia, belonging to the *Elmera* species, are an increasing problem in sheep husbandry. The organism is a protozoan parasite normally present in healthy adult sheep. Under certain conditions lambs may become heavily infested leading to marked loss of condition, some scouring and high mortality. Coccidiosis is often a problem of overcrowding, associated with housing at lambing, particularly if ewes and lambs are confined after lambing in yards or small paddocks. It is also common in the feed lots of the sheep areas in the USA. The condition can be treated by prompt administration for 3–5 consecutive days, of a coccidiat such as sulphamezathine. It is best prevented by putting ewes and their lambs out on to clean grass at a low stocking rate within a 2 or 3 days after lambing and thereafter avoiding overcrowding. Care must also be taken in groups of weaned lambs that are brought together in high concentration, particularly when this change is also accom-accompanied by an abrupt change in diet.

EXTERNAL PARASITES

Sheep suffer from a variety of external parasites which are normally harmless. However, they sometimes multiply and affect the sheep's wellbeing or they may form the agent for transmitting more serious conditions.

Ticks and Tickborne Diseases

The tick (*Ixodes ricinus*) is an important parasite of the sheep. In Britain ticks have mainly confined to the hill areas of Northern England and Scotland. In themselves they cause little harm, in small numbers, but they are the agent for the transmission of disease organisms and the wounds they leave can allow invasion by disease organisms. These include Louping ill, a severe virus disease of sheep transmitted by ticks. Tick-borne fever, caused by one of the *Rickettsia* species can cause loss of condition in susceptible sheep and is also associated with some abortion in ewes; and *Tick pyaemia*, caused by an infection of *Staphylococcus aureus*, a cause of heavy losses in lambs.

Apart from that for louping ill, there is no satisfactory vaccine available and prevention depends on the control of ticks by the regular dipping of sheep flocks in affected areas.

The Sheep Blowfly

The blowfly is a major parasite of the sheep and can cause heavy losses during the summer season. Blowfly attacks are primarily caused by flies of the *Lucilia* species—*Lucilia sericata* being the most important European member and *Lucilia cuprina* the most important in Australia. Some of the *Calliphora* species (the brown blowflies) can also cause primary attacks.

Secondary attacks by species such as the *Calliphora* and *Chrysomyia* species are also an important factor. The blowfly lays its eggs in damp, soiled areas of wool around the hind-quarters of a scouring sheep, although during warm humid weather attacks around the shoulder and back can be observed. The larvae of the blowfly called 'maggots' burrow into the skin of the sheep and feed on the living flesh. The attacks can be prevented by dipping ewes and lambs during the summer period using a long acting insecticide. In Australia the 'Mules' operation was developed to prevent blowfly attack, originally in Merinos with heavily wrinkled folds around the hindquaters. 'Mulesing', in its modern form, involves the exision of pieces of skin on either side of the vulva to create a healed area which is smooth and wrinkle free. This operation can give a marked reduction in the incidence of blowfly attacks (Belschner, 1959).

Head-fly

A problem that has increase in certain areas, e.g., Southern Scotland, in recent years is that due to *Hydrotea irritans*. This fly is widespread and although it is a non-biting species it can cause severe irritation to sheep by congregating around the head. In severe cases the sheep may rub its head causing self inflicted wounds which are further aggravated by the flies.

There is no simple remedy for the problem and although repellent insecticidal preparations are available they have not so far proved entirely successful. It is claimed that hornless breeds with woolly heads are relatively immune but it is not always possible to use such breeds in the areas affected. There is a possibility that the problem is one of temporary unbalance in population numbers and that in time the balance may be restored.

Nasal fly

The fly *Oestrus ovis* is found all over the world and can be a serious problem in some circumstances. The adult fly itself is a severe nuisance congregating around the head of the sheep and attempting to deposit its hatched larvae in or near the sheep's nostril. The larvae themselves in the nasal mucosa also cause some irritation resulting in coughing and sneezing. Prevention is seldom economic but in severe outbreaks some control can be achieved by treating the sheep to eliminate the larvae in the nostrils. (Marsh, 1965).

Sheep Scab or Scabies

Sheep have long been afflicted by skin conditions associated with various parasitic mites. The main problem is caused by the psoroptic mite, *Psoroptes communis ovis*. The disease is effectively controlled by dipping, using dips containing acaricidal compounds. So effective is this treatment that the condition has been eradicated from many sheep keeping areas. Australia has been free from sheep scab during this century and countries like the UK have eradicated the parasite in recent years. Many countries have adopted legislation to enforce regular dipping to prevent sheep scab.

Bacterial Diseases

Many diseases of sheep, of varying importance, are associated with the presence of bacteria. Some of these can be prevented quite easily by vaccination. Others are much more complex conditions where the bacterial attack can be regarded as secondary to the primary predisposing factors, which triggered off the outbreak. With increasing intensification of sheep production the stress on the sheep's defences is more marked and much more thought has to be given to reducing such stress, as well as to the adoption of rational veterinary preventative procedures.

CLOSTRIDIAL DISEASES

Several sheep diseases are associated with Clostridial bacteria and these organisms, like many others causing disease in sheep, are naturally present in normal healthy sheep. The main diseases include:

Lamb dysentry—a condition that usually proves fatal and attacks lambs in the first week of life.

Enterotoxaemia (pulpy kidney)—a common cause of sudden death in lambs and adult sheep. It often affects lambs in good condition and is sometimes associated with a change to a better diet.

Tetanus—the causative organism is present in the soil and invades the sheep usually following operations such as castration, tail docking or shearing.

Blackleg—is another soil borne organism of the group which invades the sheep under similar conditions to those causing tetanus and causes losses following specific operations.

Braxy—this particular condition has often been associated with the death of weaned lambs in their first autumn, particularly when feeding on frosted crops and grass.

Black disease—This is associated with fluke infestation and the organism gains entrance to the sheep's tissues due to the damage caused by immature fluke worms. Prevention of fluke infestation is, therefore, one method of preventing Black disease.

These and other clostridial diseases can now be controlled by regular vaccination and, where necessary, it is economical to administer a compound vaccine, which gives simultaneous protection against several of these diseases. Booster vaccination of ewes just before lambing ensures high levels of protective antibodies in the colostrum which can protect the lamb for the first two or three months of life. Subsequent vaccination should allow for the time lag in developing higher immunity levels and should be timed to ensure maximum protection at times when sheep are known to be most vulnerable to the disease. The appropriate timing and frequency of vaccination varies from country to country.

Pasteurella organisms are associated with severe outbreaks of pneumonia. There is usually some predisposing factor that allows entry for the pasteurella and the soundest prevention is by tackling the general housing and management. In severe cases vaccination is possible.

FOOTROT

There are several conditions which can affect the sheep's feet which can be dealt with together as a group.

True footrot is caused by a mixed infection of *Fusiformis nodosus* and *Fusiformis necrophorus*, neither of which alone can cause the disease. *Fusiformis nodosus* can live on pasture for no more than two weeks but can be harboured by carrier sheep for many months, without outward signs of ill effects. *Fusiformis necrophorus* is normally found in the sheep's digestive tract and is, therefore, always present where there are sheep. Many have attempted eradication and failed, most probably because complete segregation of ostensibly healthy sheep was not followed up by a sufficiently long period of preventative foot bathing and regular examination, so that any carriers harbouring the organism could be recognized and dealt with.

The eradication process amounts to a thorough examination of the sheep's feet with segregation of apparently healthy from affected sheep. Healthy sheep have their feet trimmed and are run through a formalin footbath (10 per cent solution) before returning to clean pasture. From then on, these are kept completely isolated from other sheep and grazed on pasture that has been rested from other sheep for at least two weeks. The healthy sheep are run through the footbath at regular intervals and a sheep with any sign of lameness promptly examined and segregated. The affected sheep are subjected to a course of intensive treatment, starting with a thorough hoof paring and if possible are run through a footbath every day for two or three weeks. Any badly affected sheep should be sent for slaughter or kept permanently isolated and the treated sheep only allowed to join the healthy group after they have shown no symptoms for six months. Running through a footbath is a misleading phase, in that it is essential that the sheep should stand for some minutes in the solution for adequate penetration of the hoof.

This process is best carried out in ewes after the lambs are weaned, during the late summer, when dry conditions are likely to prevail.

The second approach to the footrot problem has to be adopted in the flying flock or where total self containment is impracticable. This involves control of the infection without complete eradication. It again involves thorough foot trimming and regular foot bathing although a low level of infection remains.

Vaccination against Footrot

Recently a vaccine for footrot has been developed in Australia and is widely available (Egerton & Roberts, 1971). It was a surprising finding by the Commonwealth Scientific and Industrial Research Organisation (CSIRO) in Australia in the late 1960s, that sheep infected with footrot could be cured by vaccination with suspensions of *F. nodosus* and that subsequently these sheep showed considerable resistance to infection on later exposure. The use of *F. necrophorus* for vaccination has not been successful, although inactivating one of the necessary organisms is sufficient to give the required protection. Footrot vaccine now available is prepared from cultures of *Fusiformis nodosus* inactivated by formalin and treated with aluminium hydroxide gels or potash alum. This, when injected subcutaneously, gives a degree of protection for several months due to high levels of circulating antibody. Following two initial injections, at about 8 weeks apart, immunity can be boosted by two further doses per annum. These booster doses should be given to ensure highest protection at the times of maximum challenge. Vaccination within the last 6 weeks of pregnancy is not recommended because much of the antibody produced passes to the lamb through the colostrum rather than being retained to give the required protection to the ewe.

The vaccine is a useful step forward in containment of the disease but it is expensive and only partly effective and must be supported by the other prceautions normally part of good sheep management.

OTHER FOOT CONDITIONS IN SHEEP

Scald

This is where the skin between the claws of the hoof becomes inflamed and the sheep become lame. Organisms such as

Fusiformis necrophorus or *Spirochaeta penortha* may be associated with the condition, and it is sometimes, but not always, the prelude to the development of true footrot.

Foot Abscess

Another condition, sometimes secondary to true footrot, is again often associated with *Fusiformis necrophorus*. Where this condition occurs in flocks where *F. nodosus* is not present, it usually affects a smaller proportion of the flock than in true footrot outbreaks, and sometimes only one hoof of an individual sheep may be involved. Treatment of affected cases with antibiotics is usually effective, but prevention is more difficult.

Strawberry Footrot

This condition is associated with species of *Dermatophilus* fungi and causes inflammation and ulceration above the hoof. It is not normally a problem where adequate precautions are taken to control common footrot.

Mastitis

Mastitis in the ewe is less common than in the dairy cow but is usually much more severe when it does occur. The acute gangrenous mastitis that occurs most commonly in sheep is associated with a *Staphylococcus* organism but other organisms can be found, particularly species of *Pasteurella* in the USA. The condition usually affects ewes in full lactation and develops so rapidly that little can be done to save the udder of the affected sheep. If the sheep survives, the udder usually blackens and sloughs off. Less acute mastitis, resulting in a hardening of a quarter, also occurs and may be associated with management at weaning. There is little published evidence on the degree and pattern of incidence in various countries but there appears to be a relatively high incidence in the North Country Cheviot of Scotland. This may be associated with the management of the sheep rather than the breed. Because of the lack of knowledge of the incidence of mastitis and the stages at which it is most prevalent, little evidence is available by which to evaluate means of preventing the condition.

Bacterial diseases that can affect lambs early in life include *Escherichia coli* infection, already referred to as a possible problem with artificially reared lambs. It can also affect lambs where lambing is concentrated and may cause severe scouring and death in lambs that are only a few days old. Other bacteria gain entrance into the lamb's body at birth through the navel and cause conditions such as 'joint ill'. Prevention is best accomplished by dressing the navel soon after birth using aerosol bactericidal sprays.

Other Diseases of Sheep

Some diseases, associated with organisms other than bacteria, are important in sheep. They include those such as foot and mouth disease, which are of general importance for pigs, cattle and sheep are not dealt with here.

SCRAPIE

This is a disease of sheep and goats that has been known in Europe for more than two hundred years. The disease has long defied full understanding partly because it takes a long time to develop in the sheep and is not usualy seen in animals less than 18 months old. The disease results in progressive nervous disturbance characterized by rubbing against various objects, the development of an unusual posture and gait, and in most cases the sheep eventually succumbs. There has been some controversy over the mode of transmission of the disease but it is now established that it is associated with the presence of a minute virus-like organism which can be transmitted from sheep to sheep and between sheep and goats. One possible route for this transmission is from the fetal membranes of scrapie-affected sheep (Pattison et al., 1972) which is consistent with the findings of Dickinson (1967) that the main transmission of scrapie is via the breeding ewe. The claims that the disease is hereditary or congenital cannot be fully accepted but it is established that susceptibility to the scrapie agent is under a measure of genetic control such that some genotypes may show some resistance or show a much delayed development of the disease. Several countries such as Australia, New Zealand, Canada and USA have been able to fend off the disease by strict import controls and by the adoption of a slaughter policy for all flocks in which affected sheep appear. Little is known about the present incidence in Europe, partly because there is some reserve about reporting it. Scrapie probably occurs in many European sheep breeds although its incidence in any flock may be low and confined to the older breeding animals.

DISEASES CAUSED BY VIRUS OR FUNGAL ORGANISMS

Contagious Opthalmia (*Pink Eye*; *Heather Blindness*)

This condition of the sheep's eye is similar to the eye infection of cattle (New Forest disease). It is associated with the presence of the virus like rickettsial organism *Ricketssia conjunctivae* and is found all over the world. The eye is much inflamed and the sheep may be temporarily blind during the course of the disease, but it usually subsides within two weeks and although there may be some residual opacity and greyness of the cornea in many cases, this finally clears and the sheep returns to normal. Treatment is often uneconomic and there are few prevention procedures possible.

Mycotic Dermatitis (*Lumpy Wool*)

This condition is associated with a fungus of the *Dermatophilus* genus. It most commonly results in a development of infection on damp areas of the back, sides and sometimes the head. The invasion of the epidermis and wool follicles causes a dermatitis with the secretion of an exudate which dries into black crusts in the matted, shortened wool and gives it the characteristic 'lumpy' wool areas. The condition usually clears up after shearing and there is little than can be done to control its incidence.

Contagious Pustular Dermatitis (*Orf, Sore Mouth*)

This skin disease is associated with a virus which is present widely in sheep all over the world. The symptoms of the disease include ulcers around the lips and nostrils, sometimes extending inside the mouth. Less frequently, the feet may be affected and the udder of ewes suckling infected lambs. It is most common in lambs from a few weeks old to several months and in a severe outbreak it markedly affects the lambs' well being.

Where the disease is common it can be controlled by vaccination, preferably under veterinary supervision.

DISEASES CAUSED BY PLANTS

There are a number of conditions which affect the sheep, stemming from the ingestion of certain plants. Some involve poisonous plants in the accepted meaning of the term. These include plants containing toxic alkaloids like the lupins and hemlocks.

Ragwort (*Senecio jacobea*) is known as a plant containing alkaloids toxic to all farm animals. Sheep appear to be able to tolerate larger doses than cattle, possibly because of a greater capability for degrading alkaloids in the gut. However, ragwort consumption has been associated with unthriftiness in fattening sheet and with abortion (J. C. Forbes, 1974; private communication).

Other plants act more indirectly, for example the oestrogenic plants, where the ingestion of high oestrogen levels from plants, such as some strains of subterranean clover in Australia, causes upsets in reproductive functions. This results in infertility in ewes as well as the development of side-effects in wether sheep.

Several plants cause photosensitization where the skin becomes hypersensitive to the action of direct sunlight. In the chronic forms there is an irritation of the skin at the extremities with consequent scab formation and sloughing off so that in some cases the ears gradually wear away. Several plants all over the world may have photosensitizing properties; in the UK the condition is often associated with the grazing of rape.

Sheep Housing and Handling Pens

Housing is a less important feature of sheep production than of any of the other major farm livestock systems. This is a reflection of the fact that sheep are usually associated with systems where grazing is the major source of feed throughout the year. Sheep are also well adapted in terms of their fleece and their foraging ability for pasturing during unfavourable winter weather conditions.

Nevertheless, there is a tradition of the use of buildings, primarily for winter housing, in high latitude countries such as those of Scandinavia and Iceland where snow covers the ground in winter. Night housing or penning has also been widespread all over the world where predators have been a problem. In areas where sheep milking in small peasant flocks is practised, the sheep flock is often kept in after the evening milking, sometimes in the ground floor of the owner's house, so that the flock can be milked again before spending the day out on pasture.

Under present day conditions the role of housing for sheep is still a very limited and specialized one. These are:

1. As an alternative to the traditional practice of renting wintering land for sheep in mountain areas, primarily for ewe lambs in their first winter. Housing is rarely cheaper than 'away wintering' when fully costed (MAFF, 1969) but it can sometimes provide stability and independence for the hill farmer in a situation where there are other demands on suitable wintering land (Owen, 1960).

2. On lowland farms with wet, heavy land where the advantages in terms of resting winter pastures and the possibility of better control of feeding and lambing, outweigh the higher feed costs normally incurred with winter housing (Cooper, 1966).

The major constraints on house design to meet these two

requirements are those of cost and health. Cost must be minimized by using adaptations of existing buildings or by relying on economy buildings, providing the simple essential features. The chief aspect as far as health is concerned is to ensure adequate ventilation and dry conditions underfoot.

The main types of winter housing available are as follows:

Unroofed yards. One method of keeping sheep that may not strictly be defined as 'housing' is to confine the sheep to an area which serves only as yard space, with no vegetation growth, and all the feed has to be provided. Examples of this type of confinement, on a large scale, are found in the feed lots of the mid West and Western states of the USA. Such feed lots are commonly confined to low rainfall areas, not far from the cereal growing belt, on sites where the land is reasonably free draining.

Under certain conditions woodland provides an ideal site for wintering sheep. Care has to be taken that trees of the appropriate species and stage of development are used and that sheep are not short of feed so that they damage the bark of the trees. Normally a much greater area of woodland would be allowed per sheep than for normal open yard systems.

For more intensive confinement under wetter climatic conditions it is necessary to make provision for the maintenance of dry lying conditions. Fig. 8.1 illustrates such a yard based on slatted floors suitable for wintering mature ewes at 1 to 1.5 m^2 per ewe. The design of the slatted floors is shown in Fig. 8.2.

Semi open sheds. A common type of sheep house is one where one side (or the front) of the building is open to ensure adequate ventilation. Houses such as the example shown in Fig. 8.1 need careful siting to avoid excessive exposure to severe weather. Flooring can be in the form of slats, as in the example shown, or in the form of a drained solid floor either bedded with straw or other litter, or partly mechanically scraped.

Enclosed sheds. Although it is possible to provide a fully enclosed, controlled environment house, for sheep there are as yet few situations where such cost can be justified. The usual enclosed house for sheep is a naturally ventilated building, an

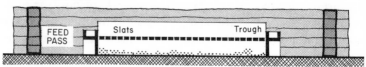

Open yard

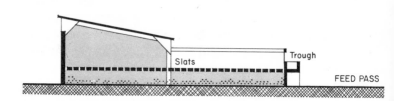

Open fronted shed

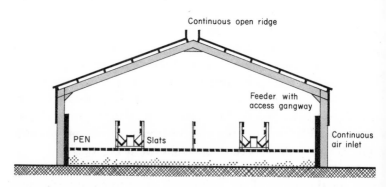

Enclosed shed

Fig. 8.1. *Slatted floor sheep housing.*

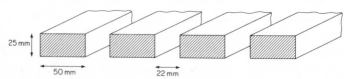

Fig. 8.2. *Wooden slatted floors suitable for sheep buildings (cross-section). (By courtesy of Mr. D. S. Soutar, Scottish Farm Buildings, Investigation Unit, Aberdeen.)*

example of which is shown in Fig. 8.1. Such a building can be flexibly used and usually provides the most congenial environment for lambing ewes.

SPACE ALLOWANCES AND BUILDING DIMENSIONS

Only a very general indication can be given of space allowances for sheep. The appropriate allowance depends very largely on the size of group in which the sheep are subdivided, the size of the sheep, the behaviour and temperament of the sheep and whether provision for an out-run is available. The greater the size of the group running together the smaller the necessary floor space allowance per sheep within the group, to give the same comfort. Floor space allowances can vary from $0.5 \ m^2$/sheep for small ewe lambs in a shed provided with an outrun to as much as $1.5-2.0 \ m^2$/sheep for accommodating mature ewes during pregnancy and lambing time.

The dimensions of a building are very much influenced by the feeding system employed since rationed feeding depends on the availability of adequate feeding space for each sheep. Since the requirement for a mature sheep may be in the region of 50 cm, a building giving $1.5 \ m^2$ per sheep will need to be 3 m in depth. A double sided building involving a central passageway is still likely to be relatively long and narrow unless the design is doubled up as shown in Fig. 8.1. When feeding is based on the ad libitum consumption of complete diets feeding space can be reduced to about 10 cm per adult sheep thus giving more flexibility in house design as well as the advantages in labour saving and reduction of disturbance in the sheep house. Complete diets can be based on mixtures of silage, coarsely ground dry roughage and cereals or on dry mixtures without the silage.

Fig. 8.3 illustrates the design of self-feeders for dry complete diets and mixer trailers of the type that can be used to make a complete mix based on any common feedingstuff, e.g., silage, roots, chopped straw, distillers' grains and cereals are available, which are suitable for sheep.

Whatever the size and design of a sheep house, it is desirable,

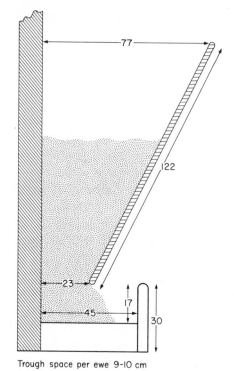

Trough space per ewe 9-10 cm

Fig. 8.3. *Feeding trough (dimensions in cm).*

as far as possible, to retain flexibility of subdivision within it, so that in-wintered sheep can be divided into groups of appropriate size. If the house is to be used for lambing, provision for individual penning is needed. This may involve 1 lambing pen per 4–10 ewes in the group depending on the intensity of care and the length of time ewes are kept separate for proper mothering. There is little critical information on the optimum size of group for housing and work on other species may not be applicable to the sheep.

Intensity of use of sheep housing. One of the major problems in justifying expenditure on sheep housing is the difficulty of making sufficiently intensive use of the buildings. Few sheep systems justify housing the ewes for more than a few months of the year, although the use of such houses may be extended to a limited extent for operations such as shearing and for the intensive fattening of store lambs. The most satisfactory solution in some situations, is to integrate sheep housing with other complementary uses. Buildings used for storing crops such as potatoes or feedingstuffs such as hay or grain, may often provide space for in-wintering sheep in late winter and at lambing time.

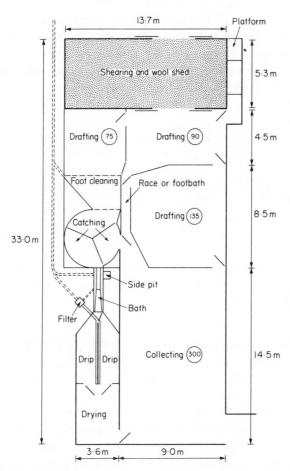

Fig. 8.4. *Sheep dipping and handling pens (circles show appropriate sheep capacity.)*

Other possibilities include the use of turkey rearing houses where space may be available in late winter and early spring.

Sheep handling pens

Handling pens, unlike housing, are essential for most sheep units but they suffer even more acutely than housing, in that they are used intensively for very short periods and may remain unused for a large proportion of the year. In many ways portable pens have advantages, particularly for a sheep flock kept on a mixed farm and moved in rotation from one part of the farm to another. Unfortunately, intensive use under wet conditions demands that at least part of the area be concreted to make handling sheep tolerable.

The main essentials of a suitable sort of handling pen system, illustrated in Fig. 8.4 are:

(1) An adequate collecting pen into which all the sheep can be easily driven and held.

(2) A drafting race leading on through a sorting gate with access to two or three drafting pens as well as the main collecting pen.

(3) A catching pen for dosing and handling sheep with means of maintaining sheep density as the numbers in the pen decrease.

(4) A foot bath.

(5) Dipping and/or spraying facilities.

Construction materials need to be cheap but strong enough to withstand mass pressure from many sheep, and free from obstruction likely to cause injury to the sheep and to impede free flow. Wooden posts and rails are the most common construction materials.

Details of materials and construction are available in many bulletins in different countries, and those suitable for UK conditions are summarized by the MAFF (1969) which is also the source of Fig. 8.4.

Fig. 8.5. *Sheep handling on a New Zealand farm. (By courtesy of the High Commissioner for New Zealand, London.)*

Genetic Improvement 9

Development of Sheep Breeds

In dealing with the genetic improvement of sheep it is useful first to survey the breeds of sheep available, as raw material for the present day breeder, and to consider how present day breeds were developed. Sheep and man have been associated for a very long time. Domestication is thought to have occurred in about 10 000 B.C., some time after the dog and before cattle were domesticated (Zeuner, 1963).

The domestication of sheep is an example of how two species became gradually more closely associated, in this case presumably by the dependence of early man on the wild sheep for food and clothing, until eventually both species occupied so close an ecological niche that domestication was almost inevitable. It is likely that this initial association occurred in mountainous territory, the natural habitat of the sheep and laid the foundations of 'transhumance' systems described earlier (Chapter 1).

The earlier domestication of the dog was a possible factor in the domestication of the sheep, seeing how valuable the dog has become in the herding and handling of the sheep.

Domesticated sheep are thought to be descended from some of the races of wild sheep still found today (Ryder & Stephenson, 1968). The sheep first domesticated was probably the Urial type, of which two varieties are still found today in South West Asia. Another kind of wild sheep—the Argali, found in central

321

Asia probably contributed to the Asiatic groups of present-day sheep, whilst the Mouflon still found in some of the Mediterranean islands like Corsica and Sardinia, probably contributed to European groups. The other main type of wild sheep still existing, the Bighorn, is found in the Rocky Mountains of the USA, although there is no evidence that it was ever domesticated. As human civilization spread outward from its origin, domesticated sheep were carried with it and intermingled with the local types of wild sheep to provide the wide variety of sheep that are present today. The original sheep, like the Soay sheep of Northern Britain today, were probably short-tailed and had a double coated fleece of long hairy fibres growing through a close jacket of short fine wool.

Domestication followed by selection of the various types of sheep has resulted in significant changes from the original sheep in three main ways.

The most noticeable is the development of the wool characteristics so that in the Merino the old outer coat has been virtually eliminated and a fleece composed entirely of the soft fine wool developed. Secondly, sheep have in some areas been developed as a dairy animal and in many peasant communities of the Mediterranean, Middle East and Eastern European countries the sheep is largely a dairy animal yielding meat as a by-product. The other noticeable change brought about in the sheep has been the development of early maturity, in the post-Bakewell era of the eighteenth and nineteenth centuries, which has resulted in breeds that have a high proportion of fat in the carcass at a low weight, when well fed.

WORLD CLASSIFICATION OF SHEEP BREEDS

The sheep belongs to the Genus *Ovis* which is closely related to the Genus *Capra*. The sheep and the goat have been closely associated during man's history and it is sometimes difficult, particularly with fossil evidence, to distinguish between the two species. However, the goat differs from sheep in several respects, particularly in that it does not have the wool fibres in its coat and is adapted to a different biological niche, in that it can penetrate and utilize grazing areas on steep and craggy slopes and cliffs which are not utilized by the sheep. In domesticated use the lack of wool has meant that the goat has been more narrowly specialized as a dairy animal than the sheep. Some types of sheep, such as the Barbary of North America, really belong to a group intermediate between sheep and goats. The list of breeds given in Table 1.3 (*see* pp. 12–13) is not meant to be comprehensive but it includes most of the breeds that are important, not only in terms of numbers, but in terms of their potential future use as genetic material in sheep improvement.

Fig. 9.1 is an attempt by Dr M. L. Ryder of the Animal Breeding Research Organization, Edinburgh, to put some functional and developmental significance into the rather arbitrary groupings in Table 1.3.

There are several interesting groups. The group descended from the Northern Short Tail sheep which includes breeds like the Finnsheep and the Romanov, are characterized by a high level of prolificacy, a character which, until recently, was not highly desirable. The sheep groups are dominated by the Merino and its near cousins, and its importance reflects the traditional emphasis on wool. The Merino has also had an influence as a more minor component of breeds such as the Dorset Horn, an influence often unacknowledged and unrecorded. The Merino's rôle in the history of agricultural development is thus important and far-reaching (Carter, 1964).

The recent search for previously localized breeds with special characteristics, like prolificacy, is likely to intensify and for northern latitudes there is likely to be an emphasis on breeds that can fit into frequent breeding systems. There is some suggestion that there may be an association between length of breeding season and prolificacy (Land, 1974). Some within-breed studies have failed to reveal such an association (Purser, 1972) and much more evidence both between and within breed, is required to see how helpful such an association can be in developing sheep for high production systems.

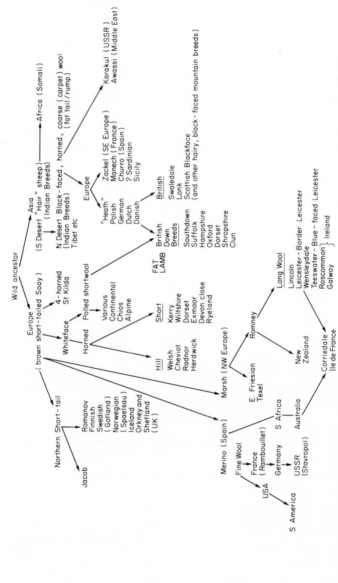

Fig. 9.1. *Classification and affinities of sheep.* (*By courtesy of Dr M. L. Ryder, Animal Breeding Research Organization Edinburgh.*)

Fig. 9.2. *Romanov sheep in the northern European part of the USSR. (By courtesy of the Soviet Embassy, London.)*

Fig. 9.3. *Merino ram in the Altai district, Siberia. (By courtesy of the Soviet Embassy, London.)*

The fat tailed sheep like the Awassi, of widespread importance in the drier parts of the world, are an example of adaptation to drought conditions, although in future such adaptations may have less significance where the general level of animal husbandry is raised through the provision of supplementary feed and better water supplies.

THE FORMATION OF PRESENT-DAY SHEEP BREEDS

The development of officially designated sheep breeds, as known today, started in the Western World in the eighteenth century and reached its peak in the nineteenth century. In Europe, breed or flock book societies were initially the result of a few breeders getting together to form a society to develop a sheep breed, largely based on the local type of the area, sometimes with the introduction of one or more favoured individual sheep from other localities. The Englishman, Robert Bakewell, one of the pioneer breeders of the eighteenth century, developed the English Leicester breed by such a process and stood out among many of his followers in that he strove to introduce an objective basis to selection. Only a few of the present-day sheep breeds as listed by Mason (1969) are completely pedigreed, in the sense that both ewes and rams are individually identified and form a virtually closed population. The official formation of a breed society, with a committee and its officers, was often associated with the exposition of the society's aims and included the definition of the objective of the breed. Usually this comprised a list of 'points' describing standards of excellence to be aimed at in the breed, based partly on relatively unambiguous standards such as colouring, and on a variety of less definable characteristics such as 'spring of rib', 'boldness of eye', 'character' (NSBA, 1968). Performance characteristics when included are described in general terms such as 'deep milking' and 'early maturing'.

As breed societies developed public demonstrations of the interpretation of these ambiguous criteria were given at agricultural shows where the sheep were exhibited for competitive ranking and judged by breeders authoritative on breed type. Present-day breeds have gone through a series of changes in 'fashion', amounting to a re-interpretation of the original aims, sometimes coupled with the introduction of genes from other breeds.

Breed societies form a medium of contact between breeders, just like any other society, and many breeds are dominated for some time by a relatively small handful of active leading members who form the top of the breed hierarchy and supply the major contribution to the gene pool of the breed. The average breeder, however, tends to have a limited stay in pedigree breeding (Table 9.1, MLC, 1972) although it is quite common for some families to be associated with a breed for many generations.

Table 9.1. *Statistics of some registered sheep flocks.* (*MLC, 1972*).

Breed	No. of flocks	Average no. of years reg.d	Average no. of breeding ewes	Average no. of rams per flock	Per cent of home bred rams
Bluefaced Leicester	350	19*	10	1.4	†
Border Leicester	397	†	24	2.3	9
Clun Forest	320	†	129	3.1	14
Devon Closewool	190	18	191	3.5	8
Dorset Down	77	14	103	3.0	16
Dorset Horn	107	15	87	2.9	21
Hampshire Down	66	15	59	2.2	24
Leicester	43	29	32	†	†
Lincoln	20	20	43	1.4	14
Oxford Down	32	30	34	1.6	8
Polled Dorset Horn	37	6	94	3.4	37
Romney	57	17	271	8.1	53
South Devon	93	20	53	1.8	0
Southdown	25	†	64	2.5	32
Suffolk	915	12	40	2.2	13
Teeswater	195	22*	6	1.7	†
Wensleydale	17	22*	10	1.3	†

* Average age of flocks (flock book not in existence for some of the period). Source: Data drawn from breed society flock books.
† Data not available.

The trend to objective measurement of economically important traits has been a more recent and more restricted phenomenon in the sheep than in other livestock (Owen, 1971). Notable exceptions are the recording schemes associated with the Finnsheep and the East Friesian since the early years of the century.

Selection in Improvement

There are two distinct ways in which improvement in any form of animal production may be achieved. One is to make better use of the existing genetic material by better feeding and management (environment) and the other is to change the material itself by genetic improvement. In practice both forms of improvement go together, although in certain instances more dramatic improvement can be made from one method than the other.

Some important terms need definition at the outset, others will be defined later in the chapter.

Population: The ideal population refers to a large randomly mating group of animals genetically isolated from other groups. Real populations, such as breeds of sheep or large flocks, do not fulfil the ideal in that they are finite in size, not strictly randomly mated and not always completely isolated from, or closed to, matings with animals of other breeds.

Phenotypic variation: The variation shown in any character or trait, possessed by members of a population is called phenotypic variation and is made up of a non-genetic component, due to such factors as year of birth and level of feeding, and a genetic component due to the genetic make-up of members of the population.

Sometimes phenotype is mistakenly thought of as the outward appearance of the animal. It is in fact the tangible manifestation of the animal that can be observed and measured in various ways. It includes the various aspects of performance such as weight, milk yield and carcass traits in addition to external measurements and conformation.

Genetic variation: The genotype is an abstract concept and can be thought of as being related to the phenotype in the same way as an architect's plan of a cathedral is to the completed building itself. In animal breeding it is conventional to conceive of the genotype of an individual animal in terms of 'breeding value' which can be thought of as the additive effect of all genes that are passed on to any offspring.

Genetic variation arises partly because of variation in the frequency (or proportion) of desirable as against undesirable genes, and partly because of the way the genes are combined to form good or less good combinations. Hybrid vigour, for instance, arises from the way the genes are distributed in their various combinations and not from the fact that the frequency of desirable genes is necessarily higher. In special circumstances, therefore, depending on the sheep it is mated to, the breeding value of a sheep may exceed its predicted breeding value.

Selection: The major weapon available to the breeder in the task of effecting genetic improvement is the selection of superior animals from existing stock and the judicious mating of these selected parents to produce the ensuing generation of new stock. Selection obviously must act on some variability in the characters in question, whether it be in the choice of one breed against another or in the choice of individuals within one breed. The scientific aspects of selection depends on the recognition of the components of the variability within and between animal populations and the manipulation of these components within a selection scheme, to the best economic advantage.

If any one character of a breed of sheep is examined, e.g., the mature weight of ewes, the variability can be expressed in the form shown in Fig. 9.4. This illustrates diagrammatically that if all the ewes in the breed were enumerated a large number of them would have mature weights near the true mean of the breed (μ) but a few animals would differ fairly substantially above or below this mean.

In genetic improvement it is not only the amount of the total or phenotypic variation that is important but that portion of it

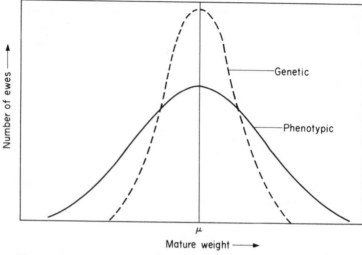

Fig. 9.4. *Distribution of ewes within a breed according to mature body weight.*

due to genetic differences. Within the bell shaped normal curve shown in Fig. 9.4 the genetic variation is represented by another curve which has the same mean value but less variation.

Heritability: The heritability of a trait is an important parameter and measures the proportion of the total variation (variance) in the trait which is due to additive genetic effects (those effects that depend on the frequency of the genes concerned). In its condensed form it is expressed as:

$$h^2 = \frac{V_G}{V_p}$$

where h^2 = heritability (which is the square of h, the correlation between additive breeding value and the phenotypic value)

V_G = additive genetic variance

V_p = phenotypic (total) variance

Simply inherited characters: Simply inherited characters are influenced by only a few pair of genes—often only 1 or 2 pairs—so that the results of matings can be observed and analysed in terms of the segregations of the individual genes. None of the main objectives of sheep improvement, which will later be considered to have priority, fall into the class of simply inherited characters. Nevertheless, such characters are sometimes important, particularly if some undesirable gene needs to be eliminated. All characters that show genetic variation are influenced by one or more pairs of genes, each pair located at a specific point on the chromosome, with each member of a pair being a random selection from the corresponding pair possessed by the parent. The effect of a pair of genes may be the mean of the effect expected if the members of the pair were paired with an identical gene; in this case there is no dominance. In other cases the effect of the pair of genes is nearer to the value expected if the pair were made up of two genes corresponding to one of the members; the member gene in question then shows dominance over the other (recessive) member.

If dominance is complete then the effect of the recessive member of the pair is completely overshadowed. If sufficient data on the results of individual mating are available, it can be determined whether a character is simply inherited or not and what the precise nature of the gene pairs involved is. Several examples of such gene effects in the sheep have been reviewed by Rae (1956).

Fleece colour—dominant black as in the Karakul and Black Welsh Mountain; recessive black as found in most white breeds with varying gene frequency; there are several other examples of colour and colour patterns apparently influenced by one or very few pairs of genes.

In white breeds which give rise to the occasional black individual the difference in colour is usually the effect of a single pair of genes with the white gene (allele) dominant to the black allele. If the white allele is denoted by *W* and its black allele by *w*, then when black sheep (*ww*) are mated together they can only give rise to black progeny. If black sheep (*ww*) are mated with true breeding whites (*WW*), the resulting lambs (*Ww*) are white. However, if sheep of the *Ww* genotype (the heterozygotes) are mated together in sufficient numbers the result should be the normal Mendelian ratio of $1\,WW:2\,Ww:1\,ww$, i.e., three whites for each black sheep.

If true breeding blacks (ww) are mated to heterozygous whites (Ww) in sufficient numbers, the progeny should show a ratio of one white to one black sheep.

A fuller account of simple inheritance in sheep has been given in other texts (Nichols, 1957).

Face and leg colour—White fleeced sheep breeds vary in face and leg colour from black through various gradations of dilution (solid brown or dun) and speckled (broken white and black) to white. Two or more pairs of genes are usually involved in the development of these colours and colour patterns.

Multiple teats—Ewes occasionally show an extra pair of supernumerary teats which are non-functional. More rarely a ewe may have more than one pair of extra teats and there may be some secretion from one pair of extra teats; it is possible that this character is associated with differences in only one or two pairs of genes. Although breeds like the Finnsheep and Romanov seem to show a higher frequency of this character it is hard to support the view that it is associated with high prolifacacy and there is no evidence of a clear association with milk yield.

Birth coat in the lamb—The degree of hairiness of the lamb birth coat appears to be partly influenced by relatively few genes.

Horns—Sheep breeds differ in respect to the presence of horns in the sexes—some being horned in both sexes, e.g., Scottish Blackface, 'Cheviot', Swaledale and Dorset Horn.

Some are polled in both sexes, e.g., the Down breeds, Clun Forest, Finnsheep, others where only the ram is horned, e.g., Welsh Mountain and the Merino.

The inheritance of horns in sheep has been subject to some debate but it has been suggested that the results of crosses such as Dorset Horn × Suffolk are best explained as being that hornlessness is dominant in both sexes but the dominance is incomplete in the male so that the first cross rams grows reduced horns.

Another hypothesis which seems to fit the known observations is that in sheep there are two pairs of genes influencing the horned or polled condition. The first pair contains a polled gene dominant to its (horned) allele. The other pair contains a horn modifying gene which suppresses the horned condition in the female.

Abnormalities—There are several abnormalities, many of them influenced by recessive genes which vary in their effect:

Slight defects such as cryptorchidism (where one testicle in the ram is retained in the body cavity) and jaw defects where the lower jaw appears too long 'undershot' or too short 'overshot'.

Lethal and seimi-lethal defects such as nervous inco-ordination ('daft' lambs) and dwarfism.

Blood Groups—There is increasing evidence on a number of distinct blood groups in sheep. The presence of these blood groups can already be used to characterize individuals and breeds and there is some indication in animals generally that certain blood group differences can be associated with differences in economic characters. However, so far there is no indication of a substantial practical application of knowledge on blood groups apart from the occasional use in parentage verification and in helping to understand the evolution and inter-relationship of modern sheep breeds.

GENES IN POPULATIONS

Within a flock or a breed, it may be important to know what proportions of genes at a particular *locus* (position) on the chromosome belong to one type or another, e.g., we might wish to know what is the proportion or *frequency* of the black gene in a white breed. Since individual genes can only express themselves through their effect within a pair of genes the frequency of the genes themselves has to be deduced from the frequency of the genotypes or gene pairs in the population. The relation between gene frequency and genotype frequency (gene distribution) follows the Hardy–Weinburg principle and can be conveniently expressed in the binomial

$$(p + q)^2 = p^2 + 2pq + q^2$$

Where p = the frequency of one type of gene

q = $1 - p$ the frequency of the other gene

p^2 = frequency of gene pairs containing both genes of the first type

q^2 = frequency of gene pairs containing both genes of the second type

$2pq$ = frequency of the gene pairs containing both types of gene (i.e. the heterozygotes).

This formula can be used to deduce the frequency of a gene such as a recessive black gene in white sheep since the number of homozygous recessives, i.e., sheep with both black genes, is the q^2 of the above formula and its square root is therefore the desired gene frequency. This is only an approximate estimate of what occurs in practice because the ideal conditions required for the strict operation of the Hardy–Weinburg principle, e.g., random mating, are not fulfilled.

This reasoning also shows that straight selection against homozygous recessives, with a recessive gene at low frequency, is relatively difficult since so few genes (q^2) are revealed for culling. On the other hand, selecting for a dominant white gene in a predominantly black sheep population will initially be very efficient since all the white genes, being dominant, are exposed to selection.

Quantitative Characters. Most of the important applications of genetic theory are involved with the improvement of characters which are influenced simultaneously by many gene pairs and by the environment. With such characters the binomial or histogram type of distribution, associated with relatively small numbers of gene pairs and where there is no effect of environment, is not evident. 'Normal' variation, described earlier by the 'normal' curve is more common; most variation in the characters of the sheep can be assumed to be of this kind.

Individual ewes cannot, of course, have fractions of lambs, but the means of groups of several ewes are distributed approximately normally. Variation of characters in sheep production can, therefore, be conveniently expressed in terms of the normal curve with the resulting advantage of conciseness and amenability to mathematical manipulation.

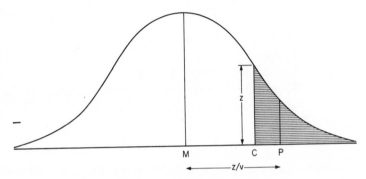

Fig. 9.5. *Response to selection.*

The process of selection. The selection procedure at its simplest involves the cutting off of a segment of the population for breeding (Fig. 9.5). The smaller the proportion of the population retained for breeding purposes, i.e., the segment cut off or truncated at C, the greater the superiority of the mean of the parents (P) over the mean of the whole population (M). This difference $P-M$, called the selection differential (S), is conveniently measured in units of standard deviation and denoted by i; i can be derived from the proportion of the population retained as parents using the following expression:

$$i = \frac{z}{v}$$

where

z = the ordinate of the normal curve $\Big\}$ (See tables by
v = the fraction of animals retained $\Big.$ Fisher & Yates, 1943)

When the parents are mated to produce another generation, the mean of the new generation will be the product of the selection differential and the heritability of the character $Sh^2 (= i\sigma_p h^2)$ and the expected improvement per annum measured in real units (Ry) is estimated by:

$$Ry = \frac{i\sigma_p h^2}{A} = \frac{ih\sigma_G}{A}$$

where i = selection differential in standard units

σ_p = the standard deviation

σ_G = the genetic standard deviation

h^2 = the additive genetic variance as a proportion of the total phenotypic variance.

A = the generation interval measured as the average age of parents when their young are born.

The additive genetic variance which forms the raw material for selection is that part of the phenotypic variability which is due to the average effects of the genes (considered singly) in the population. The other component of genotypic variance is due to the particular way the genes in question are combined in the particular individuals. Especially favourable or unfavourable gene combinations (due to dominant effects, etc.) are not necessarily repeated when the members of gene pairs are broken up and subsequently recombined during mating. Thus it is only the additive genetic variance that can be used to ensure progressive improvement during selection.

Reverting to the expression that selection response per annum

$$Ry = \frac{i\sigma_p h^2}{A}$$

it must be remembered that the selection differential (S) usually differs between rams and ewes in a sheep breeding scheme since much fewer rams than ewes are required to maintain a flock of a given size.

For example, assume a flock of 2000 ewes with a crop of 2000 lambs per annum, selected purely on the basis of lamb weight at castration time (corrected for age). Assume that 10 rams per annum are required to replenish the necessary team of 40 stud rams and that 500 ewe lambs need to be retained each year to maintain the flock of 2,000 ewes in regular ages.

If the sex ratio is 50:50, then the 10 rams are selected from 1000 possible candidates, a proportion of 0.01 and the 500 ewe lambs also from 1000 possible candidates, a proportion of 0.5.

If it is assumed that the standard deviation of lamb weight at this stage (the same for rams and ewes) = 1.5 kg and the heritability = 0.2

	Rams	Ewes
Proportion selected	0.01	0.5
selection intensity ($i = z/v$)	2.64	0.8
Phenotypic standard deviation (σ_p)	1.5 kg	1.5 kg
heritability (h^2)	0.2	0.2
Assumed generation interval (the average interval that elapses between birth of the parents and the birth of the lambs)	3.0	3.5

The rate of progress per annum from this hypothetical breeding scheme can be estimated by adding up the value of $i\sigma_p h^2$ computed separately for ewes and for rams and dividing by the sum of (Σ) the separate generation intervals, i.e.,

$$\frac{\Sigma i\sigma_p h^2}{\Sigma A}$$

This becomes

$$\frac{(2.64)(1.5)(0.2) + (0.8)(1.5)(0.2)}{3.0 + 3.5} = 0.16 \text{ kg}$$

In practice the situation is generally more complicated because rams are often subjected to selection at castration time and again at a later stage and the ewe lambs are often selected on quite different criteria from ram lambs.

More realistic examples of the calculation of response to selection will be given later.

Methods of Selection

Individual selection

So far the discussion has focussed on the selection of individuals within a population, based on measurements of their own performance with respect to the selected character. This is called individual selection. It is a direct and simple form of selection and has wide applicability and, where possible, it is always one, if not the only, method employed.

There are certain circumstances where it is obviously not applicable, for example:

(1) It is not possible to apply it to the selection of rams, on characters such as prolificacy or mothering ability, which the rams themselves do not exhbit, i.e., sex limited characters.

(2) It is also impossible to use individual selection directly for improvement of carcass attributes since, to obtain the necessary information, the sheep has to be slaughtered first.

In other situations, additional information can be used to augment that from the measured phenotype of the candidates for selection.

The other forms of selection are based on the information available on the relatives of the candidates in question—the ancestors, the collateral relatives (sibs) and the progeny.

Pedigree selection

Selection on the basis of the average performance of ancestors has the great merit of enabling selection to be carried out more or less at birth, thus cutting down the generation interval and the costs involved in delaying selection (e.g., not castrating ram lambs). It has the drawback of usually being the least 'accurate' form of selection giving only a very limited evaluation of the animals breeding value. Put in another way, the heritability of values of mean performance of ancestors is low, largely because there are so few of them that are closely related. Given the heritability of a character, the appropriate weighting factors can be calculated, to estimate the breeding value of an animal from that of its ancestors.

The following is an example of the appropriate weighting factors that may be used in selecting for the number of lambs born in sheep.

Assumption—heritability of litter size at birth based on two records for the 3 year old ewe

$$= 0.2$$

Then $BVI = b_d D + b_{pd} PD + b_{md} MD$
where BVI = breeding value index at birth
$\quad b_d$ = partial regression coefficient of BVI on dam's performance
$\quad b_{pd}$ = partial regression coefficient of BVI on paternal dam's performance
$\quad b_{md}$ = partial regression coefficient of BVI on maternal dam's performance
$\quad D$ = dam record
$\quad PD$ = paternal dam (granddam) record
$\quad MD$ = maternal dam (granddam) record
For the above assumption the appropriate weightings are:
$\quad BVI = 0.1D + 0.05PD + 0.04MD$ (Pirchner, 1969)

Selection on the basis of the sheep's own performance and that of its ancestors is often the most efficient method of selection in relation to making maximum progress with least expense.

SIB AND PROGENY TESTING

As the names suggest these methods of testing depend on the assessment of breeding value from the information on groups of sibs or progeny. Of all selection methods, the progeny test is potentially the ultimate in accuracy since the breeding value of a ram is, by definition, twice the average superiority of an infinitely large group of progeny, from a large population of ewes. The sib test is less accurate than the progeny test and in the case of half sib selection (which can be considered also as selection on the basis of the parent's progeny test) is half as accurate for the same number of animals as a progeny test.

However, sib testing often affords an opportunity to cut down the generation interval and therefore may still be preferred to progeny testing. Progeny testing, in spite of its advantages in terms of 'accuracy' in identifying the breeding value, is hardly ever justifiable in sheep because of the long generation interval and the increased costs associated with it. It is shown later that selection for lambs born, for instance, can best be based on an optimum combination of individual and pedigree information rather than a laborious and costly progeny testing scheme.

SELECTION FOR SEVERAL TRAITS

As outlined already it is usually necessary to select for several traits.

Selection index: Normally it is most efficient to combine all the values for the traits in question into one figure or index value, using an equation of the following form:

$$I = W_A A + W_B B + W_C C$$

where $I =$ index value A, B and C are the measured values of the traits selected for and W_A, W_B and W_C are weighting factors which give each character a different weight in the index according to the economic value of a unit of the trait, to the heritability of that trait and also according to any correlation (genetic and non-genetic) there may be, between the trait and other traits contributing to an index.

For example, a trait of little value economically gets very little weight, even if it is highly heritable, and vice versa. Equally a trait will receive less weight if it tends to be associated with low values for the other desirable traits.

Genetic correlation: The genetic correlation between two traits, observed in members of a population of animals, measure the association (covariance) between the traits arising from genetic causes. This association arises because characters are affected by the same genes (pleiotropic effects) or by linked genes. The other component of phenotypic correlations between traits arise from common environment effects.

The use of an index as a measure of an animal's 'all round' worth is a reasonable concept which has wide applications outside breeding. An interviewing panel for a post are generally attempting, in a subjective way, to combine assessments of the various qualities of the candidates into an overall balanced assessment of their likely future usefulness. The objective implementation of this concept in practical sheep breeding is less easy, because of the difficulty of assessing the appropriate weighting for each factor. Taking a very simple case, where the economic worth of the sheep depends mainly on characters that are not correlated in any way it can be shown that the appropriate weighting for each character should be the product of the economic worth of the character and its heritability (ah^2). The economic worth of the character (a) can be defined as the change in the money value of the sheep for unit change in the character in question. In a simple case, if wool is worth £0.50 per kg, then the economic weight of wool is £0.50 since a sheep with 4 kg of wool is worth £0.50 more than one with 3 kg of wool, other things being equal.

Example: Assume that in a certain sheep system young sheep are slaughtered as yearlings for mutton, and selection is made at that time for the ewes to be retained for breeding, on the basis of their wool yield and body weight. Assuming both characters to be uncorrelated, a & h^2 for wool £0.50 and 0.40 and a and h^2 for liveweight £0.25 and 0.30 the following index would be appropriate:

$$
\begin{aligned}
I &= W_A A + W_B B \\
&= a_A h_A^2 A + a_B h_B^2 B \\
&= 0.2A + 0.075B
\end{aligned}
$$

where A = wool weight and B = body weight

Taking the case of two ewes

> ewe 1 with 4.0 kg wool and 45 kg bodyweight
>
> ewe 2 with 3.0 kg wool and 55 kg bodyweight

$$I \text{ (ewe 1)} = (0.2)(4.0) + (0.075)(45) = 4.175$$
$$I \text{ (ewe 2)} = (0.2)(3.0) + (0.075)(50) = 4.35$$

Obviously ewe 2 is preferred to ewe 1 although ewe 1 is considerably superior in terms of wool yield. The example is not realistic because it would be unwise to assume that there was no correlation (phenotypic or genetic) between bodyweight and wool yield. Also, in practice it is not usual to be able to delay all culling and selection until all the characters have been measured. However where all the parameters are known at the time of selection, i.e., economic worth, heritability, phenotypic variance, genetic and environmental correlation then appropriate methods have been developed to calculate the optimum weighting for each character (Turner & Young. 1969).

Independent culling levels: In practice another method of selecting for several traits simultaneously may be more useful. In this method an independent culling level is set for each character although commonly this may take the form of setting a certain proportion of the sheep, to be selected as breeding stock, with respect to each character, at a particular selection stage. This method is theoretically less efficient than the selection index method, particularly in certain circumstances. For instance, a sheep which is outstanding in one respect and just fails to qualify on another criterion is rejected by this method but is likely to be selected on an index method. The superiority of a selection index is more marked the more characters that are being considered for selection and the smaller the selection intensity (Turner & Young, 1969).

In sheep selection, where there is a stepwise culling of breeding stock candidates, there is often no practical alternative to the use of the independent culling method. Although this method does not depend on weighting factors as such, similar calculations are made to decide what the culling level for each trait should be or what proportion of the candidates should be selected (or culled) at any particular stage.

Earlier it was shown that:

$$Ry = \frac{ih^2\sigma_p}{A}$$

or Response per generation $= ih^2\sigma_p$

For several characters that are not correlated it can be shown that the economic response (i.e., the genetic change per generation in money units) is the sum of the gains from selection for the individual characters (Turner & Young, 1969):

$$R_{(\pounds)} = a_1 i_1 h_1^2\sigma_{p_1} + a_2 i_2 h_2^2\sigma_{p_2} + \ldots . a_n i_n h_n^2\sigma_{p_n} = \Sigma a_n i_n h_n^2\sigma_{p_n}$$

Since $i_n = z_n/v_n$

$$R_{(\pounds)} = \frac{anznh^2 n\sigma_{p_n}}{vn}$$

$$= \Sigma a_n h_n \sigma_{G_n} (z_n/v_n)$$

In this method the final proportion (v) of the breeding stock to be selected is known beforehand and the product of each selection proportion, applied independently to each of the traits, must be equal to this, i.e., $v = v_1 \times v_2 \times v_3 \times \ldots . v_n$.

The question is therefore to determine the correct ratio of $v_1:v_2:v_3$, etc., to get the greatest overall response in money terms. This can be conveniently done by an iterative (trial and error) process in most simple cases, e.g., where two uncorrelated characters are selected for, various values of $v_1:v_2$ can be calculated and the optimum chosen.

Example: Assuming that the prolificacy of the dam and the food conversion efficiency of the lamb when artificially reared are not correlated, what proportion of ram lambs should be selected at birth on their dam's prolificacy, and what proportion on a subsequent performance test when artificially reared?

Overall 15 rams are required from 150 candidate ewes. If it is assumed that:

(1) the heritability of dam's record used as a measure of the

ram's breeding value (i.e., the regression of the son's breeding value on its dam's record) is $\dfrac{h^2}{2} = \dfrac{0.25}{2} = 0.125$

(2) heritability of food conversion efficiency is 0.3

(3) the phenotypic standard deviation of dam's record is 0.7 lambs

(4) the phenotypic standard deviation of food conversion efficiency is 0.032

(5) the net income from an extra lamb if artificially reared $= £3.0$

(6) Improvement of efficiency from 0.3–0.4 results in a saving of 25 kg of feed at £60 per 1000 kg, giving a value of £15 per unit of conversion efficiency over this range.

Then the following parameters apply:

	$a(£)$	h	σ_G	$ah\sigma_G$
Prolificacy	3	0.35	0.35	0.367
Feed conversion	15	0.55	0.016	0.132

For various values of v_1 and v_2 (where $v = v_1 \times v_2$) response in money terms can be calculated

v_1	v_2	$R(£)$
0.1	1.0	0.64
0.2	0.5	0.62
0.3	0.33	0.57

On this basis an initial selection of one ram lamb from each of the top 20 per cent of ewes (based on prolificacy) followed by a performance test where a further half of the rams are selected as stock sires would be almost as good as selection on prolificacy alone. If the prolificacy of the ewe is known to be correlated with the performance of the son on test then a more complicated analysis has to be carried out, based on the above parameters together with the estimates of genetic and phenotypic correlations between the traits.

GENOTYPE ENVIRONMENT INTERACTION AND SELECTION FOR
DIFFICULT ENVIRONMENTS

No discussion of selection in sheep can be complete without
discussing the question of 'where' to select. For example, a
common debate is whether hill sheep should be selected on the
hill, without feeding or on the lowland under good conditions.

Genotype/environment interaction. Such an interaction exists
where the effect of genotype (i.e., the difference between genotypes) depends on the level of the environment under which the
genotypes are compared. Some genotype/environment interactions have been shown to occur with sheep although the
evidence is surprisingly scarce (Hohenboken et al., 1964). The
answer to the question of where to select hill sheep is that they
should normally be selected under hill conditions since there is
little evidence that there are positive advantages to selection on
the lowland (Dalton, 1967). However, in the past the fact that
commercial husbandry conditions have tended to improve with
time has sometimes justified selection under good conditions,
since the fruit of such selection has enjoyed better conditions
than those operating commercially at the time of selection.

Another allied problem is whether selection of sheep for
mountain and hill conditions should include direct selection for
adaptation or characters associated with it. Logically it could
be expected that selection of sheep that perform best in terms of
other desirable objectives would automatically tend to safeguard adaptation to environment. Insurance against infrequent
catastrophic conditions is best obtained through stocks of feed
rather than deliberate selection for sheep that could survive
such conditions. However, if some simple measurement of any
important component of hardiness became available, it is
conceivable that potential hill rams could be screened on this
basis with advantage (Sykes & Slee, 1969).

Under poor, extensive conditions prolificacy is not a desirable
objective, although hill ewes may later function as breeding
ewes for lowland lamb production and may also be crossed to

produce crossbred breeding ewes. The Scottish Blackface is one example of a breed suitable for hill conditions, which is capable of high prolificacy when kept on the lowland. Some emphasis on ewe prolificacy may therefore be justifiable under poor conditions.

In many extensive sheep systems on poor land, wool is a relatively important product and selection of rams on yearling wool characters may be justified. However, the main criterion of selection, outside fine wool growing areas, is the weaning weight of the lamb, on a suitably corrected basis, since emphasis on this character will have some effect on important mothering qualities.

Under extensive conditions on poor land, even more than on lowland, there are severe practical difficulties to any effective breeding scheme which limit the degree of sophistication. Where individual and parentage identification is impossible only a very crude selection scheme can operate. Nevertheless, a well organized scheme based on selection for weaning weight and yearling wool characters could be effective and it is really difficult to justify more sophistication in breeding hill sheep.

Minimizing environmental effects in selection

A major difficulty in sheep selection is the difficulty of recognizing genetic superiority in amidst the many environmental influences. It can be likened to the difficulty of listening to someone on a bad telephone line where the sound of the voice is swamped by extraneous crackling. There are many ways in which the background interference from environmental causes can be minimized, thus effectively increasing heritability of the traits. These fall into three categories:

By making repeated measurements of the character in question.

Obviously an animal's genotype, as commonly defined, remains the same throughout life, although characters such as the number of lambs born per lambing can vary from one year to the next—from one to as many as four or five, in really prolific sheep. Taking a simple view of heritability

$$h^2 = \frac{V_A}{V_A + V_{EP} + V_{ET}}$$

where h^2 = heritability of the character
$\quad V_A$ = additive genetic variance
$\quad V_{EP}$ = permanent environmental variance
$\quad V_{ET}$ = temporary environmental variance
If we average n records then V_A and V_{EP} remain the same but V_{ET} is reduced and

$$h^2_{Av} = \frac{V_A}{V_A + V_{EP} + V_{ET/n}}$$

which can be shown to be equal to

$$h^2_{Av} = \frac{nh^2}{1 + (n-1)r}$$

where r = the intraclass correlation between the measurements. (Pirchner, 1969)

Obviously, any benefit gained by selection on the average of several records must be weighed against the loss sustained through the higher generation interval involved in the scheme.

Very often other considerations have to be borne in mind. In the case of prolificacy in sheep the heritability of numbers of lambs born in the ewe lamb in some circumstances is considered to be so low as to make it worthless including it as a basis for selection (Turner & Young, 1969).

Performance testing under standardized conditions

A very positive step in reducing environmental interference is to bring a group of candidates for selection together into a standard environment. This method has been used widely in the selection of boars and beef bulls. The aim is to bring the young sires together as soon as practicable, either on the same farm or into a centralized station and to record performance under these more uniform conditions. Again, this is another means of increasing the effective heritability of the character by acting directly to reduce environmental variance.

With sheep it could be argued that this method can have special significance, because environmental influences— largely the maternal effects—make selection on individual field performance of ram lambs to 3–6 months of age, very difficult (Bowman, 1968). It has already been demonstrated that ram lambs can be successfully reared artificially from birth and this could provide a powerful means for selecting sires of slaughter lambs. Because of the possible importance of the method the Meat and Livestock Commission in the UK, in collaboration with the School of Agriculture in Aberdeen, are engaged in examining the validity of the technique. Ram lambs from the Suffolk breed are subjected to a performance test from birth and the best 10 per cent and the worst 10 per cent of rams, on the basis of test performance, are progeny tested to see whether the test is effective in improving the field performance of crossbred lambs. A preliminary analysis of the results (Owen, 1974; unpublished) indicates that the heritability of test performance is high (0.58) and that the correlation of test performance with breeding value for field conditions is also promising. Under standard performance tests the 90 day weight of sires of the best 10 per cent group averaged 39.5 (kg) and that of their progeny averaged 34.1 (kg) whilst the averages for the worst 10 per cent group were 30.6 (kg) for the sires and 31.5 (kg) for their progeny.

Applying corrections to raw field records

A number of non-genetic factors have a well-known effect on sheep production. They include the season, the number of lambs reared by the ewe, the age of the ewe, and the sex of the lamb. The effect of these on variation in performance records can be minimized in several ways:

Contemporary comparisons. The safest way to proceed in a really large flock is to use a form of 'contemporary comparison' where candidates for selection are only compared within groups of similarly treated lambs, e.g., ram lambs might be selected for weaning weight within a group born in the same year, to ewes of a defined age group and within litter size at birth and number suckled by the ewe.

Correction factors. In other circumstances, where the effects such as those of sex and age of dam, and their interactions with factors such as season, are well known from extensive data, it may be appropriate to apply standard correction factors to records of performance. Such a procedure can lead to biases if incorrectly applied and they should only be adopted after careful study of available evidence.

In some cases the situation largely resolves itself since other considerations may dictate that selection is made annually (within season) within sex and the selection is confined to twin lambs from ewes of specified age.

INBREEDING AND CROSS BREEDING

The sheep has benefited, as much as any livestock, from a widespread, systematic use of crossbreeding. It has long been known that the systematic mating of closely related animals has marked deleterious effects and that, conversely, the mating of animals from widely isolated populations, (e.g.; breeds within species) tends to have beneficial effects on many characters. These effects are manifestations of 'inbreeding depression' on the one hand and 'heterosis' or 'hybrid vigour' on the other. Both are closely related phenomena where similar factors are at work. The mating of relatives leads to inbreeding in the offspring although the occasional mating of remote relatives (beyond second cousin level) is not likely to lead to a significant degree of inbreeding. Inbreeding in farm animals leads to progressive deterioration, particularly in respect of important reproductive characters, including the viability of the young. The increased degree of uniformity due to inbreeding is less noticeable in the important economic characters than in the simply inherited characters such as colour and polledness. The reason for inbreeding depression is not fully understood but it is partly because more gene pairs become homozygous with inbreeding and a greater proportion of undesirable recessive genes are revealed through segregation. Both dominance and over-dominance (where the heterozygous combination is superior to either homozygous state) may contribute to the superiority of heterozygous gene pairs. However, there seems to be a pronounced general disadvantage in a reduced number of heterozygous gene pairs which leads to deterioration, particularly in important traits associated with reproduction and viability. Although some use has been made of inbreeding in commercial breeding of maize and poultry, there is no known justification for the use of inbreeding in sheep improvement.

Crossbreeding, however, has had wide and justifiable application in sheep improvement. Heterosis can be thought of as the converse of inbreeding depression and similar factors are involved in its beneficial effect. Many of our breeds of sheep have been subjected to a certain amount of inbreeding during their formation and maintenance as separate breeds, so that the level of heterozygosity, or the proportion of heterozygous gene pairs, is lower than the optimum, for many important traits. Crossing two breeds therefore gives rise to hybrid vigour in some traits, where the performance of the offspring exceeds the mean of the two parental breeds, in respect of that character.

As regards the effect of inbreeding and crossbreeding, the characters of the sheep can be divided into two main groups.

(1) Those associated with reproductive fitness, e.g., prolificacy, early lamb survival and to a lesser extent milk yield of the ewe. These characters tend to have a low proportion of additive genetic variation, i.e., the heritability is low, they are also sensitive to inbreeding depression and tend to exhibit a high degree of heterosis.

(2) Other characters such as the yield and quality of wool and carcass characteristics, which are not so closely associated with survival, tend to have a high heritability, to be much less

sensitive to the ill effects of inbreeding and show less benefit from heterosis.

It is not surprising therefore that ewes for fat lamb production where the maternal characters are important, should often be crossbred, so as to benefit from the merits of hybrid vigour. There is an added value from crossbreeding, which is that it allows the breeder to ensure favourable combinations of characters to suit his needs.

The 'stratification' of sheep breeding in various countries is particularly well exemplified in Britain. The British sheep industry has long had a substantial core of planned crossbreeding as follows.

hill ewe × long wool ram
↓
cross bred (or halfbred)
ewe   × Down ram
↓
slaughter lamb

The hill ewe may be a ewe that has been bred under mountain conditions, e.g., Welsh Mountain, Scottish Blackface or Swaledale, and then brought down to an upland farm, for crossing with a long wool ram, like the Border Leicester. This move to better conditions suits the hill ewe in her declining years and under better conditions a good crossbred lamb is produced. The ewe lamb from the cross benefits as a mother from hybrid vigour and the combination of the traits of hardiness and mothering ability from the dam breed with the larger size and prolificacy of the sire breed. The crossbred ewe is crossed with the Down ram, under the most favourable conditions, to produce a rapidly grown slaughter lamb. The hybrid vigour of the ewe and the blend of the desirable characteristics of prolificacy and mothering ability allows full exploitation of the growth potential and carcass attributes of the genetic contribution from the Down sire.

It is very doubtful whether any scientific contribution to

sheep breeding can match the simplicity and effectiveness of such an organization, developed over the years by traditional sheep breeders.

Another example of a similar stratification is found in Australia. Here, the Merino, cast from the large wool producing flocks of the dry interior, is crossed with the Border Leicester ram to give the Border Leicester × Merino. The wether lamb goes for slaughter and the ewe is used to replenish the ewe flocks of the wetter zones near the coast. The ewes in these flocks are crossed with Down rams to provide prime lamb for slaughter.

RELATIVE MERITS OF GENETIC AND ENVIRONMENTAL IMPROVEMENT

As mentioned previously both methods generally run concurrently although rarely there may be occasions when the emphasis is very largely on one rather than the other. There is also the choice, within genetic improvement of substituting one breed for another either completely or partly as in a cross-bred combination of two breeds. It might be argued that production from our hill sheep breeds such as the Blackface is limited by non-genetic rather than genetic factors, but there are few situations, including the example of the Blackface, where the variation in performance is solely genetic or solely non-genetic in origin. If quick improvement is sought, as in a five year plan, then the mechanics of effecting genetic change may be such that only changes in non-genetic factors, such as level of feeding, could give measurable benefit. On the other hand, if a system of frequent breeding is envisaged, it may only be contemplated if the genotype, in respect of length of breeding season, is such as to allow a high proportion of ewes to breed twice within the same breeding season.

Objectives of Improvement

FORMER OBJECTIVES

Highly sophisticated selection methods and breeding schemes

are not likely to succeed if sufficient attention is not paid to the objectives. Safe progress in breeding is usually achieved by aiming for a well-defined long term objective. There has been obvious progress in highly heritable, often superficial characteristics, when present-day sheep are compared with more primitive types, but there is uncertainty about the extent of the changes brought about by breeders in some of the important economic characters. Wool is one character where there has been obvious progress, a reflection of a readily identifiable character of high heritability. Early maturity also seems to have been enhanced in meat breeds, such as the Southdown and its derivatives. Other characters, particularly the mothering qualities, may have deteriorated in many 'improved' breeds, going by the reputation in this respect of relatively unimproved mountain and hill breeds which play a big role in the breeding structure of most national sheep industries.

MINIMIZING THE NUMBER OF OBJECTIVES

Spreading finite resources over more objectives results in less emphasis on each individual objective. Increasing the number of objectives for selection, therefore, seriously reduces the effectiveness of selection for any one of the objectives. Measurable progress, therefore, depends on limiting the number of characters selected to important ones known to be reasonably heritable. However important a character, it is obviously useless to include it as an objective for selection if heritability is near zero. For example, in sheep barrenness is important economically, but it cannot be justified as an objective in a breeding scheme because there is no evidence that the heritability of this trait is much different from zero. There must also be a compromise in deciding on objectives between minimizing the number of objectives and ensuring that selection is sufficiently broadly based to give sound, long term improvement. Emphasis on one highly heritable character can upset the delicate balance of characters that have been developed over centuries of selection. Within limits, therefore, it is wise to exclude characters from selection until there is evidence that their inclusion would be worthwhile, rather than the converse which has often guided breeders in the past. During the progress of a breeding scheme careful checks should be made on progress achieved so that objectives can be reviewed and amended as necessary.

OBJECTIVES AND THE FUTURE

A difficult aspect of setting objectives for sheep selection is the necessity to project to the future. In sheep selection turnover is relatively slow and objectives have to reflect conditions several years in advance. Nevertheless, some attempt at future projections is essential if 'economic worth' in any calculations is to have meaning. On examination some general objectives likely to be important in the future of sheep emerge. For instance, wool as an objective may have a diminishing importance in sheep production although it will remain a worthwhile by-product for some time. Meat production seems likely to be the chief objective of world sheep production in the future so that efficient production of lean meat, particularly from resources that cannot easily be utilized by man directly, will be important.

In various areas and on individual farms objectives will vary with circumstances and there are some areas where milk, or lamb skin, may be the major objective for several decades.

OBJECTIVES AND THE SYSTEM

In specifying objectives for sheep breeding, it is important to relate component characters to the sheep system as a whole. If a sheep flock is regarded as a discrete system with its input and output, then each objective related to a component of this system, must be evaluated in relation to the whole. For instance in relation to the whole system of sheep production variation in the rate of growth of the lamb in the period of a month or two before slaughter may be a minor component of overall efficiency justifying only a low priority for selection. The point can be illustrated by a simple model (Fig. 9.6).

If assumed values are put into such a model, the reproductive rate of the ewe stands out clearly as important in improving the overall efficiency. Examples of calculations that can help give an overall appreciation of the effect of major objectives are given in Table 9.2. The calculations indicate that increasing the numbers of lambs weaned per ewe on a once a year lambing

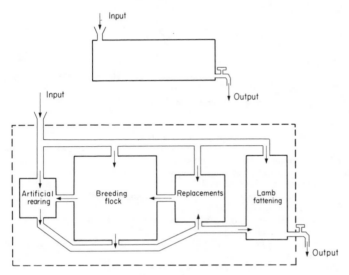

Fig. 9.6. *Intensive system model.*

system should prove profitable, judged by the effect on margin over feed cost. Increasing lambing frequency to three times in two years appears less attractive at least when no advantage is assumed in the sale price of the final product.

THE INTERRELATION OF SEVERAL OBJECTIVES

A model of a system as described is useful only if something is known about how change in a component objective affects other components. Knowledge of genetic correlations between traits is therefore an important aspect of the setting of objectives for selection. For example, in meat animals there is a complex

Table 9.2. *Feed cost and lamb output value per ewe in relation to the numbers of lambs reared per ewe lambing and of breeding frequency*

	All values expressed on the basis of a once per year lambing system with one lamb reared per ewe lambing.			
	Lambs reared per ewe lambing			
Feed costs per ewe	1.0	1.5	2.0	2.5
Lambing frequency				
Once per annum	100	106	111	152
Three times in two years	129	167	191	267
Lamb output per ewe				
Once per annum	100	150	200	250
Three times in two years	137	206	275	343

Assumptions:

Mean lambing rate: once per annum 93 per cent. Three times in 2 years 85 per cent.
Annual forage allowance: 1.5 kg forage daily per ewe.
Pregnancy allowance: 12.0 kg concentrate feed per pregnancy for a ewe bearing 1 lamb + 8.0 kg concentrate feed per extra lamb.
Lactation allowance: 15.0 kg concentrate feed per lactation for a ewe suckling 1 lamb + 15.0 kg per extra lamb suckled.
Artificial rearing: Lambs above two per ewe lambing, artificially reared on 8 kg milk powder and 100 kg concentrates.
Early weaning: On two out of three of the lambings at the higher frequency the lamb is weaned and reared on 80 kg concentrates.
Grass supplement: For every lamb above one suckled by the ewe 15 kg concentrate supplement is allowed.
Relative value of feed inputs: Ratio of price of forage:concentrates:milk powder = 1.0:3.0:8.0.

interrelation between food conversion efficiency, rate of gain, carcass composition, mature size and voluntary food intake. Of these characters, efficiency and carcass composition have a major, direct contribution to overall profitability of the system. Rate of gain may have some direct relevance where it enables a higher turnover rate and thus a lessening of general overheads; in many current sheep systems this is not the case. Rate of gain is also a factor, along with manipulation of the lambing date, in modifying the time of sale of the finished lamb.

Mature size and food intake of the animal are obviously important factors in overall profitability, affecting as they do items like replacement costs and stocking rates on pasture. An overall assessment of food conversion efficiency in any animal system includes the effect of such factors. Some of the connections between these characters in sheep breeds are illustrated in Fig. 9.7. The size of the sheep directly affects its intake, the rate of gain during the growing period and the carcass composition at any given slaughter weight. Food intake itself affects directly the rate of gain and the efficiency of conversion of feed into gain.

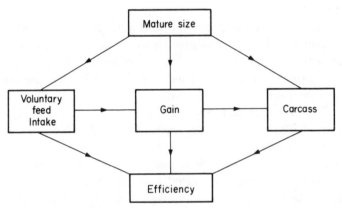

Fig. 9.7. *The interrelationship of various traits in determining efficiency of meat production in sheep.*

Efficiency of feed conversion is also in its turn influenced by the rate of gain and also by the composition of the carcass at any stage. Lean carcasses contain more water and less energy than fat carcasses so that a higher gross efficiency of conversion of feed into gain would be expected in the leaner sheep.

Mature size is associated not only with early rate of gain, rate of maturity (carcass leanness at the same carcass weight) and efficiency of food conversion during the growth of the lamb, but also with the food intake of the breeding flock which may nullify increases in output and efficiency judged in terms of an individual lamb. There are exceptions to the general between-breed trend in the interrelationship of these factors, whereby some breeds of relatively small mature size grow faster than predicted (McClelland, 1974). This is not surprising since there is bound to be variation in the shape of the growth curve between breeds.

It is important to determine the heritability of the shape of growth curve since it would be an advantage to have breeds that grow quickly to carcass weight but have a low mature size. Work with mice and broilers indicates that shape of growth curve has a reasonable level of heritability (Beilharz, 1974).

From the foregoing considerations it might be expected that selection for a high rate of growth would tend to produce animals leaner at a given weight, because of the association of early rate of gain with mature size and rate of maturity. The evidence available from sheep, cattle and pigs indicates that the genetic correlation of growth rate and leanness of carcass is not always positive (Taylor & Young, 1966; Owen & Morton, 1969; Bowman, 1968).

Further, since level of food intake is associated with rate of gain, itself positively associated with efficiency of conversion, it might be expected that voluntary feed intake and efficiency would be positively associated. The data for artificially reared lambs (Owen, 1972) shows the opposite, indicating that the direct effect of food intake as the denominator of the efficiency ratio outweighs the indirect effect on efficiency through rate of gain.

In view of such complex and often contradictory relationships, it is often difficult to reach the correct decision on objectives. In simple terms the sheep needs to have a small food requirement (and therefore probably of small mature size) but with lambs that grow fast and give lean carcasses. One solution to the dilemma could be to select for efficiency of feed conversion during the growth period in that this character is of importance itself and is associated both with carcass leanness and with the rate of gain. It is unlikely to increase voluntary feed intake substantially and it is difficult to predict its effect on mature size of the animal.

IMPORTANT OBJECTIVES AND THEIR GENETIC PARAMETERS

As far as sheep improvement is concerned, the following objectives can be regarded as important. They fall into two groups—those relating to breeding efficiency and those relating to the efficiency of the growing lamb. (Table 9.3; MLC, 1972)

These characters are in themselves complex and selection for one of them involves selection for a composite of many components. Several of these cannot be included as selection criteria on present evidence, in spite of their undoubted economic importance, because of their low estimated heritability.

Table 9.3. *The heritability of characters of major importance in sheep*

Objective Characters of the ewe	Component character	Probable Heritability
Breeding frequency	Age of puberty	
Weaning percentage	Date of first oestrus	0.25–0.35
	Barrenness—proportion of ewes	
	lambing put to ram	0·00–0.10
	litter size at birth	0.10–0.20
	lamb mortality before weaning	0.00–0.05
Easy lambing	frequency of assisted lambing	Not known
Efficiency of feed conversion in the ewe	Annual feed intake	Not known
Dairy characters	yield of milk	0.10–0.20
	milk quality	0.40–0.50
	corrected lamb weight to 50 days	0.10–0.30
Wool	wool weight	0.30–0.45
	fineness of staple (quality of fleece)	0.40–0.70
Character of the lamb		
Food conversion efficiency	Efficiency on test	Not known
Carcass quality	Fat content of carcass (composition and conformation)	0.25–0.35
Rate of gain	Gain to 100 days	0.10–0.30

PERFORMANCE RECORDS

It is one thing to decide upon the main objectives of selection, it is another to specify precisely what records the shepherd must keep to achieve this aim. Considering the improvement of sheep for meat production the following criteria appear to be the most worthy of consideration for inclusion in a breeding scheme:

(1) Litter size at birth.
(2) Time of onset of the breeding season.
(3) Lamb weight at a specified age (around 100 days) corrected for litter, sex and dam age.
(4) Feed conversion on test of the ram lamb.
(5) First fleece weight.
(6) Adult body weight.

Owen (1971) has already outlined in some detail the characteristics of sound performance recording for sheep but the measurement of the above six characters demands:

(a). Individual identification, lambs correctly assigned to ewes at lambing time and ewes correctly assigned to rams at mating time. Although it sounds simple this is the crux of a detailed breeding scheme. At mating time sire identification requires that ewes are run in a group with a single ram, or that a harnessed teaser ram is run with the ewes and marked ewes shed off from the flock and put in a pen with the ram for 12 or 24 hours. The latter procedure is usually the most efficient when large numbers of ewes and rams are involved. Assignation of ewes to rams is not essential in many schemes apart from being a matter of executing flock policy. It is surprising how little is lost in many breeding schemes if the sire is not recorded and other steps are taken to avoid the possibility of inbreeding. Assignation of lambs to ewes involves more organization, but without it the opportunities for selecting the essential characters are severely limited. If rams are properly marked at mating time, so that the time of mating is indicated by the crayon mark on the ewe, some simplification of lambing is possible. If ewes

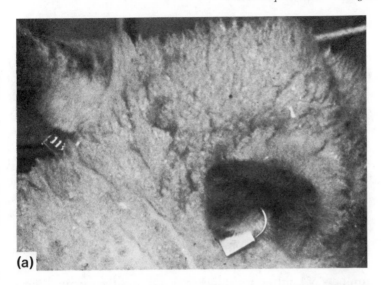

Fig. 9.8. *A pair of chicken wing tags for the newborn lamb and a larger plastic ear tag fitted at 8 months old for the young ewe provide a simple and effective means of individual identification.*

are pen-mated, so that dates of mating are available, then it should be possible to arrange that most ewes are placed in an individual pen before lambing. This can substantially simplify the shepherding of the prolific flock since a great deal of difficulty is caused by mismothering and desertion at birth. For this aim to be achieved in a flock where mating is not deliberately synchronized there should be approximately one individual pen for four to five ewes. The procedure depends on ewes and lambs being removed from their pen as soon as they are fit and tagged, so that other ewes can replace them before they are due to lamb. Several identification methods are available as illustrated, the larger tags being suitable to replace smaller ones when ewe lambs have been selected to join the breeding flock.

(b). Measurement of litter size at birth requires no more than that a record is kept of the ear number of the ewe, the total numbers of lambs born (alive or dead) and the ear numbers of the surviving lambs.

(c). Measurement of the date of onset of the breeding season requires that a harnessed teaser ram be run with the ewes from about six weeks before the first ewe normally shows oestrus; this prevents any effect of the ram itself on the onset of oestrus. The date when a ewe or ewe lamb is first marked can be recorded. For this purpose ewes need to have an easily visible number stamped on the fleece.

(d). The 100 day (or other age) weight of lambs is best recorded by weighing all lambs on one or two occasions, the first of two weights could correspond with the 100 day age of first born lambs and the last with the 100 day age of the last born lambs. In many hill flocks it is impracticable to get a 100 day weight, and a weaning weight at about 150 days is recorded. 100 day weights can only be meaningfully compared when allowance has been made for differences in the major factors influencing such weights. These factors include the number of lambs at birth, the number suckled by the ewe, the age of the ewe, sex of the lamb, environment, and date of lambing. It has already been pointed out that the most satisfactory correction procedure in large flocks is to make 'contemporary comparisons' whereby the weight of a lamb is expressed on the mean value of all lambs in the same category, e.g., it may be a ram lamb from a two year old ewe suckled as a twin. In other cases where records are available for that flock, appropriate average correction factors can be used on actual records over many years. It is not so satisfactory, although it may be the only alternative, to use correction factors derived from other data, unless there is sufficient evidence that interactions do not exist. It is rare that a sufficiently widespread sheep recording system has been in operation long enough to calculate correction factors with any general validity for a breed or area.

(e). Food conversion of the growing lamb can only be directly measured when the lamb is early weaned and artificially reared for a part of the growth period. This procedure can be applied to ram lambs from birth and a food conversion record obtained over a given weight range, say from 15–50 kg liveweight. The value of this procedure for the selection of rams depends on the heritability of food conversion, estimated in this way, and its correlation with breeding value for field conditions. Preliminary evidence on this aspect has already been presented (see p. 348).

(f). Fleece weight and body weight can sometimes be determined together when the lamb is about 15 months of age, otherwise the ewe can be weighed at mating time each year.

Records must be used effectively if they are to repay the trouble and expense of keeping and the logical tendency in scientific research to record rather more than the bare necessity has to be strongly resisted in recording schemes for commercial enterprises. Seldom under such circumstances is there any opportunity to make worthwhile use of records whose value and specific role are not well known in advance.

Breeding Schemes

In the present section examples are given of how some of the principles outlined in the foregoing discussion have been applied in practice in differing situations to the particular flock, breed or national situation in question. The procedure in setting up a sound scheme could be summarized in the form of three questions:

(1). What direction? Correct long term objectives.

(2). How fast? Maximizing the rate of progress $\dfrac{ih^2\sigma_p}{A}$

(3). How profitable? Maximizing cost/benefit from the scheme.

Relatively few breeding schemes have been reported which make a systematic attempt to incorporate the principles outlined into a scheme aimed at the improvement of meat production. This is partly because many research institutions have been involved in selection experiments, to provide a basis for the formulation of breeding schemes, rather than in operating a breeding scheme as such. Commercial undertakings on an individual farmer scale or on a large scale are usually much less well documented for various reasons.

Some of the following examples have been described previously (Owen, 1971).

THE NORWEGIAN CIRCLE SCHEME

This scheme illustrates the mechanized use of records for genetic improvement. It is designed to overcome difficulties of obtaining a reasonable progeny test when flocks are small by getting several neighbouring flocks to combine to form a breeding co-operative or ram circle of 300–400 ewes. Mating begins on the same day for each flock in the circle, each flockmaster receiving one ram on the first day. Ewes are hand mated, all ewes on heat that day being mated to the ram. Circulation of the rams from one farm to the next begins on the second day and is continuous for the mating season. In this way the progeny of each ram to be tested is spread throughout the flocks comprising the circle.

Each ram is mated to at least 30 ewes although the optimum would be 40 ewes per ram with 50–70 progeny per group. In addition to the normal records, 10 lambs are picked out at random from each progeny group and slaughtered to give records on carcass weight and quality and wool weight. Although the scheme illustrates a novel way of overcoming the difficulties of progeny testing with small flocks, there is doubt as to whether progeny testing, however carried out, can be justified as a means of sheep improvement.

THE FINNISH SCHEME BASED ON SELECTIVE REGISTRATION

Sheep improvement in Finland was directed by the Finnish Sheep Breeders' Association set up in 1918 for this purpose. The main breed included in the Association is the Finnsheep (or Finnish Landrace)—a breed of high natural prolificacy. The breeders in Finland chose prolificacy as a major objective of selection from the start and in the early years of improvement, entry into the Flock Book was on the basis of recorded performance into three prolificacy classes. As prolificacy was established at a high rate, there was a need to improve other characters. All the emphasis on recording is on meat and wool production, supervised regularly by an official recorder, to check accuracy and to give advice. Breeders use the records primarily to allow early culling of ewes, secondly to aid the sale of breeding stock and thirdly to aid ram selection.

This scheme is an example of a centrally organized scheme giving detailed information on individual animals in a form that has aided selection and has been of great help in the sale of breeding stock. Such a scheme needs to be computerized so that preparation of summaries and the calculation of indices can be calculated and returned without delay as useful information to the breeders.

THE ROQUEFORT SCHEME FOR IMPROVEMENT OF DAIRY SHEEP

The development of milk recording in the Roquefort area was closely associated with the emergence of the Lacaune as the dominant breed of the area, and also with a rapid improvement in pasture management and general feeding. In 1950 the breed was organized into a Flock Book and even prior to this, some Lacaune flocks were milk recorded. Milk recording is carried out by full-time recorders who supervise monthly recording of milk. Lamb suckling lasts for one month with a maximum allowable period of 42 days, the first recording taking place within a few days after weaning and the lactation yield calculated by extrapolation to cover the suckling period. Milk records are used to aid selection of females but the main justification for the detailed recording procedure is the use made of the records for selecting rams. The system of progeny testing now widely used, was developed as a result of a detailed statistical study of milk records in 1963. Previously ram selection was inefficient, relying largely on the dam's yield. The progeny testing scheme is used to evaluate young rams on their ability to raise yields on the basis of daughter's first recorded yield, very much on the lines of the schemes used for selecting dairy bulls. For this a certain minimum number of daughters for each sire is specified and the selected rams are used for artificial insemination as well as for natural service.

THE ABERDEEN SHEEP BREEDING PROJECT

In order to give a more complete picture of the application of some of the previous principles, a fuller description is given of a sheep breeding scheme started in Cambridge in 1964 and continued since 1972 at Aberdeen (Owen, 1971b). The scheme is designed to improve sheep for meat production and although no final judgment on the outcome can be made, it illustrates many of the practical aspects involved in putting theory to practice.

Objectives

Of the characters that have been shown to be important in sheep, it was clear at the inception of the project that prolificacy, and to a lesser extent, growth and feed conversion efficiency of the lamb, were characters most likely to be of continuing importance. At that time (1964), methods were becoming available to enable artificial rearing of lambs so removing what had hitherto been a serious obstacle to the practical operation of selection for prolificacy. It also provided the possibility of a standardized performance test for ram lambs.

The initial objectives for selection were therefore reduced to two:

(1). Prolificacy—based on the numbers of lambs born to a ewe averaged over two or more records, and

(2). growth rate—based on growth rate of the ram lamb to 35 kg liveweight under standardized conditions of artificial rearing.

The Initial selection

There are several ways to start a scheme of this kind. Many breeders have started with whatever material they possessed at the time. In many research and educational institutions, as well as in commercial practice, breeding work is often directed towards an existing herd or flock with the sole justification that the alternative is more difficult to organize. Older pioneer breeders, who initiated existing breeds, in the eighteenth and nineteenth centuries, sometimes started with a collection of the best of the native stock of the area but sometimes also included likely candidates from further afield. There seems no reason why a scheme of this kind should not be started by selecting an initial foundation group by screening all the genetic material available, within a country, irrespective of breed. The choice of genetic material from further afield needs more careful consideration unless conditions are very similar to the country in question because of the risk of unexpected adaptation problems.

The scheme was therefore commenced by selecting individual ewes from any British breed fulfilling a stringent minimum entry requirement into the foundation group. The minimum was set as three consecutive sets of triplets (based on numbers of lambs born) in the three lambings immediately preceding selection. Selection was almost entirely confined to pure bred ewes to prevent any undue advantage from heterosis that might be gained by crossbred ewes. In any event, authenticated individual records are less common from commercial flocks of crossbred ewes. On this basis, mainly in the first two years of the scheme, a group of 54 ewes was obtained representing several breeds. The breed composition of the foundation group was as follows: 34 Clun Forest, 6 Llanwenog, 3 Llŷn, 2 Radnor, 1 Kerry Hill, 3 Suffolk × Welsh Halfbreed, 1 Ryeland, 3 (Suffolk × B. Leicester) × N.C. Cheviot, 1 Bluefaced Leicester.

Table 9.4. *Lifetime records of top foundation ewes (number of lambs born)*

Ewe no.	Breed	1	2	3	4	5	6	7	8	9	10	11	12
260	Clun	2	4	3	4	4	4	4	1	4	4	–	–
103	Clun	–	3	4	4	4	3	5	3	–	4	3	1
161	Clun	–	?	?	3	4	4	4	3	4	3	2	–
3	Clun	–	3	3	3	4	4	3	–	–	–	–	–
LL1	Llŷn	2	3	4	5	4	3	1	1	4	3	–	–
L1	Llanwenog	–	3	3	3	4	3	3	–	–	–	–	–

Many of the ewes had a record of prolificacy higher than the minimum requirement (Table 9.4). The selection of ewes, although directed over a wide field, mainly by postal enquiry, was not comprehensive, and a lack of organized recording was a major drawback to efficient screening of existing material. Although selection of ewes on the basis of the average of three previous records was a justifiable procedure, no similar satisfactory basis was available for the selection of rams which could at best only have been evaluated on the basis of their dam's performance. Rams to mate with foundation ewes were therefore selected from the Finnish breed known to have a high level of prolificacy. These were available at that time, mainly from the importantion to the UK by the Animal Breeding Research Organization, Edinburgh. Seven rams from this breed, as little related as possible, were mated to the foundation ewes, giving an average of about 8 ewes per foundation ram to form each of seven initial breeding groups.

Avoidance of inbreeding

When a new population of animals is developed from a relatively narrow base, steps have to be taken to avoid inbreeding and to maintain a high effective population size, since it has been shown that inbreeding is likely to be undesirable, particularly for characters like prolificacy. Mating in the first several generations was therefore on a strict cyclical basis based on the initial seven groups A to G (Fig. 9.9). According to this

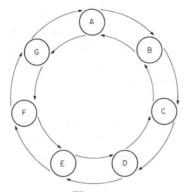

Fig. 9.9.

procedure a decision was made at the outset that some rams and ewe lambs went along the clockwise outer route and the remainder along the anti-clockwise inner route. Thus, some of the progeny of the ram and ewes of the original group A followed the clockwise route and so were mated to B sheep in the first instance giving A B progeny which continued along the cycle by being mated to sheep from C to form A B C and so on. By using two opposing cycles with various starting points it ensured that at the end of one circuit a clockwise group starting at A say, would have only a very small relationship to the original A group and have a large component ($\frac{1}{2}$) of G. The anti-clockwise group starting at A likewise would be very little related to Group A at the end of the cycle and have a large component of B. Maintenance of such a strict cycling procedure in its simplest form depends on the continued existence of foundation ewes for the various groups and becomes less necessary as total population size increases.

Cyclical mating was discontinued after the first eight years but two features that minimize inbreeding are maintained:

(1). Ram numbers in any season are not allowed to fall below 10

(2). Using a computer mating system, mating is confined to individuals that have no common ancestor nearer than one great grandparent. The process involves a search of the family tree of each ram and ewe as far as the great grandparents. Mating is then permitted only if there are no common ancestors or if only one common ancestor is present at the great grandparent level.

In the first matings that took place the F_1 (Finnish/British) ram lambs and the resulting F_2 rams were back crossed to the British foundation ewes so that the genetic contribution from the Finnish breed was substantially reduced in the initial matings.

SELECTION PROCEDURE

Having dealt with the mechanics of the initial matings the subsequent selection of young breeding replacements and the mating procedure can be described.

As a criterion of selection the evidence suggests that prolificacy is best measured as number of lambs born, averaged over the first two lambings for any young ewe. This is because the heritability of numbers born seems to be higher than any other component of prolificacy. The average of the first two records is taken as the best compromise between increasing effective heritability (by the averaging of records) and the need to measure the character as early in life as possible, to reduce the generation interval. Consideration has also to be given to the considerable doubt that exists about the heritability of ewe lamb prolificacy. As to the method of selection for prolificacy in the case of rams the choice lies between selection on the basis of ancestor information, to enable the use of selected rams as lambs in their first year and only a limited selection at the early stage, a smaller number of candidate rams being later selected on half sib or progeny performance. The mechanics of progeny testing for prolificacy are daunting in practice since, to ensure at least two records per daughter, final selection cannot be made until the candidate ram is at least $4\frac{1}{2}$ years old. Going purely on experience with other species, to achieve a reasonable selection differential, at least five times as many candidates would have to be tested as the final number of selected rams required, and it is unlikely that mating each candidate to fewer than 40 ewes would give a reasonable number of surviving daughters. These considerations alone indicate that progeny testing for prolificacy is not likely to be practicable. Using information on half sisters is an alternative possibility provided candidate rams can be retained until their half sisters are $3\frac{1}{2}$ years of age. As an alternative to progeny testing such a scheme has been suggested for selecting dairy bulls (Owen, 1975).

Because of the cost and complexity of progeny testing it was decided to base the selection of rams for prolificacy on the information available on the first two lambing records for the dam; later some weighting on the performance of the two grand dams was included. The selection policy for ewe replacements was decided by the need to expand flock numbers and by the scientific necessity to retain some age groups in each generation entirely unselected so as to give some indication of genetic progress. Initially, therefore, no female stock were culled until they had lambed twice. At that stage approximately four-fifths of the young ewes were culled and the remainder retained for further breeding.

FURTHER SELECTION OF RAM LAMBS

Ram candidates selected initially on prolificacy were removed from their dams on the second day of life and reared

Table 9.5. *Results of a ram performance test*

	Number of ram	100 day wt	days at 35 kg	FCE
1973	24	20.5	148	0.23
	25	30.5	112	0.33
	31	29.5	120	0.29
	35	30.0	111	0.29
	37	23.5	138	0.27
	38	29.0	112	0.37
	41	26.0	125	0.30
	53	27.0	120	0.37
	56	37.5	96	0.39
	69	31.5	110	0.36
	72	27.0	120	0.52
	73	28.0	120	0.32
	80	28.0	125	0.34
	84	31.5	109	0.28
	87	28.5	118	0.33
	88	30.0	115	0.29
	102	25.0	130	0.26
	105	20.0	146	0.29
	113	32.0	108	0.45
	122	25.5	120	0.31
	129	33.0	110	0.35
	135	28.0	123	0.29
	150	35.5	99	0.30
	184	27.0	126	0.28
	187	30.0	118	0.29
	195	35.5	99	0.25
	203	28.0	116	0.17
	216	28.0	120	0.30
	226	28.5	120	0.20
	235	24.5	147	0.32
	234	31.0	115	0.27
	177	28.0	122	0.23
		28.7		
S.D.		3.85	12.6	0.058
per cent		13.4		

artificially. Each ram lamb was given a restricted allowance of milk replacer for the first 30 days of life and allowed unrestricted access to a pelleted complete diet from 14 days of age. Approximately 50 per cent of the ram lambs were culled on the basis of growth rate to 100 days in accordance with indications of the theoretical weighting to be applied (Table 9.5). In the later years of the scheme selection for growth rate has been mainly applied within brother groups since a high proportion of rams are born with at least one brother. A summary of performance in some of the tests is given in Table 9.5.

SUMMARY OF SELECTION PROCEDURE

The main aspects of the selection procedure can be summarized in a simple form (Fig. 9.10). A more realistic stable situation in a flock of 400 breeding ewes (i.e. mature ewes + ewe lambs put to the ram) is assumed.

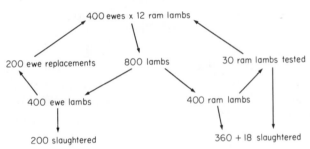

Fig. 9.10. *Outline of selection procedure as applied to a stable flock of 400 ewes.*

THEORETICAL RATE OF PROGRESS

Prolificacy

The annual rate of progress for a breeding scheme is estimated as follows from the expression:

$$Re = \frac{ip\sigma_G}{A}$$

This is similar to the previous equation (p. 336) except that p is a more generalized form of h and represents the correlation of the observed measurement, be it on a single animal or on the mean of several, with the breeding value of the candidate.

The quantities $i p \sigma_G$ and A have to be calculated separately for each pathway of transmission of genes from one generation to the next (Table 9.6)

Table 9.6. *Progress per annum in prolificacy from selection assuming* $p = 0.5$ *and* $\sigma_G = 0.35$.

	i	*h*	*ih*	*A*
RR	0.0		0.0	1.0
RE	0.0		0.0	1.0
ER	1.5	0.5	0.2625	2.5
EE	0.8	0.5	0.14	2.0
			0.4025	6.5

$$R_e = \frac{0.4025}{6.5} = 0.062 \text{ lambs/annum}$$

i.e., in ten years expected improvement amounts to 0.62 lambs/ewe

Rams to breed replacements (Ram to ram (RR)); (rams to ewe (RE)): It is assumed that growth performance is not correlated with prolificacy so that selection on growth affects prolificacy only through the consequent direct decrease in selection intensity.

Using ram lambs the age of the sires when their sons and daughters are born is one year.

Ewes to breed rams (ewe to ram (ER)): The ewes to breed the 30 rams selected for prolificacy are selected from 170 candidate 2 and 3 year olds. Allowing for the fact that a small proportion do not give birth to a ram, the proportion selected is under 20 per cent which corresponds to a selection differential $i = 1.5$.

The age of the ewes when the rams are born is 2.5 (assuming that half came from 2 year old and half from 3 year old ewes).

Ewes to breed replacements (ewe to ewe (EE)): The ewes to breed ewe lambs are selected for prolificacy from the best half of

Table 9.7. *Progress per annum in feed conversion efficiency assuming* $p = 0.55$ *and* $\sigma_G = 0.016$. *(15 out of 30 rams required to ensure 12 working ram lambs).*

	i	h	ih	A
RR	0.80	0.55	0.007	1.00
RE	0.80	0.55	0.007	1.00
ER	0.00		0.00	2.50
EE	0.00		0.00	2.00
			0.014	6.5

$R_y = \dfrac{0.014}{6.5} = 0.002$ on a mean efficiency of 0.3

Table 9.8. *Lambs born per ewe in the younger ewes for the period 1970–1974. Aberdeen prolific ewe project*

Year	No. of ewes	Total lambs born	No. lambs /ewe
1-year-old			
1970	36	60	1.66
1971	30	55	1.83
1972	44	78	1.77
1973	27	41	1.52
1974	55	94	1.71
2-year-old Ewes			
1970	39	88	2.26
1971	74	154	2.08
1972	86	192	2.23
1973	31	79	2.55
1974	9	25	2.78
3-year-old Ewes			
1970	49	119	2.43
1971	29	70	2.41
1972	5	15	3.00
1973	71	199	2.80
1974	24	71	2.96

the ewes (selection intensity $i = 0.8$). The average age of ewes when the replacement lambs are born is 2 years.

The scheme allows selection on another characteristic, the feed conversion efficiency of the ram lamb (a character correlated with rate of growth and probably also with carcass leanness). Progress in this characteristic will be slower than for prolificacy but some selection is required on these important traits.

Assuming that there is no correlation between the feed conversion efficiency and dam's prolificacy, progress can be calculated as for prolificacy (Table 9.7).

Table 9.8. summarizes lambing results over the last five years of the scheme. The scheme is simple to operate and involves only the minimum of recording, although several additional traits have been recorded in order that selection objectives can be reviewed periodically. The high level of prolificacy from the initial selection appears to be a key factor in that it gives much more variation to select from an early stage. Another important feature is the restriction of suckling load by artificial rearing since it reduces the competitive disadvantages of being born in a large litter.

As a result of the scheme a new breed—the Cambridge—has been formed which is undergoing trials on commercial farms as a possible sire for commercial crossbred ewes.

Improved Systems 10

Having dealt with the main components of sheep production it is useful to conclude by a discussion of improvement in sheep systems composed of these elements. A system is not a simple sum of its component parts, it is a new organism sometimes possessing features not easily predicted from a study of the components in isolation. In the past it was assumed that the role of the scientist was to develop the components and of the farmer to assemble and test new systems, with the guidance and encouragement of agricultural advisers. Development of new ideas into sheep farming has not been rapid for various reasons and in future more emphasis will have to be given to carrying through promising developments so that they can be evaluated in the context of a 'real' system with all its human and economic constraints.

To further this aim three categories of sheep systems are examined in the present chapter to consider what the main features of an efficient system should be, in the light of principles discussed in the previous chapters.

Hill and Mountain Sheep Systems

Although the numbers of sheep on the lowlands have ebbed and flowed according to economic conditions, the hill and mountain areas have maintained their sheep numbers with greater constancy apart from the devastation of occasional severe seasons. These areas have been the main traditional sheep-keeping areas of the world during man's recorded history. The predominance of sheep in such areas is bound up with the intense seasonal variations of such areas. Increases in altitude, like increases in latitude, are associated with a fall in mean temperature and an increase in mean precipitation and an enhanced seasonal difference. Although summers are cooler they are also wetter, providing good conditions for grass growth, but because of the lowering of winter temperatures the non-growing season increases. The mountain environment therefore is one of short summers and long severe winters. Compared with cattle, sheep are better adapted to such conditions, particularly where herbage conservation is impossible because they can survive the winter in conditions where cattle would perish without extra feeding. One of the reasons probably lies in the difference in size; a smallish hill ewe gathering 1 kg of herbage dry matter a day has greater mobility and a not much smaller grazing equipment than a cow requiring probably ten times as much herbage. Other species such as the deer are also well adapted to such conditions but further study is required to assess their relative value as meat producers on such land.

Much useful work relevant to hill sheep farming has been carried out in the last fifty years but little of it has been applied in hill sheep farming practice. In assessing the reasons for this and illustrating what such a development could entail, the various means of increasing output from a hill or mountain system need to be dealt with. These include:

(1) Genetic improvement of the sheep.

(2) Input of wintering fodder, either through supplementary feeding or obtaining extra wintering land.

(3) Input of good quality summer feed.

(4) Improved flock management.

Genetic Improvement

Genetic improvement alone is unlikely to lead quickly to

higher production. Traditional breeds used in these areas are already well adapted to their environment and as that environment is improved by other ways it often becomes possible to sustain crosses with more productive types of sheep, either those developed on better hill areas or from the smaller and hardier of the lowland breeds. The problem therefore is one of matching existing genotypes to the conditions rather than radical within-breed improvement of existing stock.

Inputs of Winter Feed

This is often the main key to improvement, since winter feed supply is the limiting factor of many such systems. Inputs during the winter, by allowing higher overall stock numbers to be carried, eventually help improve summer feed, since the poor quality of summer herbage is partly a result of under-use and accumulation of large reserves of lignified material.

The balance of summer and winter feed supply—One method of achieving the right balance between winter and summer feed supply has already been discussed—the age old migration of men and their sheep flocks between vast fertile winter plains and the high altitude summer pastures.

The present day remains of the system in the UK is the intensive use of the mountain land of Wales and parts of Northern England (by contrast to Scotland) with hill farm units based on a combination of arable land with hill land and the use of away wintering. The result in these areas is a high summer stocking of about two ewes and their lambs per hectare (Owen, 1955), giving a high removal of summer growth, inhibition of species like heather, and resulting in short grassy herbage at high elevations. Even on the rocky terrain each green ledge of grass is grazed. Stark contrasts in terms of heather content can often be seen on either side of fenced sheep walks.

Cattle and wethers on mountain pastures—The use of cattle for the control of mountain grazing is often advocated but there is little evidence that the animal species is important if the grazing pressure is adequate, in spite of the sheep's greater powers of herbage selection. Where sheep systems depend heavily on wool income a high proportion of wether sheep are kept, often until they are three or four years of age. Such a sheep flock structure is probably better suited for mountain land since the wethers are better able to withstand heavy grazing pressure on poor land and they consequently exert earlier and heavier grazing pressure than that desirable in a flock consisting entirely of ewes with young lambs.

Two means of increasing winter capacity without a full transhumance system are 'away wintering' and supplementary feeding.

Away-wintering

Traditional practice of hill sheep farming is a modification of transhumance to fit into an enclosed agriculture, based on individual farm holdings. A mountain farmer hires from a lowland neighbour, usually on a headage basis, the right for his sheep to graze the land during the winter after the crops are harvested and the cattle housed. Traditionally, the most vulnerable part of the hill flock, the lambs in their first winter, received preference in this respect to ensure that they received enough feed and minerals to make their early growth; the weaker old ewes and the younger ewes were given next priority depending on the wintering resources at home. The cost of away wintering has always been an important factor in hill farm economy and the lowland farmer also has had to weigh the price received for wintering sheep against the disadvantages of the wear and tear to fences and walls together with the cost of the resulting delay in the availability of keep for cattle in the spring. Equally the hill farmer has to weigh the cost of alternatives to away wintering, which amount to supplementing with feeds—either hay, concentrates and roots—possibly in conjunction with winter housing. These alternatives, if they are to give the same relief to the home wintering resources as away wintering, are often as expensive (Owen, 1960).

The most economic form of away wintering is where the farmer owns both a hill and lowland farm and runs the two units as an integrated enterprise. This combination often gives the best of both worlds where the farmer, planning the whole unit as one, can adapt the joint system for the benefit of both. The mountain pasture can take the dry stock during the summer, allowing greater emphasis on productive stock and conservation on the better land. The arrangement also provides a pool of breeding stock, such as cast hill ewes, for crossing on the better pastures. Unfortunately the arrangement is less easy where the tract of hill or mountain is large and unbroken so that integrated units involve a long distance between the hill and the lowland members. Other factors also militate against such an arrangement, such as the gaming, tourist and forestry interests.

Supplementary feeding—The simple way to correct the imbalance of winter/summer keep on an existing hill unit, with limited cultivable (inbye) land, is to use purchased feed. Because of the high cost of feed and the limitations on individual ewe output, feed has to be judiciously allocated to gain a useful return. Supplementary feeding on the hill farm has the merit that it allows full rein to flexibility of allocation, so that the feed input can be injected into the ewe's productive cycle at the optimum time (Chapter 6). In the hill situation better feeding at other times can have an effect on production, because the hill ewe is adapted to utilizing body reserves to cope with seasonal variation in feed supply. For example, better nutrition even after weaning in late summer allows the ewe to achieve better peak condition and may still benefit that ewe the following spring when her reserves are at their lowest.

The high cost of feed means that it is often only justified where stocking rate is increased and given on a regular annual basis only to gimmers and ewes in poor condition; other ewes are given feed only as pasture availability and climate dictates. This ensures a continuing thread of feeding experience in the flock so that ewes take easily to feeding when necessary.

Such judicious feeding is unlikely to inhibit the grazing activity of the ewe. In a hard winter it is likely to have the reverse effect since correct supplementation can increase the intake of the poor roughage available.

Input of Good Quality Summer Feed

Although the shortage of winter keep is the main barrier to more effective use of hill land another serious obstacle is the fact that although summer keep may be plentiful, its quality sets a very low ceiling to animal performance. The lamb is shielded from the full effect of this because of the milk it receives from the ewe and the young lamb makes reasonable progress for the first three months of life. Indeed by July when hill flocks in Britain are sheared, April born lambs have made some 70 per cent of their eventual weight as yearlings in the following April. This gives some indication of how low the growth of the hill lamb is after this early stage. The initial capital expenditure on feeding stuffs to provide winter keep may therefore not be justifiable on the basis of increasing stock carry and the production of more second-rate store lambs. The increased grazing pressure and greater removal of surplus summer growth is in the long run likely to improve the quality of the summer keep on mountain pastures which suffer from under-grazing. The process of improvement may be accentuated by using other cultural methods where possible, particularly the application of lime and phosphates. However, in the mountain environment the speed of improvement in itself may create problems by upsetting delicate mineral balances, resulting in trace element deficiencies.

Surface seeding—An example of the modification of low-ground techniques that has found a useful place in the context of hill land improvement is the technique of surface seeding. It can be used on terrain not suitable for ploughing and heavy cultivations or where there is poor thin soil or on areas of thick peat, where maintenance of the surface turf is essential. The method involves application of lime and fertilizer together with some grass and clover seeds on to the pasture surface. Depending on the nature of the existing vegetation preparatory cultivations vary from nil to a rigorous discing or rotovating, following burning where shrub vegetation was present (Warboys, 1970; Dowling et al., 1971).

Improved Flock Management

The key step in hill farm improvement is the integration of the various components—pasture improvement, change of stocking rate, input of winter feed—into a balanced, commercially viable, system in a progressive scheme which yields planned repayment of capital investment. The lack of sufficient emphasis on this stage has resulted in disappointing results from adoption of new techniques and in the small impact on practice resulting from increased knowledge that is apparently relevant.

The Welsh 'ffridd' system—There are many examples of existing traditional systems which are well balanced in themselves and also form a framework within which new techniques can be profitably exploited. One example, mentioned earlier, is the traditional Welsh *'ffridd'* system in Western Britain where the lower, more sheltered part of the mountain grazing is enclosed and used strategically to meet the needs of the flock at lambing, mating, for twin suckling ewes and for improving the condition of wether lambs prior to sale. The enclosed *'ffridd'* area usually contains the land most suitable for improvement and inputs into the *'ffridd'* in terms of lime, fertilizer and pasture improvement, are therefore integrated into the whole system at the optimum time of the production cycle.

The two-pasture system—Recent work in Scotland and other parts of the UK (Eadie, 1972) has culminated in a basically similar design for improvement called 'the two-pasture system'.

This system also emphasizes the incorporation of the pasture improvement within a system of higher intensity in which increased stocking and increased individual ewe output both

combine to meet the initial capital and subsequent maintenance cost of the system. The improvement is directed to the
more amenable and well sheltered lower reaches of the hill
capable, at their best, of supporting fescue/agrostis/white
clover pasture. The improved land is fenced and the pasture
thereon saved for use at the critical times of the ewe's productive cycle—at tupping time to ensure reasonable condition
and a good ovulation rate, in the period around lambing and
subsequently for ewes with twins and for weaned lambs.

A HILL FARM IMPROVEMENT SCHEME

The implications of a programme of hill farm improvement
are best illustrated in the form of a hypothetical example,
which although necessarily simplified, brings out some of the
important practical issues.

The model: The unit is assumed to be a hill farm of 400 ha
with a range of altitude from 150–900 m above sea level with
rainfall in the 1200–2500 mm range in latitude 50–60°N. Such
a farm has a range of climatic aspects and is assumed to have
20 ha cultivable 'inbye' land.

Before improvement such a system is assumed to support
one hill ewe per 2 ha of total area*. Ewe lambs (6–12 months)
are assumed to be wintered off the farm at a fixed charge per
head. It is assumed that no supplementary feed is used.

Assumed production level:

lambs weaned per ewe mated	80 per cent
Ewe mortality	8 per cent
Sales weight of wether and other sale lambs	25 kg
Wool sold per ewe	2 kg

The model corresponds approximately to farms of the same
size that might be found within the wetter highlands of the
United Kingdom.

---

* Numbers of ewes based on autumn census including ewe lambs but
excluding cast ewes.

In the UK such a system is dependent on state support, since gross sales are low in relation to the two main items of cost—away wintering and rent.

The age structure of such a flock could be:

Ewes each autumn

6 months	18 months	$2\frac{1}{2}$	$3\frac{1}{2}$	$4\frac{1}{2}$	$5\frac{1}{2}$ for sale
46	43	40	37	34	30

From the 154 ewes in the four productive age groups mated a total of 122 lambs are weaned and 76 are available to sell.

Total sales: 76 lambs, 30 cast ewes, wool from 184 ewes.

At current price levels the margin of gross sales over wintering charges plus rent is in itself an insufficient income for a family without including other costs that are inevitably incurred. Such a system is viable only because of state support and due to other family activities, including tourism.

An important step in an attempt to improve such a system is to set a target stocking rate appropriate to the potential of the land. It is assumed in the model that, if wintering capacity was not a limiting factor, 850 ewes could be summered (over two ewes per hectare).

The two main steps in devising a progressive improvement scheme for the unit described are:

(1) The acceptance of a target summer stocking rate of 852 ewes (including ewe lambs) to be achieved over a period of six years.

(2) The provision of adequate resources, partly by surface seeding fenced areas and partly by supplementary feeding, to winter the eventual number of 652 ewes (assuming that all ewe lambs are away wintered).

A reasonable target for fenced improved areas would be 40 ha in addition to the 20 hectare of inbye land giving an overall ratio of 14 ewes per ha of improved land. The optimum amount of land improvement is difficult to specify but it would depend on the quality of the existing hill pasture.

CALENDAR OF DETAILED OPERATION OF THE SCHEME

The First Year (commencing in the Autumn)

Accelerated Expansion. When the decision is made to embark on the scheme only two new possibilities are open in the first autumn, if the flock is a hefted or acclimatized flock.

The first is to retain a larger number of young ewe replacements by minimal culling (say 56 retained from 61 possibles) together with the purchase of a small number of suitable ewe lambs to make the number up to 75. If all these ewe lambs are sent together as one group for wintering, the small proportion of strange lambs will be assimilated into the home group before embarking on the open hill grazing in the spring.

An additional possibility is to retain cast ewes for one further year to help out on flock expansion.

Embarking on the Feeding Programme

The older ewes would be initiated into a programme of supplementary feeding for ten weeks commencing six weeks before lambing. The supplement could consist of whole barley or whole maize given at a gradually increasing rate, reaching $\frac{1}{4}$ kg per head just before lambing and maintained at that rate until one month after lambing. Total consumption for each ewe equals 12 kg of grain. Since there is usually a gap between the homecoming of the ewe hoggs and the availability of pasture for them on the hill, these young ewes could benefit from a low level of supplement for one month after their return. Whole grain given at $\frac{1}{8}$ kg per day for 32 days—a total supplement per lamb of 4 kg—would be suitable. This supplement could give a double benefit—that of preventing the serious loss of condition that often occurs at this stage and also that of training these aspiring stock ewes to accept feed readily.

Pasture Improvement

During the following summer the first of four enclosures, extending to 10 ha each, would be fenced after a detailed survey of the whole farm to determine the areas considered most amenable to improvement from the point of view of land quality, aspect and herding convenience. Following fencing, the area would be prepared by burning and surface cultivation as necessary followed by a moderate lime dressing (2–5 tonnes ground limestone or its equivalent per hectare) phosphate and nitrogen fertilizer and grass and clover seeds, at a total of about 50 kg seed per hectare.

The new growth would be grazed off for the first time by putting all the ewes and lambs on it in mid August. A reasonably successful take should allow better growth than the usual system with consequent benefit to ewes and lambs for sale and for the ewes to be tupped. The enclosed pasture would be rested from late September until two or three weeks prior to lambing.

The Subsequent Years

Table 10.1 summarizes the number of sheep in the regular age groups, assuming a constant 8 per cent annual mortality and that initially a small proportion of ewe lambs are purchased, to allow the required flock expansion in the early stages. In years 3, 5 and 7 further enclosures of 10 ha each are added to the system to complete the improvement programme.

The rate of expansion and of completion of the improvement could be increased if the hill grazing were enclosed in a ring fence so that higher purchases of ewe lambs and some older ewes could be made in the expansion stage.

Whatever the rate of progress, the main aspects of the original system can be compared with the improved system on the assumption that the following features are applicable:

(1) The system remains a one man or one family system— greater organization and planning, together with some withdrawal from other activities, to make greater efficiency of labour use possible. Experience of large animal units in the USA has shown that mechanization, coupled with good

Table 10.1. *Number of ewes of various ages kept in the model flocks before, during and after improvement. Assumed mortality rate in each group 8 per cent per annum*

	Total productive ewes	$\frac{1}{2}$	$1\frac{1}{2}$	$2\frac{1}{2}$	$3\frac{1}{2}$	$4\frac{1}{2}$	$5\frac{1}{2}$	$6\frac{1}{2}$
Old System	153	46	43	40	37	33	30*	
New System								
First Autumn	183	75	43	40	37	33	30	27*
Second Autumn	209	100	69	40	37	33	30	27*
Third Autumn	255	130	92	63	37	33	30	27*
Fourth Autumn	326	180	120	85	58	33	30	27*
Fifth Autumn	437	200	166	110	78	53	30	27*
Sixth Autumn	560	200	184	154	101	72	49	27*
Seventh Autumn	653	200	184	170	140	93	66	45*
Eighth Autumn	652	200	184	170	155	130	86†	58*
Ninth Autumn	652	200	184	170	155	143	120*	–
Final Autumn	652	200	184	170	155	143	131*	–

* Sold as draft ewes.
† Part sold as draft ewes

organization, can increase labour output far beyond levels currently contemplated in the UK.

(2) All ewe lambs and possibly a proportion of the weaker or younger ewes, to be wintered away or otherwise 'off the farm' on purchased feed in a wintering enclosure or house.

(3) All remaining ewes to be supplemented with 12 kg of feed grain as outlined previously and given an allowance of conserved roughage to appetite.

(4) Assuming that production per ewe remains unchanged after improvement gross sales after completion of the improvement will include 320 lambs, 130 cast ewes and wool from 650 ewes.

The main aspects of the budgets for the two systems are given in Table 10.2.

Few other problems, specifically related to more intensive stocking of sheep on pasture, can be predicted provided the aim of adequate feeding is achieved. The improvement pro-

Table 10.2. *Simplified budgets for the original and new systems indicating the change in margin over main variable costs. Assumptions: Main sales—store lambs £7 each, draft ewes £7, wool 80p per ewe. Main costs—rent £400, away wintering £2.50 per lamb, cereals £50 per 1000 kg*

	Original system (£)	New system (£)
Sales		
Lambs	532	2240
Ewes	210	910
Wool	147.20	520
Total (a)	889.20	3670
Costs		
Rent	400	400
Away wintering	115	500
Winter feed	–	431.20
Total (b)	515	1331.20
Margin (a–b)	374.20	2338.80

Capital costs associated with the change:	(£)
40 ha surface seed fenced £125 per ha	= 5000
Feed store	= 2000
Sheep handling pens	= 1000
Total	= 8000

gramme and the maintenance of the more intensive system would, however, involve a higher level of managerial capacity.

State support in the form of improvement grants for the first five years of improvement would seem to be a better national investment and a better way to encourage a self sufficient hill sheep industry than a system based solely on annual headage payments.

Intensive Grass Systems

The background to the intensive use of grass has been fully discussed in Chapter 7 and in this section the aim is to describe an all sheep system designed to produce high lamb output from temperate grass, based on traditional sheep and techniques. Unlike the hill farm situation, where any improvement scheme involves a gradual process of upgrading taking several years, the adoption of an intensive grass system is a matter of changing policy within the framework of existing resources and fertility levels. The comparison with an existing traditional system is less easy than in the hill farm model because an appropriate existing system is likely to be a mixed farm with a complex interaction of arable crops, cattle and sheep.

THE MODEL

Ninety hectares of pasture are assumed in a temperate climate such as that of lowland Britain, rainfall 750–1500 mm with reasonably even annual distribution. It is assumed that the grass is utilized only by sheep although, as mentioned previously, a mixed cattle and sheep system has many advantages. For illustrating the problems of practical implementation of principles, however, a system based entirely on sheep is more easily modified to a mixed system than vice versa.

It is also assumed that the 90 ha are permanent pasture although the system is easily adapted to suit an arable farm on which the 90 ha form a 2-year grass 'break' on a 450 ha farm. Again problems on such a farm would be expected to be less than on permanent pasture and stocking rates could well be increased, if a substantial area of stubble grazing was available in autumn and winter.

The grass is assumed to be ring fenced and sub-divided into three approximately equal areas each containing some dryish areas suitable for wintering sheep. It is assumed that the land quality is appropriate to support 900 ewes. The ewe is assumed to be the crossbred daughter of a hill ewe and this ewe is mated with a Down breed, such as the Suffolk. Replacements are assumed to be purchased as $1\frac{1}{2}$ year old gimmers in September, following the sale of cull ewes.

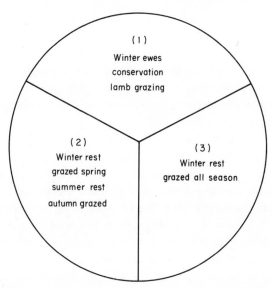

Fig. 10.1. *Plan of pasture use in the three areas in one year.*

The three areas would be used for a different function each year on a rotational basis (Fig. 10.1).

In any one year (year 1) the management programme for the areas could be:

Period	Area 1	Area 2	Area 3
1 Dec.–15 April	All ewes	Rest	Rest
15 April–30 June	Rest and conserve	Ewes and lambs	Ewes with single lambs
1 July–15 Sept.	Weaned lambs	Rest	Weaned ewes
15 Sept.–30 Nov.	Rest	Ewes	Ewes

In year 2, Area 1 gets the treatment applied to Area 2 in year 1, Area 2 the treatment given to Area 3 in year 2 and Area 3 the treatment given to Area 1 in the previous year.

WINTER PERIOD

During this period of 135 days it is assumed that the ewes are confined to one section of the grass. Whatever the soil type it is desirable for winter feeding to provide a slatted platform abutting on to a hard road so that feed from a self-unloading trailer can be dispersed into troughs. With twice a day feeding of a complete diet, 100 cm per ewe of trough length is allowed. The width of the platform depends upon soil type and the possible necessity to confine the sheep wholly on the platform during wet weather (7–10 m).

Fodder available for winter feeding, in the form of barn dried hay or high dry matter chopped silage, amounts to the produce of 30 ha cut once in June. This is assumed to supply 120 tonnes of hay or 360 tonnes of high dry matter (33 per cent) silage, which amounts to approximately 1 kg per ewe per day of hay or 3 kg per ewe of silage. Both hay and silage would be given in the chopped form for ease of handling. Using a mixer/ self unloading trailer, grain would be added to the fodder at a rate of up to 30 per cent six weeks before lambing, and continued until the ewes are moved to summer grass. According to experience a low level of chopped straw could also be added to the mix. The fodder would be dispensed once or twice a day according to the storage properties of the diet.

Lambing is assumed to start on the fifth of April so that practically all the ewes have lambed and settled with their lambs by the twenty-fifth of April. Mating therefore commences on the tenth of November. Rams are harnessed with coloured crayons to allow the separation of four groups, each of about 225 ewes, according to expected time of lambing; provision is made for these groups in turn to be brought into a separate lambing enclosure, with access to part of the slatted feeding area and fitted with overhead lighting for adequate night supervision; 100 individual pens, made from hurdles are assumed to be available to allow penning of ewes when they have lambed. These pens are about two metres square and allow access to a feed trough and a water supply. When the ewe has lambed, and safely adjusted to her lambs, she is dosed with anthelminthic and turned out to one of the two spring grazing areas. The spring grazing areas are given fertilizer, including up to 150 units of nitrogen per acre in mid-March, and according to grass availability, will be supplied with several hay racks and lamb shelters made of straw bales. The ewes with singles that lamb first go on to the pasture that was rested since the end of November and the remainder, including all ewes with twins, go to the pasture rested since mid September.

SPRING PERIOD

After the ewes and lambs have been moved to the spring pasture the winter pasture is repaired by seeding any poached areas, fertilizer applied and rested, preparatory to conservation in June. The spring pasture is set stocked at 15 ewes and their lambs per hectare. The ewes are sheared in late May and the lambs at that time, or preferably a fortnight earlier, given a vaccine to protect them against pulpy kidney (*Clostridium welchii*).

The spring period ends with the weaning of the lambs, although many of the single lambs will have reached slaughter weight before this. The conserved area needs to have been cut, cured and removed about the middle of June; this requirement can be met by making silage but only in a few areas if grass is conserved as naturally cured hay.

SUMMER PERIOD

The lambs are weaned at the beginning of this period and all dosed against worms. Depending on grass supply supplementary feed may be made available in the slatted feeding area so that as the lambs get accustomed to eating dry feed they will consume a small proportion of concentrated feed with grass.

In the meantime the weaned ewes are confined to one enclosure at the rate of thirty ewes per hectare. If dry conditions prevail and grass growth is severely retarded then provision should be made for supplementation, preferably with hay. The third enclosure is clear of stock during the period and may be given a fertilizer dressing to encourage grass recovery.

AUTUMN PERIOD

At the end of the summer period the lambs should be cleared, the ewe stock replaced as necessary and the ewes allowed to graze two of the areas so that they should be in good condition by mating time. By the end of the autumn period the ewes have mated and the two areas well grazed before the onset of winter.

Organization at mating is the key to successful lambing management. This can be accomplished by harnessing all the rams and progressively changing crayon colour, preferably from lighter to darker colours, according to the number of ewes marked. This should enable the operator to identify four groups of about 200 ewes by their keel mark. This mark can be confirmed by a more permanent marking when the ewes are turned into their winter quarters.

TARGETS OF PERFORMANCE FOR THE SYSTEM

The aim with this system would again be to run it as a one man or one family unit and the levels of physical performance achieveable on a successful unit are given in Table 10.3.

Table 10.3. *Target levels of performance for the intensive grass flocks.*

Lambs weaned per ewe mated	1.6
Carcass weight of lamb at slaughter	20 kg
Lamb gain from birth to slaughter: single	0.35 kg/day
twin	0.25 kg/day
Grain/concentrate per ewe	40 kg
Grain/concentrate per lamb	10 kg

New High Production Systems

The aim with the two previous systems was to apply recent advances in knowledge within the bounds of existing practices using sheep genotypes in current popular use. In the present section the principles discussed in Chapters 2 & 6, together with the limited experience gained at several centres in recent years, are drawn upon to propose a less orthodox system applicable, not only to some existing popular sheep breeds and crosses, but also to ewes of much higher productivity potential. Since 'intensive' is a term capable of wide interpretation the definition is narrowed down to include any system whose aim involves one or more of the following three:

(1) A flock weaning percentage from one mating in excess of 200.

(2) A flock average lambing interval of less than 12 months.

(3) All year confinement without grazing.

Which one or more of these aims is attempted will depend very much on geographical situation. In some locations, where grass growth is poor or unreliable, a system based on complete confinement to yards or feed lots may be attractive.

The second aim of reducing the lambing interval, gets more difficult as the latitude increases from the equator—the higher the latitude the narrower the range of genotypes that are capable of frequent lambing and the greater the need to use artificial means for supporting breeding activity. Before new systems come into widespread use it is often difficult to assess the likely costs and returns involved. However the analysis in Table 9.2. (p. 356) indicates which factors are likely to have the most marked effect on the financial outcome.

The results show that increases in litter size within the possible range 1.5–2.5 appear to have a greater effect on financial outcome than decreases in lambing interval, within the possible range 12–8 months. Decreasing the lambing interval however can give greater flexibility in the time of lamb production which in itself could be an advantage. Most of the considerations involved have been dealt with in Chapter 2 and the present intention is to outline the details of a possible system of high production, based both on higher litter size and on some reduction in lambing interval, in a latitude within the 50–60° band. The system can be applied to conditions where grazing is available or to a totally confined system.

THE MODEL

Because of the limitations imposed by the latitude and the need to make the system workable with a number of sheep breeds and cross breds, lambing is projected on seven occasions during the year, with a reasonable spread of lambing to enable full and efficient use of labour and equipment.

It is assumed that the unit is made up of 800 mature ewes replaced at the rate of one-quarter per annum so that 200 ewe lambs are brought in each summer to lamb down at one year old, in addition to the 800 mature lambing ewes.

Fig. 10.2. *Mating and lambing cycles for a frequent breeding system involving two flocks.*

The ewe lambs are mated by exposure to the ram from the tenth of November with a target mean lambing date of the fifteenth April. The lambs are then weaned on the fifteenth June and assigned to one of two flocks of mature ewes with projected mating and lambing cycles shown in Fig. 10.2.

MATING MANAGEMENT

In order to attain greater management precision it is assumed that all matings for mature ewes are synchronized; this (in conjunction with PMS) helps to induce breeding activity during the sub-optimal period for ewe lambing activity. Synchronization is achieved by administering either natural progesterone or a synthetic progestagen compound, either as an intra-vaginal sponge or as a subcutaneous implant, 10–15 days prior to target mating date. According to the genotypes used and the location, the injection of 500 international units of PMS on the withdrawal of the progesterone is given for the April, July and February matings. In order to further stagger the labour load at lambing, the ewes mated in August, October and December can be split into two groups, the first to be mated at the time indicated and the second group to be mated two weeks later.

Because of the greater likelihood of mating failure in February, April and July it is preferable initially to mate these as one group and to allow the re-mating of any returns on the second cycle.

BREEDING FAILURE

Any ewes that fail to breed in a group after the two programmed opportunities, will eventually show heat. If all groups are accompanied by a harnessed teaser ram then the non-pregnant ewes can be detected and, to minimise the delay involved to the next mating, these ewes can be transferred to a group that will give the earliest opportunity for remating. There will therefore be some deviations from the expected mean number per group of 133 ewes to be mated on each occasion and the division of replacement gimmers into either flock can be adjusted accordingly.

The success of the unit will depend on good management, particularly at mating and lambing time and upon the meticulous keeping of an activity calendar for groups and of record cards for individuals within groups.

Although the programme allows on average two months and at least one clear month between the lambing of successsive groups, late December and early February do involve some overlap of peak management demand as between lambing and mating. Experience with any one system could allow better separation of management demand.

ORGANIZATION OF TUPPING

Since a unit of this size would be operated by one man, handling facilities should be such as to permit funnelling ewes into a long race for routine inspection and operations. There should also be an invertible crate so that ewes can be easily individually constrained and inverted for sponge insertion, as well as for foot treatment. Each group of ewes would have a proven teaser ram running with it, each one rotated from one group to another on a twice weekly basis to insure against risk of temporary failure of teaser ability. In addition there would be two spare teaser rams as part of the pool to be put into any group a few days before programmed mating.

For mating, a group of ewes is placed in the pre-mating enclosure equipped with a two-way separation race and all freshly marked ewes separated into a smaller mating enclosure bounded by other mating pens. During the peak mating activity for a group, the ewes would be run through the race every two hours. The group of ewes separated on each occasion would be penned separately. After eight hours have elapsed the ewes in each pen would be shared out amongst ten fertile rams in individual ram pens and allowed to stay there for two hours. The ten rams would then be changed for fresh ones and allowed two hours rest before the next mating.

An alternative that is less demanding in labour and less certain to give maximum mating success, is to allocate all the ewes to the fertile rams at the rate of about six ewes per ram as soon as the sponges are removed. After mating activity has occurred for some time all the rams could be moved to another group on a rotational basis in order to insure against any temporary infertility and to induce extra libido in the rams.

LAMBING MANAGEMENT

Management at this time centres around the use of a set of individual pens. These are similar to those described for the intensive grass system i.e., about 2 metres square with a solid floor and with access to feed and water. Sufficient pens should be made available so that each ewe can be penned before lambing and kept in the pen for one or more days afterwards to ensure sound ewe-lamb pairings.

Any lambs in excess of two per ewe are fostered to another ewe with only one lamb where possible; otherwise they are taken off the ewe for artificial rearing. Allowing for singles and losses it should be possible to average 1.75 lambs suckled overall so that there would be on average 0.5 lambs reared artificially for each ewe lambing (assuming a mean weaned litter size of 2.25).

ARTIFICIAL REARING

An artificial rearing unit equipped with up to 80 pens would be required with the expectation of an average of 67 lambs to be reared from each lambing. A suitable size of pen is 2 ft × 1 ft each fitted with a milk feeder, water container and solid feed trough. Lambs would stay in this unit for six weeks—five of these on twice a day milk feeding and one week post weaning before removal to the growing unit. Lambs would be removed for artificial rearing when they are one day old, or earlier if they have clearly suckled adequate colostrum. Lambs removed from the ewe in the morning would be given a first drink of milk replacer in the evening and lambs removed in the evening given their first drink the following morning. Thereafter each lamb is fed twice a day and limited to an allowance of 1.25 l/day of milk replacer reconstituted at a 20 per cent dilution rate. Access to solid feed and water is given from the age of two weeks. After the removal of each batch of lambs from the unit the whole place is cleaned and disinfected.

MANAGEMENT OF EWES AND LAMBS

Subsequent management of ewes and lambs will be conventional, according to the time of lambing, so that full use is made of any grazing available. However, following the

January, March and December lambings it is advisable to wean lambs at five to six weeks old in order to enhance the chances of successful re-mating. These lambs, together with any older unfinished lambs, weaned when grazing is not available, will be transferred on weaning to the growing unit. Lambs in the growing unit would be given a high concentrate feed after a two week transition period for those coming off the ewes at this stage. The transition feeds could be similar to those shown in Chapter 6 and might involve the use of three or four intermediate diets each with a roughage level successively lowered from the high level in the first one.

MANAGEMENT OF DRY EWES

On weaning ewes are sometimes confined and their food curtailed, to suppress excessive lactation and hasten the drying off period—they would then remain as a group running with their teaser until the mating procedure commenced again. Management demand during this time is minimal and allows some periods during the year when unskilled relief labour can take over the operation of the unit.

TARGET PERFORMANCE FOR THE UNIT

Prolificacy—With the use of high prolificacy genotypes weaned lambing percentages of more than 230 are achievable for mature ewes, lambing once per annum. Under the system described, for such genotypes it is assumed that a lambing percentage of 225 per cent for each group mated is achieved.

Lambing interval—Allowing for the percentage successful matings to vary between 60 and 95 per cent according to the season, an average lambing frequency per annum would be 1.3 (about $9\frac{1}{4}$ months mean interval).

EWE LAMB PERFORMANCE

The lambing performance of immature ewe lambs depends a great deal on age at mating and on the genotype involved.

Under the conditions described these high production genotypes should give successful matings in 80 per cent of these
young females with the expectation of 120 per cent lambing
percentage (weaned lambs per ewe mated).

Total lamb production from the unit would therefore be:

Mature ewes	$800 \times 2.25 \times 1.3 =$	2340
Ewe lambs	$200 \times 1.5 \times 0.8 =$	240
	Total lambs	2580
Number artificially reared	$800 \times 1.3 \times 0.5 =$	520
Proportion artificially reared	$=$	20 per cent

This level of lamb production achieved by a one man/one
family unit should be profitable if lowest cost feeds available
are used throughout. Wool sales together with culled ewe sales
could be expected to cover the cost of ewe lamb replacements.

References

Acker, D. (1971) *Animal Science and Industry.* New Jersey: Prentice Hall Inc.,

Agricultural Research Council (1965) *The Nutrient Requirements of Farm Livestock.* 2. Ruminants: Summaries of Estimated Requirements. London: Agricultural Research Council.

Alexander, G. (1962) Temperature regulation in the new-born lamb. 4. The effect of wind and evaporation of water from the coat on metabolic rate and body temperature. *Aust. J. Agric. Res.,* **13**, 82–99.

Alexander, G. & Williams, O. B. (1973) *The Pastoral Industries of Australia,* Sydney University Press, Australia.

Allden, W. G. (1962). The herbage intake of grazing sheep in relation to pasture availability. *Proc. Aust. Soc. Anim. Prod.,* **4**, 163–166.

Andrews, R. P & Ørskov, E. R. (1970a) A note on the effect of bulk density and digestibility on the voluntary intake of concentrate diets by sheep of two ages. *Anim. Prod.,* **12**, 335–338.

Andrews, R. P. & Ørskov, E. R. (1970b) The nutrition of the early weaned lamb. 1. The influence of protein concentration and feeding level on rate of gain in body weight. *J. Agric. Sci., (Camb.),* **75**, 11–18.

Andrews, R. P. & Ørskov, E. R. (1970c) The nutrition of the early weaned lamb. 2. The effect of dietary protein concentration, feeding level and sex on body composition at two live weights. *J. Agric. Sci., Camb.,* **75**, 19–26

Anon. (1970) *Intensive Grazing for Fat Lamb Production.* Annual Report 1969–1970: West of Scotland Agricultural College.

Arnold, G. W. (1963). The grazing behaviour of sheep. *Wool Technology and Sheep Breeding,* **10**, 17–19.

Arnold, G. W. (1966) The special senses in grazing animals. 1. Sight and dietary habits in sheep. 2. Smell, taste, and touch and dietary habits in sheep. (1) *Aust. J. Agric. Res,* **17**, 521–530. (2) *Aust. J. Agric. Res.,* **17**, 531–542.

Arnold, G. W. & Dudzinski, M. L. (1967) Studies on the diet of the grazing animal. 2. The effect of physiological status in ewes and pasture availability on herbage intake. *Aust. J. agric. Res.,* **18**, 349–59.

Ashton, W. M., Owen, J. B. & Ingleton, Jean W. (1964). A study of the composition of Clun Forest ewe's milk. *J. Agric. Sci., (Camb.)*, **63**, 85–90.

Ashton, W. M. & Yousef, I. M. (1966) A study of the composition of Clun Forest ewe's milk. mineral constituents. *J. Agric. Sci., (Camb.)*, **67**, 77–80.

Austin, R. B. (1944) *The Merino—Past, Present and Probable*. Sydney: Grahame Book Company.

Balch, C. C. & Campling, R. C. (1962) Regulation of voluntary food intake in ruminants. *Nutr. Abstr. Revs.*, **32**(3), 669–686

Bastiman, B. & Williams, D. O. (1972) In-wintering of ewes. 1. Effect of housing. *Expl. Husb.*, **24**, 1–6.

Ben-Saud, S. (1971) The Intake Utilisation of Food and Water by Ruminants. Ph.D. Thesis, University of Cambridge.

Ben-Saud, S. (1972). Voluntary intake of roughage diets by ruminants. *Proc. Nutr. Soc.*, **29**, 32A–33A.

Bhattacharya, A. N. & Harb, M. (1973) Sheep production on natural pasture by roaming Bedouins in the Lebanon. *J. Range Mgmt*, **26** (No. 4), 266–269.

Beilharz, R. G. (1974) Possibility of changing the shape of the growth curve through breeding. Proceedings of the 1st World Congress on Genetics applied to Livestock Production. Vol. III, 547–551.

Belschner, H. G. (1959) *Sheep Management and Diseases*. Sydney: Angus & Robertson Ltd.

Black, J. S. (1968). 3. The digestibility of indigenous hill pasture species. Hill Farming Research Organisation, 4th Report, 1964–1967, 33–37.

Blaxter, K. L. (1964) Dietary factors affecting energy utilisation. *Proc. Nutr. Soc.*, **23**, 3–11.

Blockey, M. A. de B. & Cumming, I. A. (1970) Mating behaviour of Merino ewes. *Proc. Aust. Soc. Anim. Prod.* **8**, 344–352.

Bond, J., Carlson, G. E., Jackson, C. Jr. & Curry, W. A. (1967) Social cohesion of steers and sheep as a possible variable in grazing studies. *Agron. J.* **59**, 481–483.

Botkin, M. P., Field, R. A., Riley, M. L., Nolan, J. C. & Roehrkasse, G. P. (1969) Heritability of carcass traits in lambs. *J. Anim. Sci.*, **29**, 251–255.

Bourke, M. E. (1967). A study of mating behaviour of Merino rams. *Aust. J. Expl. agric. Anim. Husb.* **7**, 203–205.

Bowden, P. J. (1971) *The Wool trade in Tudor and Stuart England*. London: Frank Cass & Co. Ltd.

Bowman, J. C. (1966) Meat from sheep. *A.B.A.* **34**, 293–319.

Bowman, J. C. (1968) Genetic variation of body weight in sheep. *Proc. 14th Easter School in Agric. Sci., Univ. Nottingham.*

Boxall, R. (1972). Utilisation of molassed sugar beet pulp and urea in ruminant diets. Ph.D. Thesis, University of Cambridge.

Braden, A. W. H. & Moule, G. R. (1964) Effects of stress on ovarian morphology and oestrus cycles in ewes. *Aust. J. Agric. Res.* **15**, 937–949.

Bradford, G. E. (1974) Breeding plans for improvement of meat production and carcass merit in the meat breeds of sheep. Proc. 1st World Congr. on Genetics applied to Livestock Production, Vol. I, 725–738.

British Wool Marketing Board (1974) *Wool on the Farm.* Occasional leaflet.

Broadbent, P. J. (1964) The use of grazing control for fat lamb production. II. The effect of stocking rates and grazing systems with a fixed severity of grazing on the output of fat lamb per acre. *J. Br. Grassld. Soc.*, Vol. **19**, 15.

Brockway, B. (1975) *Planning a sheep handling unit*, Report, Farm Buildings Centre, UK.

Bureau of Agricultural Economics, Canberra (1972) *The Fibre Review,1971–1972.* Australian Government Publishing Service: Canberra.

Carter, H. B. (1964) *His Majesty's Spanish Flock, Sir Joseph Banks and the Merinos of George III of England.* Sydney and London: Angus & Robertson Ltd.

Clapham, J. (1966) *A Concise Economic History of Britain.* Cambridge: England, Cambridge University Press.

Clegg, M. T. (1959) Factors affecting gestation length and parturition. *In : Reproduction in Domestic Animals. I.* Eds Cole, H. H. & Cupps, P. T. New York: Academic Press.

Cole, D. J. A., Hardy, B. & Lewis, D. (1971) *Nutrient Density of Pig Diets.* 18th Easter School in Agricultural Science: University of Nottingham. 243–257.

Conway, A. A. (1972) Irish grassland has vast potential for development. *Farm Fd Res.*, **3**, 76–79.

Cook, C. Wayne, Blake, J. T. & Call, J. W. (1963) Use of oesophageal-fistula cannulae for collecting forage samples from both sheep and cattle grazing in common. *J. Anim. Sci.*, Vo . 22, No. 3, 579–581

Cook, C. W., Harris, L. E. & Young, M. C. (1967) Botanical and nutritive content of diets of cattle and sheep under single and common use on mountain range. *J. Anim. Sci.* **26**, 1169–1174.

Coombe, J. B., Wardrop, I. D. & Tribe, D. E. (1960). A study of milk production of the grazing ewe, with emphasis on the experimental technique employed. *J. Agric. Sci.*, *(Camb.)*, **54** 353–359.

Coop, I. E. (1950) The effect of level of nutrition during pregnancy and during lactation on lamb and wool production of grazing sheep. *J. Agric. Sci.*, *(Camb.)*, **40**, 311–340

Coop, I. E. & Hill, M. K. (1962). The energy requirements of sheep for maintenance and gain. 2. Grazing Sheep. *J. Agric. Sci.*, *(Camb.)*, **58**, 187.

Coop, I. E. (1966) Effect of flushing on reproductive performance of ewes. *J. Agric. Sci.*, *(Camb.)* **67**, 305–323.

Cooper, M. M. (1966) In-wintering of sheep. *Outlook on Agriculture*, **5**, 80–84.

Cooper, M. McG. & Morris, D. W. (1973) *Grass Farming.* Ipswich: Farming Press Ltd.

Corbett, J. L. & Farrell, D. J. (1970) Energy expenditure of grazing sheep. *Proc. XI int. Grassld. Congr. 1970*, 754–757.

Corbett, J. L., Greenhalgh, J. F. D., McDonald, I. & Florence, E. (1960) Excretion of chromium sesquioxide administered as a component of paper to sheep. *Br. J. Nutr.*, **14**, 289–299.

Culpin, S., Evans, W. M. R. & Francis, A. L. (1964) An experiment on mixed stocking of pasture. *Expl. Husb.*, **10**, 29–38.

Cuthbertson, A. (1974) *Carcass Composition and Eating Quality*. British Council Specialist Course 324—Management and Diseases of Sheep. Edinburgh, April, 1974.

Cuthbertson, A., Read, J. L., Davies, D. A. R. & Owen, J. B. (1973) Performance testing ram lambs. *Proc. Br. Soc. Anim. Prod.* **2**, 83 (*Abs.*).

Cuykendall, C. H. & Marten, G. C. (1968) Defoliation by sheep-grazing versus mower-clipping for evaluation of pasture. *Agric. J.*, **60**, 404–408.

Dalton, D. C. (1967). Selection for growth in mice on two diets. *Anim. Prod.*, **9**, 425–434.

David, L. E., Marten, G. C. & Jordan, R. M. (1967) Applicability of chromogen and nitrogen as internal indicators of forage digestibility. *Agric. J.*, **59**, 544–546.

Davies, D. A. R. (1972) The use of complete diets of varying straw levels for early weaned lambs. *Proc. Br. Soc. Anim. Prod.*, (*abstr.*), 145.

Davies, G. M. (1950) The wintering of Welsh Mountain ewe lambs. *Agriculture, Lond.*, **57**, 379–383.

Denamur, R. (1971) Reviews of the progress of dairy science. Section A, Physiology: Hormonal control of lactogenesis. *J. Dairy Res.* **38**, 237.

Dent, J. W. & Aldrich, D. T. A. (1968) Systematic testing of quality in grass varieties. 2. The effect of cutting dates, season and environment. *J. Br. Grassld. Soc.*, **23**, 13–19.

Dickinson, A. G. (1967) Factors controlling various aspects of the incidence in related animals of the neurological disease scrapie. *Proc. 9th int. Congr. Animal Prod.*, pp. 27–31. Edinburgh & London: Oliver & Boyd.

Doak, B. W. (1952) Some chemical changes in the nitrogenous constituents of urine when voided on pasture. *J. Agric. Sci.*, (*Camb.*), **42**, 162–171.

Doney, J. M. (1966) Breed differences in response of wool growth to annual nutritional and climatic cycles. *J. Agric. Sci.*, (*Camb.*), **67**, 25–30.

Dowling, P. M., Clements, R. J. & McWilliam, J. R. (1971) Establishment and survival of pasture species from seeds sown on the soil surface. *Aust. J. agric. Res.*, **22**, 61–74.

Draz, O. (1974) *Management and Rehabilitation of the Natural Grazing Lands*. Paper presented at the Arid Lands Agriculture Development Programme Regional workshop for sheep and forage production, Beirut, Feb. 1974.

Ducker, M. J. & Bowman, J. C. (1970) Photoperiodism in the ewe. 3. The effects of various patterns of increasing daylength on the onset of anoestrus in Clun Forest ewes. *Anim. Prod.* **12**, 465–471.

Ducker, M. J. & Fraser, J. (1973) A note on the effect of husbandry at lambing on lamb viability and subsequent performance. *Anim. Prod.* **16**, 91–94.

Ducker, M. J., Thwaites, C. J. & Bowman, J. C. (1970) Photoperiodism in the ewe. 2. The effects of various patterns of decreasing daylength on the onset of oestrus in Clun Forest ewes. *Anim. Prod.* **12**, 115–123.

Dudziński, M. C. & Arnold, G. W. (1973) Comparisons of diets of sheep and cattle grazing together on sown pastures on the Southern Table lands of New South Wales by principal components analysis. *Aust. J. Agric. Res.*, **24**, 899–912.

Dýrmundsson, O. R. (1973) Puberty and early reproductive performance in sheep. 1. Ewe lambs. *A.B.A.* **41**, 273–284.

Eadie, J. (1968) 4. The nutrition of grazing hill sheep; utilisation of hill pastures. Hill Farming Research Organisation, 4th Report, 38–45.

Eadie, J. (1972) Sheep production systems development on the hills. Hill Pasture Improvement and its Economic Utilization, Colloquium Proc. No. 3, Potassium Institute Ltd., Edinburgh.

Edey, T. N. (1969) Prenatal mortality in sheep: A review. *A.B.A.* **37**(2), 173–190.

Edmond, D. B. (1966) The influence of animal treading on pasture growth. *Proc. 10th Int. Grassld. Congr.*, Section 2, 103–108.

Egan, A. R. & Moir, R. J. (1965) Nutritional status and intake regulation in sheep. *Aust. J. Agric. Res.*, Vol. **16**, No. 3, 437.

Egerton, J. R. & Roberts, D. S. (1971) Vaccination against ovine foot-rot. *J. comp. Path.*, **81**, 179–185.

Elsley, F. W. H., McDonald, I. & Fowler, V. R. (1964) The effect of plane of nutrition on the carcases of pigs and lambs when variations in fat content are excluded. *Anim. Prod.* **6**, 141–154.

Epstein, H. (1969) *Domestic Animals of China.* Commonwealth Agricultural Bureaux. London and Edinburgh: Morrison & Gibb.

Eyal, E. (1972) *Biological and environmental factors affecting assessment of the true production and the genetic potentials of dairy sheep.* Symposium on 'Milk Recording Practices for Sheep and Goats', Mar. 1972: Israel.

Faruque, O. & Walker, D. M. (1970) Vitamin A and protein inter-relationships in the milk-fed lamb. *Br. J. Nutr.*, **24**, 11.

Faulkner, D. E. (1974) *The traditional system of sheep production in the Near East and North Africa.* Paper presented at the Arid Lands Agricultural Development programme Regional workshop for sheep and forage production, Beirut Feb. 1974.

Ferguson, K. A. (1959) Influence of dietary protein percentage on growth of wool. *Nature, (Lond.)*, **184**, 907.

Fisher, R. A. & Yates, F. (1953) Statistical Tables. Edinburgh: Oliver and Boyd.

Folman, Y., Volcani, R. & Eyal, E. (1966) Mother offspring relationship in Awassi sheep. 1. The effect of different suckling regimes and time of weaning on the lactation curve and milk yield in dairy flocks. *J. Agric. Sci.,(Camb.)*, **67**, 359–68.

Food and Agriculture Organization of The United Nations (1972) *Production Yearbook*, **26**, Rome.

Forbes, J. M. (1967) Factors affecting the gestation length in sheep. *J. Agric. Sci., (Camb.)*, **68**, 191–194.

Forbes, J. M. (1970) The voluntary intake of pregnant and lactating ruminants: a review. *Br. vet. J.*, **126**, 1.

Fraser, A. F. (1970) Clinical examination of rams for fertility. *Vet. record*, **87**(7), 200. B.V.A. Congress, 13–16 Sept. 1970. Warwick.

Garner, F. H. (1963) The palatability of herbage plants. *J. Br. Grassld. Soc.*, Vol. **18**, No. 2, 79–89.

Gibson, T. E. (1963) The use of the critical and the controlled test for the evaluation of anthelmintics against gastro-intestinal worms. *Proc. of Symposium on: The evaluation of anthelmintics, Hanover*. pp. 55–61 Ed. E. J. L. Soulsby. New York: Merck, Sharp and Dohme International.

Gordon, I. (1968) Artificial insemination in sheep. *In: Artificial Breeding in Farm Animals*. Eds J. P. Crowley & B. Gilsenan. Pub. An. Foras Taluntais.

Gordon, I. (1971) Induction of early breeding in sheep by standard and modified progestation—PMS treatments. *J. Agric. Sci.*, (*Camb.*), **76**, 337–341

Gunn, R. G. (1968) Levels of first winter feeding in relation to performance of Cheviot hill ewes. Life time production from the hill. *J. Agric. Sci.*, (*Camb.*), **71**, 161–166.

Gunn, R. G. (1968) A note on difficult birth in Scottish hill flocks. *Anim. Prod.* **10**, 213–215.

Gunn, R. G. (1969) The effects of calcium and phosphorus supplementation on the performance of Scottish Blackface hill ewes, with particular reference to the premature loss of permanent incisor teeth. *J. Agric. Sci.*, (*Camb.*), **72**, 371–378.

Gunn, R. G., Doney, J. M. & Russel, A. J. F. (1969) Fertility in Scottish Blackface ewes as influenced by nutrition and body condition at mating. *J. agric. Sci.*, **73**, 289–294.

Gunn, R. G. & Doney, J. M. (1973) A note on the influence of the pattern of liveweight and body condition recovery between weaning and mating on food consumption and reproductive performance of Scottish Blackface ewes. *J. agric. Sci.*, **81**, 189–191.

Gunn, R. G. & Robinson, J. F. (1963) Lamb mortality in Scottish hill flocks. *Anim. Prod.* **5**, 67–76.

Hadjipieris, G., Jones, J. G. W. & Holmes, W. (1965) The effect of age and live weight on the feed intake of grazing wether sheep. *Anim. Prod.*, **7**, 309–317.

Hafez, E. S. E. (1952) Studies on the breeding season and reproduction of the ewe. *J. agric. Sci.*, **42**, 189–265.

Hafez, E. S. E. (1969) *The Behaviour of Domestic Animals*. London: Baillière Tindall.

Hafs, H. D., Purchas, R. W. & Pearson, A. M. (1971) A review: Relationships of some hormones to growth and carcass quality of ruminants. *J. Anim. Sci.*, **33**, 64–71.

Halliday, R. (1968) Serum × globulin levels in lambs from hill flocks. *Anim. Prod.*, **10**, 177.

Hamilton, D. & Bath, J. G. (1970) Performance of sheep and cattle grazed separately and together. *Aust. J. Expl. agric. anim. Husb.*, **10**, 19–26.

Hammond, J. (1932) *Growth and the Development of Mutton Qualities in the Sheep.* Edinburgh: Oliver and Boyd.

Hammond, J. (1960) *Farm Animals—their Breeding, Growth and Inheritance.* 3rd edn London: Edward Arnold.

Hart, R. H. (1972) Forage yield, stocking rate, and beef gains on pasture. *Herb. Abstr.,* **42**, 345–353.

Harkins, J., Edwards, R. A. & McDonald, P. (1974) A new net energy system for ruminants. *Anim. Prod.,* **19**(2), 127–255.

Heap, R. B., Allen, D. M. & Lamming, G. E. (1963) Influence of the induction of breeding activity in anoestrus sheep on the levels of some chemical constituents of uterine washings. *J. Reprod. Fert.* **5**, 209–215.

Heaton-Harris, D., (1970) *Repercussions of a Multiparous State in Ewes.* Ph.D. Thesis, University of Cambridge.

Hight, G. K. & Jury, K. E. (1969) Lamb mortality in hill country flocks. *Proc. N.Z. Soc. Anim. Prod.* **29**, 219–232.

Hilder, E. J. (1966) Distribution of excreta by sheep at pasture. *Proc. 10th Int. Grassld. Congr.,* Section 4, 165–169.

Hoffmann, L. (1969) The suitability of energetic index numbers for performance prediction- 'Energy Metabolism of Farm Animals'. Proc. 4th Symposium, EAAP Pubn. No. 12, Oriel Press Ltd., England.

Hood, A. E. M. (1974) Intensive set-stocking of dairy cows. *J. Br. Grassld. Soc.,* **29**, 63–67.

Hoogvliet, W. (1973) The Australian Sheep Industry Survey, 1971–1972. *Q. Rev. Agric. Econ.,* **26**(3), 171–185.

Hohenboken, W. D., Corum, K. & Bogart, R. (1964) Genotype and mating system times environment interactions for reproduction in sheep. Proc. 1st World Congr. applied to livestock production. Vol. III, 995–999.

Hornstein, I. & Crowe, P. F. (1963) Meat flavour: lamb. *J. Agric. Food Chem.,* **II**, 147–149.

Hudson, L. W., Glimp, H. A., Woolfolk, P. G., Kemp, J. D. & Reese, C. M. (1968) Effect of induced cryptorchidism at different weights on performance and carcass traits of lambs, *J. Anim. Sci.,* **27**, 45.

Hughes, R. E., Milner, C. & Dale, J. (1964) Selectivity in grazing. *In: Grazing in terrestrial and marine environments.* Ed. D. J. Crisp. Oxford: Blackwell.

Hulet, C. V., Price, D. A. & Foote, W. C. (1974) Effects of month of breeding and feed level on ovulation and lambing rates of Panama ewes. *J. Anim. Sci.,* **39**, 73–78.

Hulet, C. V., Shelton, M., Gallagher, J. R. & Price, D. A. (1974a) Effects of origin and environment on reproductive phenomena in Rambouillet ewes. 1. Breeding season and ovulation. *J. Anim. Sci.,* **38**(6), 1210–1217.

Hulet, C. V., Shelton, M., Gallagher, J. R. & Price, D. A. (1974b) Effects on origin and environment on reproductive phenomena in Rambouillet ewes. 2. Lamb production. *J. Anim. Sci.,* **38**(6), 1218–1223.

o

Hulet, C. V. & Stormshak, F. (1972) Some factors affecting response of anoestrous ewes to hormone treatment. *J. Anim. Sci.*, **34**(6), 1011–1019.

Hunter, G. L. (1968a) Increasing the frequency of pregnancy in sheep. 1. Some factors affecting rebreeding during the post-partum period. *ABA*, **36**, 347–378.

Hunter, G. L. (1968b) Increasing the frequency of pregnancy in the sheep. 2. Artificial control of rebreeding, and problems of conception and maintenance of pregnancy during the post-partum period. *ABA*, **36**(4), 533–533.

Hunter, R. F. (1960) Aims and methods in grazing behaviour studies on hill pastures. *Proc. 8th Int. Grassld. Congr.*, p 4.

Hunter, R. F. (1962) Hill sheep and their pasture: a study of sheep grazing in South East Scotland. *J. Ecol.*, **50**, 651–680.

Hunter, R. F. & Davies, G. E. (1963) The effect of method of rearing on the social behaviour of Scottish Blackface hoggets. *Anim. Prod.*, **5**, 183–194.

Hutchinson, K. J. (1971) Productivity and energy flow in grazing/fodder conservation systems. *Herb. Abstr.*, **41**, 1–10.

Hutton, J. B. (1963) Effect of lactation on intake in the dairy cow. *Proc. N.Z. Soc. Anim. Prod.*, **13**, 39.

Huxley, J. (1932). *Problems of Relative Growth.* London: Methuen.

Inskeep, E. K. (1973) Potential uses of prostaglandins in control of reproductive cycles of domestic animals. *J. Anim. Sci.* **36**(6), 1149–1157.

Ivins, J. D. (1955) The palatability of herbage. *Herb. Abstr.*, **25**, 75–79.

Jackson, T. H. (1974) *Effects of Nutrition on the Carcass.* British Council Course 324, Mar.–April, 1974: Edinburgh.

Jagusch, K. T., Norton, B. W. & Walker, D. M. (1970) Body composition studies with the milk-fed lamb. 2. The effect of the age of the lamb and the protein content of the diet on the chemical composition of the body and its organs. *J. Agric. Sci., (Camb.)*, **75**, 279–285.

Jones, D. I. H. & Miles, D. G. (1967) *Herbage quality—Feeding Trials*, p. 59. Welsh Plant Breeding Station report.

Jones, Ll. Iorwerth (1967) *Studies on Hill Land in Wales.* 2. Ecological studies of hill land. Aberystwyth: W.P.B.S. Tech. Bull. No. 2.

Jones, M. G. (1933a) Grassland management and its influence on the sward. Pt. 2. The management of a clovery sward and its effects. *Empire J. Expl. Agric.*, **1**, 122–127.

Jones, M. G. (1933b) Grassland management and its influence on the sward. Pt. 3. The management of a 'grassy' sward and its effects. *Empire J. Expl. Agric.*, **1**, 223–234.

Jordan, R. M. & Marten, G. C. (1970) Forward-creep grazing vs. conventional grazing for production of suckling lambs. *J. Anim. Sci.*, **31**, 598–600.

Keane, M. G. (1974) Effect of previous lambing on body weight and reproductive performance of hoggets. *Ir. J. agric. Res.*, **13**, 191–196.

Kneale, W. A. & Bastiman, B. (1974) Inwintering of ewes: Part II. Effect of nutrition. *Expl. Husb.*, **25**, 52–57.

Kon, S. K. & Cowie, A. T. (1961) *Milk: The Mammary Gland and its secretion.* Vol. II. London: Academic Press.

Labussière, J. & Ricordeau, G. (1970) Suitability of Prèalpes and crossbred Friesland × Prèalpes ewes for machine-milking: a study of different stages of lactation. *Ann. Zootech.,* **19,** 159–190.

Land, R. B. (1974) Physiological studies and genetic selection for sheep fertility. *ABA,* **42,** 155–158.

Lamming, G. E., Swan, H. & Clarke, R. T. (1966) Studies on the nutrition of ruminants. 1. Substitution of maize by milled barley straw in beef fattening diet and its effect on performance and carcass quality. *Anim. Prod.,* **8,** 303–311.

Langlands, J. P. & Bennett, I. L. (1973) Stocking intensity and pastoral production. 3. Wool production, fleece characteristics and the utilization of nutrients for maintenance and wool growth by Merino sheep grazed at different stocking rates. *J. Agric. Sci., (Camb.),* **81,** 211–218.

Large, R. V. (1965). The artificial rearing of lambs. *J. agric. Sci.,* **65,** 101–108.

Lawson, R. A. S. & Rowson, L. E. A. (1972) The influence of breed of ewe and offspring on litter size after egg transfer in sheep. *J. Reprod. Fert.,* **28,** 433–439.

Lees, J. L. (1969) The reproductive pattern and performance of sheep. *Outlook on Agriculture,* **6,** 82–88.

Lees, J. L. & Weatherhead, M. (1970) A note on mating preference of Clun Forest ewes. *Anim. Prod.* **12,** 173–176.

L'Estrange, J. L., Owen, J. B. & Wilman, D. (1967) Effects of a high level of nitrogenous fertilizer and date of cutting on the availability of the magnesium and calcium of herbage to sheep. *J. Agric. Sci., (Camb.),* **68,** 173–1782

Liggins, G. C., Grieves, S. A., Kendall, J. Z. & Knox, B. S. (1972) The physiological roles of progesterone, oestradiol–17β and prostaglandin F2α in the control of ovine parturition. *J. Reprod. Fertil. Suppl.* **16,** 85.

Lipson, E. (1953) *A short history of wool and its manufacture.* Melbourne, London, Toronto: Heinemann.

McClelland, T. H. (1974) Lamb growth and carcass quality of some breeds and cross breeds. Contribution to *Management and Diseases of Sheep.* Edinburgh. Mimeographed proceedings: British Council Course 324.

McMeekan, C. P. (1956) Grazing management and animal production. *Proc. VII Int. Grassld. Congr.,* Palmerston North, New Zealand. Nov. 1956. 146–156.

Maijala, K. & Kangasniemi, R. (1969) *Experiences of out of season and twice a year lambings in Finn-sheep.* Helsinki, June 1969: E.A.A.P.

Martin, D. J. (1964) Analysis of sheep diet utilising plant epidermal fragments in faeces samples. *In: Grazing in terrestrial and marine environments.* Ed. D. J. Crisp. Oxford: Blackwell.

Markson, L. M. & Terlecki, S. (1968) The aetiology of cerebrocortical necrosis. *Br. vet. J.,* **124,** 309–315.

Mason, I. L. (1969) *A World Dictionary of Livestock Breeds, Types and Varieties.* Edinburgh: C.A.B. Tech. Communication No. 8 (rev.).

Mason, I. L. & Maule, J. P. (1960). The indigenous livestock of Eastern and Southern Africa. Technical Communication No. 14 of Commonwealth Bureau of Animal Breeding and Genetics, Edinburgh: CAB Farnham Royal, Bucks., England.

Mattner, P. E. & Braden, A. W. H. (1967) Studies in flock mating of sheep. 2. Fertilisation and pre-natal mortality. *Aust. J. Expl. agric. Anim. Husb.*, **7**, 110–116.

Mattner, P. E., Braden, A. W. H. & Turnbull, K. E. (1967) Studies in flock mating of sheep. 1. Mating behaviour. *Aust. J. Expl. agric. Anim. Husb.* **7**, 103–109.

Meadley, D. R. (1952) Seasonal pattern of receivals of wool into store. *Q. Rev. agric. Econ.* **5**, 108–110.

Meat and Livestock Commission (1972) *Sheep improvement.* Scientific Study Group Report, Meat and Livestock Commission, Bletchley Oct. 1972.

Meat and Livestock Commission (1973) *Feeding the Ewe.* Technical Report No. 2. M.L.C. Sheep Improvement Service.

Meat and Livestock Commission (1973) *Planned Crossbreeding and Lamb Carcass Weights.* Bletchley, Milton Keynes.

Meat and Livestock Commission (1974) *Ewe Weights.* Sheep Improvement Services Publication.

Miller, E. L. (1968) Crude protein requirement of intensively fed lambs. *Anim. Prod.*, **10**, 243.

Minev, P. (1972) *Sheep breeding in the People's Republic of Bulgaria.* 56 pp, Sofia, Bulgaria: Centre for Scientific, technical and economic information in agriculture and forestry.

Ministry of Agriculture, Fisheries and Food (1969) *Wintering of ewe lambs in Welsh hill flocks.* Agricultural Land Service Tech. Report 22, London: HMSO.

Ministry of Agriculture Fisheries and Food (1969) *Sheep Handling pens and baths.* Fixed equipment of the Farm. Leaflet 14, London: HMSO.

Ministry of Agriculture, Fisheries and Food (1972) Nutrient Standards for Ruminants, Reports of the Working Parties, MAFF, ADAS, London: HMSO.

Ministry of Agriculture, Fisheries and Food (1972) *Winter feeding systems for mountain ewes.* Pwllpeiran Farm Guide and Report, London: HMSO.

Ministry of Agriculture, Fisheries and Food (1973) *Fatstock Guarantee Scheme, 1973/74,* pp. 32, London: HMSO.

Moore, R. W. (1966) Genetic factors affecting the milk intake of lambs. *Aust. J. agric. Res.* **17**, 191–199.

Morag, M., Raz, A. & Eyal, E. (1970) Mother-offspring relationships in Awassi sheep. 4. The effect of weaning at birth, or after 15 weeks, on lactational performance in the dairy ewe. *J. Agric. Sci., (Camb.)*, **75**, 183–187.

Morgan, J. A. & Owen, J. B. (1973) The nutrition of artificially reared lambs. *Anim. Prod.* **16**, 49–57.

Morgan, P. D., Arnold, G. W. & Lindsay, D. R. (1972) A note on the mating behaviour of ewes with various senses impaired. *J. Reprod. Fert.* **30**, 151–152.

Morris, I. G. (1968) Gamma-globin-globulin absorption in the new-born, In: *Handbook of physiology*, Section 6, Vol. III, 1491–1512. Washington: American Physiological Society.

Morris, R. M. (1969) The pattern of grazing in 'continuously' grazed swards. *J. Br. Grassld. Soc.*, **24**, 65–70

Moseley, S. R. & Lamming, G. E. (1969) The induction of breeding activity in lactating sheep by artificial light patterns.

Mott, G. O. (1960). Grazing pressure and the measurement of pasture production. *Proc. 8th Int. Grassld. Congr., 1960*, 6–11.

Moule, G. R. (1970) Australian research into reproduction in the ram. *A.B.A.*, **38**(a) 185.

Munro, Joan & Inkson, R. H. G. (1957). The effects of different suckling frequencies on the quality of milk consumed by young lambs. *J. Agric. Sci., (Camb.)*, **49**, 169.

Mylrea, P. J. (1966) Digestion of milk in young calves. 1. Flow and acidity of the contents of the small intestine. *Res. vet. Sci.*, **7**, 333–341.

National Sheep Breeders Association (1968) *British Sheep*. NSBA.

Newton, J. E. (1969) *Modern aspects of reproduction in sheep.* Tech. Report No. 7: Grassland Res. Inst.

Newton, J. E. & Betts, J. E. (1972). A comparison between the effect of various photoperiods on the reproductive performance of Scottish Half-bred ewes. *J. agric. Sci.* **78**, 425–433.

National Institution of Agricultural Botany (1973/4a) *Recommended Varieties of Herbage Legumes.* National Institute of Agricultural Botany Farmers leaflet, No. 4

National Institute of Agricultural Botany (1973/4b) *Recommended Varieties of Grasses.* National Institution of Agricultural Botany Farmers Leaflet No. 16.

North of Scotland College of Agriculture (1974) *Increasing the output of ewes to three lamb crops in two years.* Research Investigation and Field Trials: North of Scotland College of Agriculture.

North of Scotland College of Agriculture (1974) *Wastage in Caithness Sheep Flocks.* Research Investigation and Field Trials, North of Scotland College of Agriculture.

Northern Ireland Agricultural Trust (1974) *Lamb production—The development of a new system.*

Ørskov, E. R. & Fraser, C. (1972) Effect on type of rumen fermentation and digestibility of feeding whole as opposed to processed barley to sheep. *Proc. Nutr. Soc.*, **31**, 101A–102A.

Ørskov, E. R., Fraser, C. & Corse, E. L. (1970) The effect of protein utilisation of feeding different protein supplements via the rumen or via the abomasum in young growing sheep. *Br. J. Nutr.*, **24**, 803–809.

Ørskov, E. R., Fraser, C. & Gill, J. C. (1973) A note on the effect of time of weaning and weight at slaughter on feed utilisation of intensively fed lambs. *Anim. Prod.*, **16**(3), 311–315.

Onions, W. J. (1962) *Wool: An Introduction to its Properties, Varieties, Uses and Production*. London: Ernest Benn Ltd.

Ormerod, F. (1918) *Wool*. London: Constable.

Owen, J. B. (1955) 1. *A survey of hill sheep farming in Caernarvonshire*. 2. *A study of the lactation and growth of hill sheep*. Ph.D. Thesis, University of Wales.

Owen, J. B. (1957) A study of the lactation and growth of hill sheep in their native environment and under lowland conditions. *J. Agric. Sci, (Camb.)*, **48**, 387–412.

Owen, J. B. (1960) Wintering the hill flock. *Agriculture, Lond.* **67**, 225–227.

Owen, J. B. (1961) Fat Lambs from Grass. *J. agric. Soc. Univ. Coll. Wales, Aberyst.* **42**, 22–26.

Owen, J. B. (1971) *Performance Recording in Sheep*. 132 pp., Technical Communication No. 20: Commonwealth Agricultural Bureau.

Owen, J. B. (1971) Complete diets for ruminants. *Agriculture, Lond.* **78**, 331–333.

Owen, J. B. (1971a) *Performance Recording in Sheep*. C.A.B. Tech. Communication No. 20.

Owen, J. B. (1971b) Increasing reproductive efficiency of sheep. *Prog. 10th Int. Congr. of Anim. Prod.*, Versailles.

Owen, J. B. (1972) *Performance testing of ram lambs*. Report to Meat and Livestock Commission (unpublished).

Owen, J. B. (1972) Beef and sheep systems on arable farms. *Br. Grassld. Soc.*, Occasional Symposium **No. 7**, 67–72.

Owen, J. B. (1974) *Artificial Rearing of Lambs with Milk Replacers in England*. Roche Information Service.

Owen, J. B. (1975) Selection of dairy bulls on half sister records. *Anim. Prod.* (in Press).

Owen, J. B. & Davies, D. A. R. (1965) Artificial rearing of lambs. *Agriculture, Lond.*, **72**, 54–57.

Owen, J. B., Davies, D. A. R. & Ridgman, W. J. (1967) The efficiency of utilisation of grass by lactating ewes. *J. Agric. Sci.,(Camb.)*,**69**, 399–404.

Owen, J. B., Davies, D. A. R. & Ridgman, W. J. (1969a) Effects of varying the quantity and distribution of liquid feed in lambs reared artificially. *Anim. Prod.*, **11**, 1–9.

Owen, J. B., Davies, D. A. R. & Ridgman, W. J. (1969b). The control of voluntary food intake in ruminants. *Anim. Prod.*, **11**, 511–512.

Owen, J. B. & Ingleton, J. W. (1961) A method of collecting faeces from ewes. *Anim. Prod.*, **3** 63–64.

Owen, J. B. & Ingleton, J. W. (1963). A study of food intake and production in grazing ewes. 2. The interrelationships between food intake and productive output. *J. Agric. Sci., (Camb.)*, **61**, 329–340.

Owen, J. B. & Morton, J. R. (1969) Association of food conversion ratio, age at slaughter and carcass quality in pigs fed *ad libitum*. *Anim. Prod.* **11**, 317–324.

Owen, J. B. & Ridgman, W. J. (1968) The design and interpretation of experiments to study animal production from grazed pasture. *J. Agric. Sci.*, (*Camb.*), **71**, 327–335.

Owen, J. B., Ridgman, W. J. & Wyllie, D. W. (1971) The effect of food restriction on subsequent voluntary intake of pigs. *Anim. Prod.*, **13**, 537–546.

Owen, J. B. & Sinclair, K. B. (1961) The development of hypomagnesaemia in lactating ewes. *Vet. Rec.* **73**, 1423–1424.

Ozin, F. V. (1966) Artificial insemination in sheep—an outstanding achievement of scientists in the U.S.S.R. *Zhivotnovodstvo*, **28**(3), 27–31; (**4**), 56–61. Transl.: (A.B.A. **34**, 527; Abstr. 3082).

Pálsson, H. & Vergés, J. B. (1952) Effects of plane of nutrition on growth and development of carcass quality in lambs. Parts 1 and 2. *J. Agric. Sci.*, (*Camb.*), **42**, 1–149.

Pattison, I. H., Hoare, M. N., Jebbett, J. N. & Watson, W. A. (1972) Spread of scrapie to sheep and goats by oral dosing with foetal membranes from scrapie affected sheep. *Vet. Rec.*, **90**, 465–468.

Peart, J. N. (1972) Effect of stage of lactation on milk composition of Finnish Landrace × Blackface ewes. *J. Agric. Sci.*, (*Camb.*), **79**, 303–313.

Peart, J. N., Edwards, R. A. & Donaldson, E. (1972) The yield and composition of the milk of Finnish Landrace × Blackface ewes. *J. Agric. Sci.*, (*Camb.*), **79**, 303–313.

Perrin, Dawn R. (1958) The chemical composition of the colostrum and milk of the ewe. *J. Dairy Res.* **25**, 70–74.

Pirchner, F. (1969) *Population Genetics in Animal Breeding*. San Francisco: W. H. Freeman.

Poe, S. E., Glimp, H. A., Deweese, W. P. & Mitchell, G. E. (1969) Effect of pre-weaning diet on the growth and development of early weaned lambs. *J. Anim. Sci.*, **28**, 401–405.

Purser, A. F. (1972) Variation in the date of first oestrus among Welsh Mountain ewes. p. 133. *Proc. Br. Soc. Anim. Prod.*, Edinburgh: Longman.

Purser, A. F. & Karam, H. A. (1967) Lamb survival, growth and fleece production in relation to birthcoat type among Welsh Mountain sheep. *Anim. Prod.*, **9**, 75–85.

Purser, A. F. & Young, G. B. (1959) Lamb survival in two hill flocks. *Anim. Prod.*, **1** 85–92.

Quittet, E. (1965) *Races Ovine Françaises*. 96 pp. Paris: La Maison Rustique.

Rae, A. L. (1956) The Genetics of the sheep. *Adv. Genet.* **8**, 189–265.

Reid, D. (1970) The effects of a wide range of nitrogen application rates on the yields from a perennial ryegrass sward with and without white clover. *J. Agric. Sci.*, (*Camb.*), **74**, 227–240.

Reid, J. F. S. (1973) An assessment of anthelmintic control programmes adopted by British sheep farmers for their breeding flocks. *Vet. Rec.*, **93**, 281–284.

Reid, J. T., Bensadown, A., Bull, L. S., Burton, J. M., Gleeson, P. A., Han, I. K., Joo, Y. D., Johnson, D. E., McManus, W. R., Paladines, O. L., Stroud, J. W., Tyrrell, H. F., van Niekerk, B. D. H., Wellington, G. H. & Wood, J. D. (1968) Changes in body composition and meat characteristics of cattle, pigs and sheep during growth. *Proc. Cornell Meat Conf. 1968*, 18–37. New York, Oct. 1968

Reid, R. L. (1968) The physiopathology of undernourishment in pregnant sheep, with particular reference to pregnancy toxaemia. *Adv. vet. Sci.*, **12**, 163–238.

Reis, P. J. & Tunks, D. A. (1969) Evaluation of formaldehyde-treated casein for wool growth and nitrogen retention. *Aust. J. agric. Res.*, **20**, 775–781.

Ricordeau, G. & Flamant, J. C. (1969) Cross breeding between Prealpes du Sud and East Friesland sheep. 3. Milk yield. *Ann. Zootech.*, **18**, 151–168. *A.B.A.* **38** (*abstract*) 2703.

Robinson, J. F., Currie, D. C. & Peart, J. N. (1961) Feeding hill ewes. *Trans. Highl. Agric. Scot.*, **6**, 31–46.

Robinson, J. J., Foster, W. H. & Forbes, T. J. (1968) An assessmant of the variation in milk yield of ewes determined by the lamb suckling technique. *J. Agric. Sci., (Camb.)*, **70**, 187–194.

Robinson, J. J., Roster, W. H. & Forbes, T. J. (1969) The estimation of the milk yield of a ewe from body weight data on the suckling lamb. *J. Agric. Sci., (Camb.)*, **72**, 103–107.

Robinson, T. J. (1951) The control of fertility in sheep. Part 2. The augmentation of fertility by gonadatrophin treatment of the ewe in the normal breeding season. *J. Agric. Sci., (Camb.)*, **41**, 6–63.

Robinson, T. J. (1967) *The Control of the Ovarian Cycle in the Sheep.* Sidney: Sydney University Press.

Robinson, T. J., Fraser, C. & Gill, J. C. (1972) Preliminary observations on the performance of Finnish Landrace × Dorset Horn Ewes in an intensive system. *Proc. Br. Soc. Anim. Prod.,* Paper 19, 54th meeting.

Ross, D. B. (1965) Copper poisoning in housed lambs. *Anim. Prod.*, **7**, 280.

Rutter, W., Laird, T. R. & Broadbent, P. J. (1972) A note on the effects of Clipping Pregnant Ewes at Housing. *Anim. Prod.*, **14**, 127–130.

Ryder, M. L. (1965) Wool growth in sheep. *In: Comparative Physiology and Pathology of the Skin.* pp. 161–189. Eds A. J. Rook & G. S. Walton, Oxford: Blackwell Scientific Publications.

Ryder, M. L. & Stephenson, S. K. (1968) *Wool Growth.* London: Academic Press.

Salamon, S. (1972) Fertility of deep-frozen ram spermatozoa stored for three years. *In: VIIth Congress on Anim. Prod. Munich 1972* 295–296.

Salamon, S. (1962) Studies on the artificial insemination of Merino sheep. 3. The effect of frequent ejaculation on semen characteristics and fertilising capacity. *Aust. J. agric. Res.*, **13**, 1137.

Salerno, A. & Malossini, F. (1968) Milk production in Sopravissana, Württemberg, Ile-de-France and Berrichon sheep, with particular reference to the first months of lactation. *Annali 1st. sper. Zootec.*, **1**, 59–91. *A.B.A.* **38**, 1424.

Schmidt, G. H. (1971) *Biology of Lactation.* San Francisco: W. H. Freeman.

Scottish Agricultural Colleges (1975) *Farm Management Manual.* Loose leaf manual.

Sharafeldin, M. A. (1974) Possible paths to improve lamb production. Paper presented at the Arid Lands Agricultural Development programme Regional workshop for sheep and Forage production, Bierut. Feb., 1974.

Sharafeldin, M. A. & Kandell, A. A. (1971) Post lambing maternal behaviour. *J. Agric. Sci., (Camb.)*, **77**, 33–36.

Sharafeldin, M. A., Ragab, M. T. & Kandell, A. A. (1971) Behaviour of ewes during parturition. *J. Agric. Sci., (Camb.)*, **76**, 419–422.

Shepherd, C. S. (1974) *Desequand layout for sheep handling pens*. Bulletin 159, West of Scotland Agricultural College.

Slen, S. B., Clark, R. D. & Hironaka, R. (1963) A compariaon of milk production and its relation to lamb growth in five breeds of sheep. *Can. J. Anim. Sci.*, **43**, 16–21.

Spedding, C. R. W. (1965) *Sheep Production and Grazing Management*. London: Bailliére, Tindall and Cox.

Spedding, C. R. W. (1970) *Sheep production and Grazing Management*. 2nd ed. London: Bailliére Tindall.

Spedding, C. R. W. & Diekmahns, E. C. (1972) Grasses and legumes in British Agriculture. Bulletin 49, Commonwealth Bureau of Pastures and Field Crops, *C.A.B.*

Speedy, A. W. (1973) *Increasing the Frequency of Lambing in Sheep*. Ph.D. thesis, University of Cambridge.

Stern, E. (1973) Upsurge in block feeding expected as more turn to low-cost roughage. *Live Stk. Fmg.*, Oct. 1973.

Streeter, C. L. (1969) A review of techniques used to estimate the *in vivo* digestibility of grazed forage. *J. Anim. Sci.*, **29**, 757–768.

Sykes, A. R., Field, A. C. & Gunn, R. G. (1974) Effects of age and state of incisor dentition on body composition and lamb production of sheep grazing hill pastures. *J. Agric. Sci., (Camb.)*, **83**, 135–143.

Sykes, A. R., Field, A. C. & Gunn, R. G. (1974b) Effects of age and state of incisor dentition on the chemical composition of the skeleton of sheep grazing hill pastures. *J. Agric. Sci., (Camb.)*, **83**, 145–150.

Sykes, A. R. & Slee, J. (1969) Cold exposure of Southdown and Welsh Mountain Sheep. 1. Effects of breed, plane of nutrition and acclimatization to cold upon resistance to body cooling. *Anim. Prod.*, **11**, 65–75.

Symons, L. (1972) *Russian Agriculture—a Geographic Survey*. London: G. Bell and Sons Ltd.

Taylor, St. C. S. & Young, G. B. (1966) Variation in growth and efficiency in twin cattle with live weight and food intake controlled. *J. Agric. Sci., (Camb.)*, **66**, 67–85.

Terrill, C. E. (1968) Sheep and goats. *In: The Artificial Insemination of Farm Animals*, 4th ed. 215–243. Ed. E. J. Perry. New Brunswick: Rutgers University Press.

Terrill, Clair E., Lindahl, I. & Dolnick, E. H. (1970) Chemical de-fleecing under field conditions. *J. Anim. Sci.*, **31**, 947–949.

Terry, R. A. & Tilley, J. M. A. (1964) The digestibility of leaves and stems of perennial ryegrass, cocksfoot, timothy, tall fescue, lucerne and sainfoin as measured by an *in vitro* procedure. *J. Br. Grassld. Soc.* **19**, 363–372.

Thomas, B. & Smith, A. N. (1954) The nutritive value of *Calluna vulgaris*. 3. Digestibility at four and ten years after burning. *J. Agric. Sci., (Camb.),* **45**, 104–109.

Thomas, R. J. (1974) Pasture management gives effective worm control. *Scott. Fmr,* Aug. 1974, II–III.

Thorpe, E. F. (1963) Certain aspects of the intensive production of fat lambs from grass. *J. Br. Grassld. Soc.,* **18**, 139–145.

Tomkins, T. & Bryant, M. J. (1972) Mating behaviour in a small flock of lowland sheep. *Anim. Prod.* **15**, 203–210.

Timon, V. M. (1968) Genetic studies of growth and carcass composition in sheep. *In*: *Growth and Development of Mammals*, Eds G. A. Lodge & G. E. Lamming. London: Butterworths.

Treacher, T. T. (1971) Effects of nitrition in pregnancy and in lactation on milk yield in ewes. *Anim. Prod.* **13**, 493–501.

Tribe, D. E. & Coles, G. J. R. (1966) *Prime lamb Production.* 239 pp. Melbourne, Canberra, Sydney: F. W. Cheshire.

Turner, Helen Newton (1969) Genetic improvement of reproduction rate in sheep. *A.B.A.,* **37**(4), 545–563.

Turner, Helen Newton & Young, S. S. Y. (1969) *Quantitative Genetics in Sheep Breeding.* Melbourne: Macmillan.

Twardock, A. R., Symonds, H. W., Sansom, B. F. & Rowlands, G. J. (1973) The effect of litter size upon foetal growth rate and the placental transfer of calcium and phosphorus in superovulated Scottish half-bred ewes. *Br. J. Nutr.,* **29**, 437.

Underwood, E. J. (1966) *The Mineral Nutrition of Livestock.* Commonwealth Agricultural Bureaux.

United States Department of Agriculture (1970) *U.S.D.A. Yield Grades.* Marketing Bulletin No. 52, U.S. Dept. of Agriculture Consumer and Marketing Service.

Vetter, R. L., Norton, H. W. & Garrigus, U. S. (1960) A study of pre-weaning death losses in lambs. *J. Anim. Sci.,* **19**, 616–619.

Voisin, A. (1959) *Grass Productivity.* London: Crosby Lockwood & Son Ltd.

Waite, F., Wenham, G., Sharman, G. A. M., Jones, A. S., Rattray, E. A. S. & McDonald, I. (1969) Stomach function in relation to a scour syndrome in the piglet. *Br. J. Nutr.,* **23**, 847.

Wallace, L. R. (1948) Growth of lambs before and after birth in relation to the level of nutrition. I, II, III. *J. Agric. Sci., (Camb.),* **38**, 93–153, 243–300, 367–407.

Walker, D. M. & Faichney, G. J. (1964) Nutritional diarrhoea in the milk-fed lamb and its relation to the intake of sugar. *Br. J. Nutr.,* 18(2), 209–216.

Walker, D. M. & Norton, B. W. (1971) Nitrogen balance studies with the milk-fed lamb. 9. Energy and protein requirements for maintenance, live-weight gain and wool growth. *Br. J. Nutr.,* **26**(1), 15–29.

Walker, D. M. & Stokes, G. B. (1970) The nutritive value of fat in the diet of ᵗhe milk-fed lamb. 1. The apparent and corrected digestibilities of different dietary fats and of their constituent fatty acids. *Br. J. Nutr.*, **24**, 425–433.

Warboys, I. B. (1970). Some effects of mechanical treatments and surface sowing on rough hill grazings. *J. Br. Grassld. Soc.*, **25**(3), 210–213.

Weston, R. H. (1971) Factors limiting the intake of feed by the sheep. 4. Feed intake in the ruminant lamb in relation to the administration of a nutrient solution per abomasam. *Aust. J. agric. Res.* **22**, 469–479.

Wheeler, J. L. (1962) Experimentation in grazing management. *Herb. Abstr.*, Vol. 32, No. 1, Mar. 1972, 1–7.

Wheeler, J. L., Reardon, T. F. & Lambourne, L. J. (1963). The effect of pasture availability and shearing stress on herbage intake of grazing sheep. *Aust. J. agric. Res.*, **14**, No. 3, 364.

Whitehead, D. C. (1970) The role of nitrogen in grassland productivity. *C.A.B.* Bull. 48.

Whitten, W. K. (1966) Pheromones and mammalian reproduction. *Advances in reproductive physiology*. Vol. 1. Ed. A. McLaren. London: Logos and Academic Press.

Wiener, G., Duble, F. K., Broadbent, J.S. & Talbot, M. (1973) Breed variation in lambing performance and lamb mortality in commercial sheep flocks. *Anim. Prod.*, **17**, 229–244.

Williams, H. L. & Thwaites, C. J. (1974) The reproduction performance of Border Leicester ewes in contrasting photoperiodic environments. *J. Agric. Sci., (Camb.)*, **83**, 101–104.

Wilson, P. N. & Osbourn, D. F. (1960) Compensatory growth after under-nutrition in mammals and birds, *Biol. Rev.*, **35**, 324–363.

Winfield, C. G., Williams, A. H. & Makin, A. W. (1972) Some factors associated with the peri parturient behaviour of ewes. *Proc. Aust. Soc. Anim. Prod.*, **9**, 365–370.

W.P.B.S. (1968) Herbage quality—feeding trials. Report of the Welsh Plant Breeding Station.

Yeates, N. T. M. (1949) The breeding season of the sheep with particular reference to its modification by artificial means using light. *J. Agric. Sci., (Camb.)*, **39**, 1–43.

Zeuner, F. G. (1963) *A History of Domesricated Animals.* London: Hutchinson.

Index

A

Aberdeen sheep breeding scheme, 366
abomasum, 200
abortion, 302
Abyssinia, 53
acidosis, 157
Adali, 13
additive effect of genes, 329, 330
Afghanistan, 4, 30
Africa, 5, 47–54, 273
African long fat-tail, 13
Africander, 48, 50
afterbirth, 151
Albania, 3, 47
Algeria, 5, 47
Altai sheep, 27
amino acids, 221
anaemia, 274, 275, 299
Animal Breeding Research Organisation, Edinburgh, 368
ancestors, 168, 178, 186
anoxia, 156
anthelmintics, 296–297
appetite, 262
Arabi, 13, 25
Argali sheep, 321
Argentina, 4, 31
artificial insemination (A.I.), 27, 28, 39, 40, 44, 45, 146, 150, 161–164, 366
artificial rearing, 217, 223, 399
ash, body, 63
Asia, 4, 23–30
Askanian sheep, 27, 45
assisted lambing, 152

astrakhan, 27
Ausimi, 52
Australia, 5, 14–18, 19, 111, 273
Awassi, 13, 25, 139, 150, 326

B

bacterial diseases, 304–309
Bakewell, Robert, 326
Bali-Bali, 54
Barbary fat-tailed, 51, 52, 323
Barki, 52, 151, 153
barrenness, 144, 227, 359
Bedouins, 6, 25
Bedsonia, 191
beet pulp, 221
Beni Ahsen, 51
Beni Guil, 51
benzocaine, 161
Berber, 51
Bergamo, 13, 43
Berrichon, 40, 41, 42
Biella, 13, 43
Bighorn, 54, 322
Bikaneri, 13
bilberry (*Vaccinium myrtillus*), 270
birth coat, 101, 332
birthweight, 158
Black disease, 299, 305
Blackhead Persian, 13, 50
blackleg, 305
black sheep, 331
Black Welsh Mountain, 331
bladder worms, 301
blood groups, 333